Managing Food

Dagmar Engel, Donald MacDonald
and Claire Nash (contributing editor)

Helen Davies.
Course 22ND → 26TH
November 2010 -

O. M. G. !!

Chartered
Institute of
Environmental
Health

Contents

Introduction

Managing Food Safety takes a fresh and pragmatic approach to the vast subject of managing the safe production, sale and service of food.

Even though food safety risk management has been at the heart of legislation and good practice for many years, most books still just bolt it on to old-established ways of considering the subject. In contrast, the management of hazards and risk is at the heart of *Managing Food Safety*. It is the only book at this level to integrate risk management fully into every aspect of dealing with food.

Food safety is often just one of many demands on busy managers striving to produce excellent food on time, to budget and for profit, so the book keeps the everyday operational practicalities of food businesses firmly in mind.

Designed for managers and would-be managers with responsibility for some or all aspects of food safety in any sector of the food industry, the book provides both practicable management guidance and clear information about the science and legislation behind accepted good practice.

The book is an essential study aid towards level 4 food safety examinations (advanced or management level), such as the CIEH Level 4 Award in Managing Food Safety in Catering and the CIEH Level 4 Award in Food Safety Management for Manufacturing. The book is also being used for courses at level 3 (intermediate or supervisory level) and at introductory level in universities. It is also used as a compact source of reference.

The legislative framework outlined is that of the European Union, with detailed examples of food safety legislation in the UK. Even so, the *principles* enshrined in these laws are valid for many other countries around the world. Examples are included of food safety problems and practices around the world.

The book assumes that you have at least a basic-level knowledge of food safety and are familiar with the organisation and processes of a food business. Even so, the book explains all the topics step by step, gradually building your confidence in the management of food safety issues. Not all the topics may seem immediately relevant to your own workplace or your current job responsibilities, but it is still important for you to get a firm grasp of all the issues discussed.

For ease of reading the book sometimes uses the phrase 'your business' or 'your company', even though many managers are not proprietors and some food operations are not-for-profit organisations.

Getting the most from this book

Managing Food Safety is designed to support you while you are learning and throughout your management career.

The book consists of four parts, a Reference section and a number of feature pages.

Each part of the book asks and answers a simple question – what is food safety, why do we need to manage food safety, what do we need to manage and how should we manage food safety? After a general introduction to the topics covered in that part, the book is divided into sections and chapters.

At the start of each section is a list of **Key points** and **Key words**. The **Key points** are the foundation for effective food safety management and the **Key words** are crucial for the understanding and management of food safety matters. The **Key words** are highlighted in the text and included in the **Glossary**, often with an expanded definition. Many other words and phrases that are useful in the context of food and food safety are also included in the Glossary.

By the end of the book you should be able to discuss all the key points, giving, wherever possible, examples from your own workplace. You should also be able to explain all the key words in your own words.

If you are preparing for a level 4 food safety examination, refer to the key points and key words during your revision. You should find the **sidebars** – the brief notes in blue in the margins – useful for this purpose too.

As the role of a manager includes setting a good example to others, supervision and at least some responsibility for training, the book includes two types of summary. **Making it easier for others** summaries appear throughout the book. **Management matters** summaries appear in Parts 3 and 4. Use them to inspire you to find the best possible ways to help your staff to produce, serve or sell safe food.

Whenever you are just dipping in to the book, perhaps to refresh your memory about a particular point, do bear in mind that you may also need to glance at an earlier part of the chapter or section for a full explanation of a practice or requirement mentioned in a particular paragraph.

The **Reference** section includes additional general information, at-a-glance summaries, technical information, the Glossary and **Sources of further help**, including organisations, websites, books, articles and notes on the sources of material included in the book.

1. What is food safety?

What is food safety?

People have been known to survive without food for three weeks or longer, but it is rare for humans to live without water for more than ten days. Food and water are indeed the stuff of life and it is evident that we cannot live without them. They are, however, more than just a means of sustaining life. In societies where starvation is not an immediate threat, eating and drinking frequently feature in family, social and leisure activities, often creating pleasure and a general sense of well-being in addition to providing nourishment. What's more, food and drink have a central part in many religious customs.

In the 'developed world' we generally assume that the food we buy is safe to eat, whether we are consuming it at home or eating out. The statistics for cases of food-borne illness in the UK alone indicate that this assumption is not always valid. *Managing Food Safety* looks at ways to make food safe to eat by helping you to predict and prevent the problems that lead to illness from food.

First, however, we need to check what we mean by *food safety* and indeed what exactly we mean by *food*. This we do in 'Safe enough to eat' – the first chapter of Part 1 – where we also introduce the key concepts of *hazard* and *risk* that are then developed throughout the book. In the second chapter – 'In good hands' – we look briefly at the legal and practical responsibility for food safety that a manager may have. These themes are developed later in the book.

On page 4 you will find lists of the most important points and words to remember from Part 1. As you read through the book, you will find that the definitions of some key words are expanded. To help you further, all the key words are included in the Glossary, together with many other words and phrases that are often used in the discussion of food safety.

Staying alive

Key points

Safe enough to eat

Definitions of food and food safety.

Introduction to hazard and risk.

The central importance of hazard and risk to the management of food safety.

In good hands

The people who are involved in food safety.

Where legal responsibility lies.

Examples of typical day-to-day management responsibility for food safety.

Key words

Food
Any substance or product intended, or reasonably expected, to be eaten or drunk by people.

Food hygiene
All the individual measures involved in keeping food safe to eat.

Food safety
The protection of human health from harm from food. Also used to indicate the *absence* of harm to people from food.

Hazard
A source of danger: any thing, condition or circumstance that could cause harm (injury or illness) to the consumer. A 'food hazard' is anything in food that could make someone ill or cause them injury.

Person in charge
The person given the authority by the employer to take charge of food premises at any given time.

Place on the market
The holding, distribution, display and service of food for sale, including food that is free of charge.

Risk
A measure, or scale, of the likelihood (or probability) that a hazard will occur and cause harm.

Unfit food
Food which is not considered safe to eat because it could cause illness or injury.

Safe enough to eat

We grow up, quite literally, with food. It is so obvious that food is something we eat that adults rarely need to define it. Indeed, few books dealing with food safety bother to do so. However, it is important to understand what the law considers food to be, and to appreciate that this book deals only with the *safety* of food and cannot cover every aspect of the topic of food or of human safety.

Food defined

Dictionaries usually define food as being any substance taken into the body to maintain life and growth. As we know, however, 'maintaining life and growth' is not always the reason for eating or drinking. Many people drink alcohol for pleasure, even though it is not defined as a nutrient, or they chew gum, even though it provides little, if any, nutritional value.

Legislation describes food as being any substance, product or ingredient that is intended, or reasonably expected, to be ingested (eaten or drunk) by humans. In the eyes of the law *food* includes:

- any unprocessed (raw), processed or partly processed substance or product for human consumption
- drinks, including water
- substances that are deliberately incorporated into food during its manufacture, preparation or treatment
- chewing gum.

The legislation makes it clear that food does *not* include:

- live animals (unless they are prepared for sale for human consumption)
- feeding stuff for animals
- plants before they are harvested
- medicinal or cosmetic products
- tobacco or tobacco products
- controlled drugs
- residues and contaminants.

Food safety defined

Safe means secure from harm, injury or danger. So we could define *safety* as the condition of being free or protected from harm, injury or danger.

When it comes to discussing food safety, it is probably useful to refine this simple definition so that it covers both *actual* harm, injury and danger and *possible* harm, injury and danger. We can do so by considering safety in terms of hazards and risk.

A hazard is a source of danger – any thing, condition or situation that *could* cause harm to the consumer – while a risk is a measure, or scale, of the likelihood that a hazard will actually occur.

These two words are central to the way that food safety is discussed, legislated and inspected, so you'll learn a great deal more about them later in the book. For now, they help us to draw up a working definition of food safety – the protection of human health by preventing food hazards as far as possible and by minimising the risk from any unpreventable hazards.

Food safety
The protection of human health by preventing food hazards as far as possible and by minimising the risk from any unpreventable hazards.

You may be surprised to discover that our legislation does not give a direct definition of *food safety* or *safe* food in general. It does, however, make clear what the law deems to be *un*safe food and what is illegal to place on the market.

For example, food intended for people to eat must be fit for human consumption and it is illegal to add anything to food that would make it injurious to health. The law also specifies and limits the types, circumstances of use and quantities of additives that can be used. There is plenty more information about the laws governing food safety in Part 3.

The scope of food safety

It is probably becoming clear that food safety is concerned with issues such as undesirable ingredients (contaminants) and food which is unfit to eat, but has nothing to do with nutrition, eating habits (such as overeating, overdrinking or slimming diets) or animal welfare and is only partly concerned with questions of quality. What this means to someone who is charged with the responsibility for food safety is touched upon in the next chapter and developed in Part 4.

Food safety and food hygiene

You may be wondering at this stage whether food safety and food hygiene are the same thing. The short answer is no, but the phrases are often interchangeable so you should not worry about tripping over finer definitions.

A wider perspective – if you want it

If you are interested in such things, there is a longer explanation about the use of the terms. The expression *food safety* tends to be used to describe the achievement of the state, or condition, of food that is safe to eat. The term covers standards, composition, labelling *and* food hygiene.

In turn, *food hygiene* is used to refer to all the practical measures involved in keeping food safe and wholesome through all the stages of production to point of sale or consumption. So, you can see that food safety includes food hygiene, but not the other way around.

This usage has been reflected in British legislation. The Food Safety Act 1990 covers all the main principles involved in keeping food safe to eat, while the food hygiene regulations deal with more specific actions that must be taken to comply with the law. European legislation generally follows the same principles.

If you work in America, you'll also find that food *safety* is the usual term for the whole subject of keeping food fit for human consumption, but you may find that the word *hygiene* used on its own is describing *personal* hygiene.

The right words in the right place

Where does this leave you? Just use the phrase that feels most comfortable to you under the particular circumstances. For example, if you were talking to new employees, you might wish to say something like, 'Food safety stops our customers from getting ill from food' or, 'Good food hygiene is essential every moment that you work with food.'

In this book

We use 'food safety' to describe the whole subject of ensuring that food is safe to eat. We use 'food hygiene' to describe all the practical measures involved in keeping food safe and wholesome.

Making it easier for others

- Use words that staff are most likely to understand when explaining what food safety (or food hygiene) involves.

- Point out that food safety covers drink as well as food.

- Encourage staff to describe the actions they must take each day to help to ensure the safety of food.

In good hands

It goes without saying that food safety concerns everyone who wants to stay alive and well. We all hope and expect that our food is safe to eat. But who exactly does food safety concern in a *professional* capacity? Whose real responsibility is it to look after the safety of food?

The answer to both questions is that food safety is the responsibility of everyone who works with food or whose actions or omissions could compromise the safety of food.

Every person who works with food deals with some aspect of food safety, no matter how small that aspect is in the bigger scheme of things. Even so, someone has to take *overall* responsibility for all the people whose work could safeguard or threaten the safety of food and for all the systems and procedures that are supposed to be followed. That person is the manager, whether he or she is an owner-manager or an employee whose job is to manage.

In your care

You do not need to have the words *food safety* in your jobtitle to be the person responsible for managing the production, sale or service of safe food.

In small and some medium-size enterprises (SMEs), the full responsibility for managing food safety may fall upon one individual. In a large company the responsibility may be shared, but usually starts with a supervisor or first-line manager – someone with day-to-day decision-making powers, albeit sometimes on a small scale.

In medium-size and large-size food operations middle and senior managers usually have more responsibilities and a greater say in policy.

The ultimate responsibility usually rests with a senior management team or board of directors, or upon the most senior manager or director who makes the final decisions.

This is so even if the senior manager or director does not have 'hands-on' involvement in the production of food or is not based in the premises where food is produced, stored, served or sold.

Legally in charge

Whatever the size or type of the enterprise, legal responsibility usually lies with the person who is put in charge of food premises at any given time. You'll learn more about this in Part 3, but it is important to note here that the person with the final responsibility for food safety must ensure that the person in charge is adequately trained and has sufficient experience to be in charge.

An overview of management

So what is it that you need to manage if you are the person, or one of the people, responsible for food safety at your workplace? You'll find that everything involved is discussed in bite-size chunks throughout the book, with the chapters in Part 4 taking a highly practicable approach to everyday food safety issues. At this stage it is worth obtaining a general picture before you start to read about details.

A continuous process

One of the simplest ways to consider the job of management is as a continuous cycle (or, better still, a spiral) of planning, implementing and reviewing actions in the workplace. Tasks involved in this process are likely to include:

- planning

  - making policy and setting objectives

  - communicating objectives and specific standards

- implementing

  - organising and implementing policies and objectives – for example, setting priorities, establishing reporting relationships and allocating resources

  - monitoring, auditing and measuring performance and analysing the results and observations

- reviewing

  - checking performance against objectives and standards.

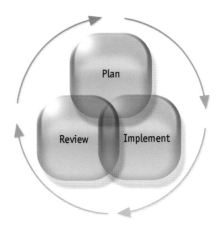

A considerable role

Of course, your own responsibilities depend upon your particular job description and job specification, and to some extent upon the part of the food industry in which you work.

Nonetheless, to become an effective manager of food safety (and to pass an accredited advanced-level food safety examination), you need to know about some aspects of food safety that you will not need to manage immediately or, perhaps, ever. For example, if you are the food and beverage manager at an hotel, you are unlikely to have to manage the canning of fish, but you still need to understand the principles involved. You need an awareness of the science underlying good practice in food safety as well as sufficient confidence and competence in your management skills.

Part 2 sets your task in a wider business context by suggesting why it is worth the bother of attempting to manage food safety in the first place. Parts 3 and 4 deal in detail with the key practical aspects of food safety management. There's no doubt that this is a huge management role – and it is possible that food safety is just one part of your total management responsibilities!

Examples of businesses that need to manage food safety

Raw food production:	farms and fisheries.
Raw food handling:	abattoirs, fish processors, dairy farms, meat processors, fruit and vegetable companies.
Food processing:	bakeries, dairies, breweries and plants producing frozen, ready-to-eat, bottled and canned products.
Transport (by road, rail, air, sea and inland waterways):	for livestock; raw food at ambient temperatures or in refrigerated conditions; processed food at ambient, refrigerated, frozen or high temperatures.
Packaging:	boxing, bagging and packeting plants.
Storage/warehousing:	at an ambient temperature or in controlled conditions.
Food sale, raw and processed:	shops, supermarkets, grocers, greengrocers, fishmongers, butchers, bakers, other specialist food shops, wholesale markets, market stalls (retail), vending machines, cafeterias and sandwich bars.
Food service and consumption:	public access and private facilities (such as company or members-only facilities) including cafeterias, restaurants, canteens, refectories, hotels, pubs, clubs, bars, sandwich bars, take-aways and leisure facilities; aircraft, ships and trains; institutional catering, including hospitals, care homes and the Armed Forces; retention facilities (such as prisons, remand centres and young offenders institutions); vending machines; mobile stalls and vehicles; outside catering facilities and events (such as barbecues and wedding marquees).
Catering/local food preparation:	catering facilities, public hall kitchens, restaurants, cafés, canteens, hospitals, regeneration facilities, fast food outlets, sandwich vans and other mobile and outside catering, and domestic kitchens used for commercial food preparation.
Transport of food within buildings, sites or building complexes:	including trolleys and motorised vehicles.
Serveries:	including canteens, self-service facilities and vending machines.

Making it easier for others

- Emphasise that every food handler has a crucial part to play in food safety.

- Explain how food safety requires full commitment from everyone.

- Ensure that people who do not handle food, but whose work could compromise food safety (such as cleaners and delivery drivers), understand the part they also play in food safety.

2. Why do we need to manage food safety?

Why do we need to manage food safety?

'We haven't poisoned anybody since we started the business, so why should we use any of our precious budget on food safety?'

You can imagine that many business owners, financial directors, managing directors and production managers in the food industry have been tempted to ask themselves a version of that question at some point.

Profit margins can be tight in many sectors of the food industry and the allocation of resources often involves difficult decisions between competing priorities. Why then should any food business spend any of its precious time or hard-earned profit on managing food safety? The simplest answer is: to stay in business.

Of course there are many other valid reasons for making food safety a priority. They might include a moral responsibility to protect consumers from illness, the desire to win the highest possible professional reputation and a need to operate within the law.

In this part of the book we consider these issues in a business context: there are short chapters about business priorities, consumer expectations, food-borne illnesses and legal priorities, especially the defence of due diligence. We use the word *business* in its broadest possible sense and include not-for-profit sectors in which 'staying in business' involves keeping within the food, purchasing or catering budgets.

Even though the management of food safety may sometimes appear to be an optional extra, we hope to persuade you by the end of Part 2 that it is an essential and integral part of any food business. Attempting to run a food business without managing food safety would be rather like trying to drive a car without gears or brakes – you might roll along quite happily for a while, but before too long you would certainly get into serious difficulty.

Staying in business

Key points

Customer concerns

Customer relationship management as a key to business retention.

The value of customer loyalty.

Levels of customer awareness.

Customer expectations and perceptions.

The need to take an active approach to food scares and consumer fears.

The impact of illness

The scale of the problem.

Problems of comparing statistics.

Assessments of the true financial costs.

Personal costs of food-borne illness.

Safeguards through diligence

The general impact of legal requirements on food businesses.

The meaning of due diligence.

Due diligence as a legal defence.

What due diligence means in practice.

Chasing profits

The balance of cost-saving measures and food safety requirements.

The competitive significance of food safety.

Key words

Case
One incidence of illness.

Due diligence
A duty of care. A legal defence where it can be shown that all reasonable steps were taken to avoid committing a food safety offence.

Food-borne illness/disease
Terms used in this book to indicate *any* type of illness that is caused, or is probably caused, by the consumption of contaminated food, water or other drink.

HACCP
An abbreviation, usually pronounced 'hassup', for Hazard Analysis and Critical Control Point. This is an internationally recognised risk management system for food. It involves identifying food safety hazards and assessing and controlling the risks from them.

Outbreak
A cluster, in time or place, of cases of illness caused by a particular organism.

Customer concerns

Without customers, there can be no business, so customer relationship management is central to all businesses. Like any other successful relationship, customer relationships take time to develop and are likely to include understanding (of customer needs), appreciation (of customer expectations) and mutual trust and respect.

How can you possibly achieve this with every customer? This is a central question of customer relationship management. It is a huge subject that we cannot examine in detail here, but it is well worth considering what the expectations of typical groups of your customers are likely to be, so in this chapter we take a brief look at customer concerns and expectations about food safety. As you will see, customer relationship management and food safety management often overlap in the food industry.

Who are your customers?

The head of a British trade organisation once said at an open meeting that he had a lot of customers who returned time and again to his shop. He added, however, that it was only customers he had and not consumers. On being asked to elaborate, he said that he had a great many happy, informed customers whose expectations were being met to their satisfaction, but consumers were something else altogether – they were people who were only interested in making trouble.

You do not have to agree with these tongue-in-cheek comments and we certainly do not endorse them. Even so, the comments do raise interesting points about the awareness, expectations, perceptions and satisfaction of the people who buy your products and services.

Purchasing and consuming

What you call the people who buy your food depends to some extent on where you work. *Guest*, *customer*, *consumer*, *shopper*, *client*, *diner* and *visitor* are all in common use, while *inmate* or *patient* may be appropriate terms in certain sectors.

In this book we use the words *customer* and *consumer* interchangeably to indicate people who buy food products and services for personal use. We use the word *client* when we need to distinguish someone, such as a manufacturer, who buys a food or ingredient for use in a product that is later sold to someone else. That 'someone else' could be another food business or an individual shopper.

(It's worth noting, that food legislation identifies the *final consumer* as being 'the ultimate consumer of a foodstuff who will not use the food as part of any food business operation or activity.' So, this is someone who *buys* the food for private use (for the family, for example), but does not necessarily eat or drink (consume) the product himself or herself.)

Customer awareness

People in the UK are probably more aware of food safety issues now than they ever have been. Newspapers frequently run food scare stories, and food safety in one form or another often features in the storylines of 'soaps', in documentaries, information from food businesses and consumer groups, school projects or the experience of friends or family. Consumers have probably heard something about *Salmonella* in eggs, chicken or chocolate bars; chicken unfit for human consumption; tuna contaminated by mercury; BSE ('mad cow disease') in cattle; Creutzfeldt-Jakob Disease (CJD) and its variants – the human forms of BSE; viruses, such as Norovirus, that produce symptoms like food poisoning; E. coli O157 connected with reheated meat products; Listeria in unpasteurized cheese; botulism in nut yoghurt; dioxins in the environment; genetically modified organisms (GMOs); irradiated food; avian influenza and so on.

You will probably be quick to point out that all this awareness is not necessarily good news for the food industry. The Food Standards Agency (FSA) has carried out consumer attitudes surveys each year since it was formed in 2000 and the general level of concern has remained consistently high. Most people interviewed (70 per cent in England in 2005, for instance) expressed some concern about food safety issues.

Great expectations

The public's concern needs to be managed, not ignored. But what can *you* do? One starting point is to consider some of the views that your customers might have about the food they eat, the food industry and the public authorities. Consider what is completely beyond your scope of influence, and what can be managed by efficient and effective food safety.

What customers might expect from their food

- Food is what it is labelled to be.

- It is safe and will not make anyone ill.

- Products are fresh and within their shelf life, which has been established scientifically.

- Food is tasty and nutritious, with any necessary additives kept to a minimum.

- Products are good value for money.

What customers might expect from the food industry

- Safe food and packaging

    - produced with appropriate care and attention (due diligence) by staff who remember that customers are going to eat the food.

- Customer relationships

    - managed with integrity and honesty

    - alert to customer expectations and requirements

    - effective complaints system in place, with recompense offered if appropriate

    - prompt product recall if there is a problem.

- Product descriptions

    - assurances about the source of the food

    - correct labelling, including for genetically modified and irradiated products

    - nutritional information provided.

- Animal welfare

    - humane treatment for the animals used for food.

What customers might expect from politicians, government departments and food inspection services

- Laws

    - made to protect consumers

    - suitable for the current requirements

    - enforced fairly, correctly and consistently.

- Staff suitably trained and experienced for the job.

- The food safety system

    - properly funded

    - no conflict of interest

    - any shortcomings identified and corrected

    - consumer protection gets priority over the food industry if there is doubt over an issue

    - controversial issues dealt with openly and transparently.

Managing perceptions

The general public's perceptions of the dangers associated with food are often in reverse order to the perceptions of specialists who work with food.

Public perception of dangers from food (in descending order)

- Pesticide residues or food additives.

- Drug residues, such as antibiotics given to animals.

- Migrating chemicals (for instance, from plasticised food wrapping).

- Natural toxicants.

Scientific evaluation of risks in food (in descending order)

- Natural toxicants.

- Pesticide residues.

- Drug residues.

- Migrating chemicals.

- Food additives.

There are many possible reasons to explain the discrepancy between the public's perceptions and scientific evaluation. They could include public mistrust of the scientific community or the government, misinformation, or misinterpretation or dislike of E-numbers. On the other hand, the discrepancy could be explained because, for example, scientists may not have got everything right in the past, may not have done enough research into the long-term effects of additives and residues or may not listened sufficiently carefully to customers' concerns.

What you can do

The real point here is that it may be as difficult to deal with a *perceived* hazard or risk as it is to deal with an *actual* hazard or risk. Even so, you should never underestimate the damage that can be done by a *perceived* problem with a food, an ingredient or a particular sector of the food industry. But what *can* you do?

On the grand scale, it is a challenge for the food industry in general and you may not wish, or be able, to participate directly in meeting this challenge. But you can make your views known by working with, or through membership of, professional and trade organisations and by keeping in close touch with the activities of local environmental health departments, food safety and environmental health bodies and the Food Standards Agency (see page 415 for contact details).

On a smaller scale, you may be able to do more. For example, during the height of the BSE scare in the UK in the 1990s business at many small family butchers shops *increased* because the public often believed that a local business would be more concerned about the source of their products than larger operations, such as supermarkets, might be. In fact, many supermarkets have schemes in place with product standards that far exceed those of smaller organisations, but there is no evidence to show that the existence of such standards always influences the public's perception.

The use or omission of additives provides another example. In the late 1970s and the 1980s the producers of diverse products, such as salad cream and tomato paste, responded to public antipathy towards E-numbers by removing the additives that helped to prolong the product's shelf life. Consequently consumers were advised to refrigerate the products after opening them, whereas previously the products could be stored safely in a cupboard for quite long periods.

It would also help to have in place a plan of crisis management to deal with sudden publicity about risks, whether perceived or actual. This is discussed in Part 4.

From satisfaction to loyalty

What then is a satisfied customer? One definition of quality is the return of the customer, not the food. This suggests a way of defining a satisfied customer: one who, given a choice of different foods, shops, restaurants and so on, consistently returns for more of the same. A customer who returns indicates that all his or her reasonable expectations have been met and all perceptions have been satisfactorily dealt with.

How then can we ensure the return of the customer? A significant part of the answer is by managing all food safety issues efficiently and effectively. After all, without effective hygiene systems, you will soon lose your customers – and without customers, there can be no business.

Making it easier for others

- Emphasise that customers expect their food to be safe to eat. If it is not safe, custom will fall with potentially disastrous consequences for the business and for jobs.

- Encourage all food handlers to understand that they have a crucial individual part to play in producing safe food and, by so doing, in meeting customer expectations.

The impact of illness

There have been periods when it has been rare for many weeks to pass without hearing something about illnesses linked to food in Britain. But has there genuinely been an increase in the number of cases of illness linked to food, or just an increase in publicity? If there has indeed been an increase, is it a worldwide problem or confined to particular parts of the world? If, instead, there has been a decrease, what in fact is working well?

A continuing global health problem

Use of terms
In this book we use 'food-borne illness' and 'food-borne disease' interchangeably to indicate all the illnesses linked to food, such as those often described as 'food poisoning' or ' food-borne infection'.

The global incidence of food-borne illness is notoriously difficult to calculate accurately. For a start, some countries have only rudimentary systems for collecting statistics. Then there is the problem of exactly how an illness linked to food is defined and this makes it extremely difficult to formulate meaningful comparisons between countries. Finally, as most cases are sporadic and may last only a short time, people may not report their illness to a doctor, so the circumstances that led to the illness may not be investigated fully.

Nonetheless, statistics from around the world show that the incidence of food-borne disease is extremely high and the World Health Organization (WHO) has reported that such illnesses are a widespread and continuing public health problem in both developed and developing countries. In 2000 alone, for example, 2.1 million people around the world, many of them children, died from diarrhoeal diseases. Many of these cases are attributed to the contamination of food and drinking water.

Even in industrialised countries where it might be reasonable to assume that food safety systems are in place, up to 30 per cent of people are thought to suffer from a food-borne disease each year. In some developing countries the high prevalence of diarrhoeal illnesses indicates the likelihood of a higher percentage, which in turn suggests underlying food safety problems, many caused by parasites.

There are an estimated 76 million cases of food-borne diseases each year in the United States of America, resulting in 325,000 hospitalisations and 5,000 deaths. While these figures are extrapolations from the actual number of cases reported, they still make depressing reading.

Examples of outbreaks

Although outbreaks of food-related illness are often fairly small and short-lived, they may also be on a massive scale. For example, in 1988 an outbreak of Hepatitis A, resulting from the consumption of contaminated clams, affected some 300,000 people in China. In 1994 an outbreak of salmonellosis from contaminated ice cream in America affected an estimated 224,000 people. In 1996 more than 6,300 schoolchildren in Japan became ill in an outbreak of a strain of *E. coli* O157.

The British picture

There is a well-respected system for gathering information about food-related illnesses in the UK which dates back to the 1960s in its present form. Even so, as in many other countries, the British statistics have often been likened to an iceberg, with only the tip of the problem visible.

An unseen problem?

A survey by the Food Standards Agency asked people to estimate the number of times that they had suffered from food poisoning in a year, based on their own diagnosis of symptoms.

The results showed that 14 per cent of people in England, 13 per cent in Scotland, 11 per cent in Wales and 10 per cent in Northern Ireland believed that they had had some form of food-borne illness in 2000. This would mean that 5 million people in the UK were ill that year from eating contaminated food, even though the official statistics showed only some 98,000 cases.

Other estimates put the likely figure even higher. The Committee on the Microbiological Safety of Food carried out extensive research in England in the 1990s and estimated that 20 per cent of the population of England suffered an 'infectious intestinal disease (IID)' in a year. However, as only three per cent of the population went to a general practitioner (GP), not every case of food-related illness was recorded in official statistics.

The committee's research included collecting data and stools, but did not distinguish between cases of IID that resulted from 'food poisoning' and cases from other causes. Even so, based on the research figures, there may be a staggering 9.5 million actual cases each year in England alone, compared to *reported* cases for England and Wales that have never reached 100,000!

Official trends

In the United Kingdom of Great Britain and Northern Ireland the *general* trend in the number of notified cases of food poisoning in the UK has been downward since the record-high levels of the late 1990s – see the graphs on page 21. In the five-year period from 2000-2005, the number of cases decreased by just over 19 per cent (from the year 2000 baseline). Even allowing for the uncertainty about the true picture shown by statistics, this is surely good news? So what is the reason for the decrease?

The Food Standards Agency (FSA) says there is no definitive answer to this question at present, but it suggests a number of factors that have helped.

Salmonella used to be the most common cause of food poisoning. Over the last decade or so, the industry has worked hard and successfully to reduce *Salmonella* contamination of poultry meat and eggs. This helped to decrease the number of cases from 1997 on.

Since 2001 the FSA has been implementing the 'Foodborne Disease Strategy' involving a wide range of measures across the whole food chain. They include reducing the microbial contamination of foods, particularly poultry and red meat; promoting better food safety management and practice; and promoting the hygienic preparation of food both commercially and in the home. An independent evaluation of the strategy highlighted

Number of notified cases of food poisoning (England and Wales)

Source: Health Protection Agency; Statutory Notifications of Infectious Diseases (NOIDs)

Number of notified cases of food poisoning (Scotland)

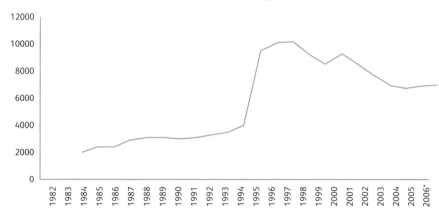

Source: Health Protection Scotland; Scottish Centre for Infection and Environmental Health.
* Provisional figure

Number of notified cases of food poisoning (Northern Ireland)

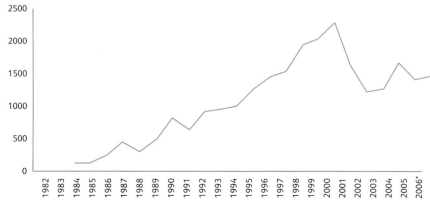

Source: Health Protection Agency; Communicable Disease Surveillance Centre, Northern Ireland.
* Provisional figure

initiatives that were felt to have contributed to the reduction in the number of cases. These included continuing work to reduce *Salmonella* and *Campylobacter* in poultry, measures to improve hygiene in abattoirs, and increased awareness of food safety and good food hygiene practices among the general public and in industry.

The FSA hopes that initiatives, such as the introduction of HACCP-based guidance for small catering businesses (see page182), will eventually contribute to a reduction in the number of cases of food-related illness.

The graphs

The graphs on page 21 are based on figures collected nationwide. There are some regional differences in the sources of the figures collated which may involve statistics from various laboratories and medical reports. This makes it difficult to compare the figures in one part of the UK with those of another.

The graphs cannot indicate the seasonal variations each year – for example, the summer barbecue season can see an upsurge in problems, such as *Salmonella* poisoning, associated with undercooked meats. Christmas can see increases in problems from inadequate thawing and undercooking of poultry.

Paralytic shellfish poisoning may also occur more frequently in the warmer months when toxic algae grow more profusely. In the winter months illness from small round structured viruses (such as winter vomiting disease in pre-school playgroups and at infants schools) can increase.

The economic penalties of food-borne illness

The true economic cost of food-borne illness in any country is almost impossible to estimate. It is relatively easy to calculate the cost of medical treatment, hospitalisation, loss of working hours, investigation of the case and action to prevent a recurrence, but it is complicated and time consuming calculating the cost of lost potential business.

As for individuals, how can you put a true price on the loss of personal amenity, temporary or permanent impairment or death?

Some food-borne diseases are of short duration only and, while they may be unpleasant at the time, usually do not cause discomfort for more than a couple of days. Others, however, may have serious, long-term consequences which affect all aspects of a person's life, including the incalculable value of the loss of amenity to the patient, the cost of the loss of his or her earnings and possibly those of family members too.

The cost to food companies can also be extremely high and can be from many sources:

- loss of working hours and production
- loss of reputation
- loss of business
- fines
- compensation payments to customers
- product withdrawals or recalls.

Putting a figure on the cost

Despite the difficulties in calculating the true cost of food-borne illness, valid attempts can be made, as you can see from the two following examples.

UK

Between 2001 and 2006 the incidence of food-borne illness decreased by 19.2 per cent. About 1.5 million fewer people suffered with an illness from food and 10,000 fewer people were treated in hospital as a result of something they ate. The Food Standards Agency estimates that this saved more than £750 million. According to these figures, the average cost of each case of food-borne illness was £500. Bearing in mind that food-borne illness is a preventable disease, this is a staggering sum of money.

In separate calculations the Committee on the Microbiological Safety of Food estimated that the proportions of the financial burden of food-borne illness nationwide are 55 per cent to employers in lost production; about 36 per cent to the National Health Service, with 'cases presenting to a GP' (people who go to their doctor) accounting for more than half of this figure; and 8 per cent in direct costs to the person suffering from the illness.

USA

With a few assumptions and some rough and ready arithmetic (and erring on the cautious side), we can gain some idea of the magnitude of the problem in the USA. Let's take the estimated figure of 76 million cases per year and assume that only half of the people were full-time workers and each had only one day off work because of the illness. If we assume that each person earned an average $30 every day, then the loss of working hours alone cost the country $1,140,000,000 per year. Of course, the true figure is likely to be far higher!

A heavy burden

Whatever the true financial cost of food-borne illness around the world, it is certainly high. Even though official statistics in some parts of the world, such as Britain, show a recent reduction in cases of illness, there is absolutely no room for complacency. Even one case is too many. What's more, it is unnecessary. With good management, you can make a significant contribution to reducing the personal, business and national burden of illness from contaminated food.

Making it easier for others

- Explain that food safety is about preventing people from becoming ill.

- Point out that more people around the world die from eating food and drinking water than from natural catastrophes, war or pestilence.

- Explain that statistics represent only the tip of the iceberg of actual cases of illness.

- Discuss the personal pain and suffering and the economic consequences from food-borne illnesses.

- Encourage staff to consider how safe food benefits everyone – the consumer, the general public at large, the business itself and the people who work in it.

- Emphasise that food safety is an integral part of staff members' roles, not an optional extra.

Feature

Living in dangerous times?

Have you ever pondered why you have to comply with so many food safety regulations when many generations seemed to survive perfectly well without protective clothing or disinfecting their hands and with only a rudimentary understanding of temperature control?

If so, you are not alone. Many busy managers have been tempted to think that they have more red tape to deal with than their predecessors, and they may sometimes think that legal demands are tougher in the country where they work than elsewhere in the world.

In fact food hygiene rules are *not* a modern invention and forms of compliance are found worldwide.

Phoenician clay slabs dating back to 3,500 BC proclaim in neat cuneiform characters, 'You shall not poison your neighbour's fat nor shall you bewitch your neighbour's wine.'

Punishments for transgressing rules about food could be far harsher than today's penalties.

In Babylon in the year 3,000 BC, for example, the adulteration of wine was punishable by death, but the offender generally had to be caught red-handed.

Early food hygiene rules were often part of religious regulations, some of which are still observed today.

Such rules might have included the prohibition of some animals, birds and fish as human food because they were regarded as 'unclean'; the separation of certain products (such as meat from milk) during preparation and storage; the use of clean and unclean sources of water and procedures for cleaning utensils after contact with animal flesh.

As many early peoples were nomadic, such rules may have helped to avoid contamination, cross-contamination and microbial multiplication in difficult conditions for food safety.

If we continued looking around the world and throughout history, we would find innumerable rules that have attempted to protect communities from the unpleasant and often life-threatening effects of illnesses from food.

So, what, if anything, has changed about the safety of our food today?

Firstly, our understanding of the causes of food-related illnesses – and subsequently the development of preventive measures enshrined in legislation – increased dramatically after Robert Koch had demonstrated at the end of the nineteenth century the connection between micro-organisms and disease.

Secondly, however, cases of food-borne disease have escalated worldwide, particularly in the two last decades of the twentieth century.

At first glance, the two developments make no sense at all. After all, it is fair to assume that a better knowledge of the causes of illnesses should *improve* food safety measures, not lead to an increase in illness.

Were our ancestors indeed getting it right, or are we just scaring ourselves silly with data that were not available in the past?

Despite frequent developments in food microbiology and technology, microbes seem always to be one step ahead of us.

Recent research shows that we have badly underestimated the adaptability of micro-organisms and their ability to 'reappear' after they were believed to have been conquered – the latter are termed *re-emergent pathogens* by the World Health Organization (WHO).

One of the most worrying of these re-emergent organisms – a strain of *E. coli* known as VTEC or *E. coli* O157 – became

a public menace within just a few years in the 1980s.

According to the WHO, other pathogens that have gained significance include *Listeria monocytogenes*, *Salmonella* species (see picture, opposite), *Vibrio cholerae*, *Campylobacter jejuni*, *Yersinia enterocolitica*, *Cryptosporidium parvum* and *Clonorchis sinensis* (a parasite).

Along with the familiar symptoms of 'classic' food poisoning (such as vomiting, abdominal pain, diarrhoea and fever) may now occur symptoms with some frightening possible long-term consequences, such as arthritis, meningitis, haemolytic-uraemic syndrome, septicaemia, cancer, blindness and spontaneous abortion.

Of course, we cannot calculate how many people died in days gone by from the effects of eating contaminated food because such statistics were not collected.

Some experts say that the rise in cases in recent decades can be attributed to increased reporting of symptoms, better medical diagnoses and improved microbiological detection methods.

But this is certainly not the whole answer. For example, in the last century or so Europe has seen enormous changes in public attitudes and expectations towards daily food and some radical shifts in our buying and eating habits.

These include an increased demand for meat, especially poultry, despite the increase in vegetarianism; more eating out; and the extension of home deliveries.

Then there is the demand for products all the year round regardless of the local harvesting season.

Other developments includes greater use of 'ready' meals; the transportation of livestock and products over far greater distances and the development of a wide range of preservation methods, packaging and equipment enabling long-distance transport, long-term storage and a shift towards far more bulk buying of food for home consumption.

Another modern trend, global tourism, has enabled pathogens to spread farther and faster than in the past. Typically, tourists catch infections, such as typhoid, hepatitis and cholera, in tropical countries and take them home, often to countries where the infections were thought to be under control.

All the changes mentioned so far are well accepted, but others, which are mentioned below, are more open to debate.

For instance, cheap ingredients in some imported animal feeds from tropical countries where animal infection is widespread may have led to an increased risk of introducing animal diseases into the UK, some of which affect humans.

Another possible problem is the increased resistance to antibiotics of pathogens such as *Salmonella* following the treatment of animal feed. This has resulted in the rapid development of strains of *Salmonella* that are immune to a range of antimicrobial products used to treat animals and humans.

The distribution of bovine spongiform encephalopathy (BSE) is yet another example quoted of how technological changes in the processing of feeds and foods may have created new hazards within a very short time span.

It may seem that some human-created problems are like a contamination carousel, on which problems just keep coming back.

There are also issues involving people in the 'at risk group' – those who are especially vulnerable to the symptoms of food-related illnesses, including pregnant women and unborn children, breast-fed infants, the very young, the elderly and people who are already ill, convalescing or who have weakened immunity to disease.

The number of older people is increasing in most industrial societies as a result of modern medicine and better nutrition. This has increased the number of people who are especially vulnerable to the symptoms of food-borne illnesses.

Those with compromised immune systems as a consequence of viruses such as HIV (human immunodeficiency virus) are also in the growing 'at risk group'.

So, are we indeed living in more dangerous times than our ancestors as far as food safety is concerned?

All the signs are that there will always be food safety hazards, but, with newly emerging and re-emerging pathogens, it is just possible that we may be facing a greater risk than generations before us – in spite of all our knowledge and technology.

What we must not forget is that the evolution of organisms has never come to an end.

Whenever we make changes, such as developing new preservation techniques, forms of transport and storage technologies, we provide new niches and possibilities for micro-organisms. They tend to adjust themselves to whatever is on offer.

So, how does someone in your job deal with constantly changing and evolving micro-organisms?

You'll find many of the answers and practicable solutions throughout the book, but here we allow ourselves a little speculation about changes that may come about.

It is possible that the risks from microbiological hazards will indeed gain greater significance.

Principles of risk management (see Part 4) will certainly help us to predict problems from microbes at various stages of the food flow and to eliminate the hazard or control its risks. Even so, we may need to acquire greater knowledge of a micro-organism than at present.

Competitive relationships between micro-organisms and interactions between microflora and packaging may become more and more important.

At the same time, the demand for foods with a longer shelf life and the distances food has to travel can only be achieved by a thorough safety guarantee from the primary producer to the consumer.

Additional, even clearer, labelling may be needed on certain products to give consumers even clearer warnings about cross-contamination, the dangers from undercooking meat and poultry and the possible presence of allergens.

Finally, consumers themselves may need to be encouraged to meet more hygiene challenges in their homes.

This could perhaps be achieved by providing even more information and education on basic food safety principles, delivered as a standard school subject in the way it is already handled in Scotland and in some other European Union member states.

Safeguards through diligence

One powerful motivation for a business to manage food safety is that the law requires it. In recent years legislation has had more and more to say about the required ways to manage the safety of food – for example, by carrying out risk assessments and by having systems in place to trace products along the food chain. No business can achieve the minimum standards demanded by legislation if food safety is simply left to chance. What's more, if something does go wrong and a business is prosecuted for breaching food safety rules, its strongest (and, possibly, its only) defence is to demonstrate that it took the greatest possible care to safeguard food – in other words, it managed food safety properly.

In Part 3 you will learn in some detail about the ways in which legislation influences the management of food safety, whether directly or indirectly. For the time being, we shall take a brief look at the principles of food safety legislation and legal compliance. If you are interested in a longer discussion about the reasons for controlling food safety by law, see the feature on pages 30 and 31.

Safety principles

Legal basics
The law expects food businesses to take all reasonable care possible to ensure that food is safe to eat, unadulterated and labelled and sold in an honest manner.

Every food business has legal obligations to supply the consumer with food that is:

- safe for humans to eat

- of the nature, quality and substance demanded by the consumer

- properly labelled and sold without misleading claims.

The wording of these three responsibilities is based upon British legislation, but similar basic legal obligations can be found in food safety laws throughout the world. They seem to be reasonable minimum standards that could legally be applied to any food business to protect public health and, in the case of the second and third obligations, to prevent fraudulent selling.

Due diligence

Many countries have the principle of **due diligence** (or *reasonable care*) at the heart of their food legislation. In Britain, it is one of only two main types of defence for a food business accused of breaking food safety rules – that the alleged offence was committed by someone else, or that there was due diligence.

The word *diligence* comes from Latin words meaning 'to choose to be industrious', or 'to choose to be persistent in your effort or work'. The word *due* comes from Old French and Latin words meaning 'something that is owed' – in other words, something where there is little choice. So, at first glance due diligence can seem to be a bit of a contradiction – something involving persistent industriousness (because you wanted to do it), but something where you really do not have a choice (because you owe it anyway)! But do not be fooled by this apparent paradox.

The legislation does not state that food businesses must be diligent. In theory, they can be as careful or as careless as they please. However (and this is the important point), all the specific legal duties add up to the clear message that food businesses owe a *due* – a duty of care – to their customers. So, if you cannot show that you are paying your debt of care to your customers, then you are most likely be found guilty of committing the offences with which you have been charged. There is no excuse for mistaking how a food business is expected to behave – if it does *everything* within its power to safeguard consumer health, then the law will not hold the business liable if something does go wrong.

Ensuring diligence

So how can a food business demonstrate due diligence if called upon to do so? The heart of your defence is to show that there is a management system in place and that it enables managers to identify and correct anything which may be unlawful.

This is relatively easy to show with respect to physical contaminants. Imagine, for example, that a customer has found a piece of metal in a jar of baby food. If the food processing company responsible can show that all its equipment, utensils and tools are well maintained, that it operates an efficient automatic metal detection system and that it follows an up-to-date HACCP plan, then a court may well acquit the company. Acquittal is less likely if the company cannot show that any of these measures is in place.

Even so, the existence of a system for managing due diligence is not enough in itself: the system also has to work properly. If food premises are infested with mice, or are in a filthy condition, then the mere existence of a system is unlikely to convince a court that due diligence was being exercised because the system is clearly *not* working effectively.

Working effectively

As you can imagine, it is much more difficult to have a strong defence for matters such as personal hygiene than it is for issues involving the composition, labelling or physical contamination of food, so this is where well-documented effective training and instruction can help to establish due diligence. There is more about training and its role in food safety in Part 4. As you read through the book, you'll find many examples of policies, systems and procedures that could help a food company to ensure that it can demonstrate due diligence.

The following list, although not comprehensive, gives an idea of some of them:

- a documented HACCP system, or similar system (see Part 4)
- evidence of supplier audits
- evidence that food has been bought from reputable sources
- cleaning and disinfection schedules
- a waste disposal policy
- a system of integrated pest management
- an accredited hygiene system
- staff training records
- policies for personal hygiene
- evidence of appropriate supervision.

As you can see, these are all management issues. Legal responsibilities and the need to establish due diligence create convincing arguments for the value of *managing* food safety, and not just leaving it to chance.

It is common to see some of these points – such as cleaning and disinfection, waste disposal, pest management, staff training and personal hygiene – referred to as *HACCP prerequisites* or *good hygiene practice* (GHP) or *good manufacturing practice* (GMP). However you describe them, they are essential aspects of every food business that need to be in place and managed.

Making it easier for others

- Make sure that everyone who handles food, or who could have an impact upon the safety of food, understands his or her own legal responsibilities.

- Emphasise that food safety and legal compliance is a team effort and make certain that staff know how best to contribute to that team effort.

- Explain what the company does to try to ensure that food is safe to eat – for instance, ensure that the food safety policy (see Part 4) is easy for everyone to understand.

- Impress upon staff the importance of complying with the spirit and the letter of the law.

- Encourage professional pride in diligence.

- Lead by example and make sure that other senior staff do so too.

Do we really need food safety laws?

Why not just let market forces determine food safety? Do we really need to control food safety by law?

In a democratic society legislation aims to achieve many things. Foremost among the objectives is the protection of society.

That protection may be from unwanted external influences, such as the importation of dangerous drugs, or from undesirable internal influences and activities, such as theft and murder.

Protection may also be from people wishing to operate outside the acceptable limits of society, for example, through terrorism. Or it could be protection from discrimination or harm directed at people who are unable, or only partly able, to protect themselves – from, for example, workplace hazards.

So where does food safety law fit into this protection?

Any state, through its government, is responsible for a great number of functions that are funded from the public purse. Some of these functions are defined by the legal system of the country. Others are part of the collective responsibility assumed by the state because 'someone has to do it' and nobody else is under any obligation to do so.

As far as food safety is concerned, a state usually assumes responsibility for the protection of public health; the suppression of fraud; the drafting, adoption and enforcement of laws; the establishment of a judiciary and a legal process; and international agreements on laws and standards.

But to what extent should a state seek to control public health and food safety?

Many people would probably agree that there should be some form of control on the causes of illnesses from food and drink. But what about nutrition? After all, bad eating habits may lie behind many illnesses and even deaths from food. Should a state seek to control an individual's diet or should it merely issue advice about it?

Most governments have restricted their function to the issuing of advice, rather than trying to control an individual's diet by legal means. Why not then merely issue advice about food safety and just leave it at that?

The simplistic answer is that diet is to a large extent a matter of individual choice (within the person's budget) and a state can usually seek to influence choice only through public education.

On the other hand, food-borne illness is often beyond an individual's control or choice – even though some people do bring about their own food-related illness because of their carelessness.

So, is it *reasonable* for a state to attempt to control the hazards and risks to public health from food? Surely the answer must be 'yes'.

After all, consumers cannot see microbes such as *Salmonella* and, even if they had daily access to powerful microscopes, most microbiological and chemical hazards, as well as physical hazards, are normally well outside their control.

What is more, although there are 'at risk groups' who are particularly vulnerable to the impact of food-borne illness, when such an illness does strike, it rarely distinguishes between the rich and the poor, the well fed and the underfed or the educated and the uneducated.

Perhaps then this gives us an idea of why most countries have introduced food safety laws – to protect, by legislation or other means, the health of the consumer in areas that are outside the consumer's normal personal control.

Of course, this does not mean that food safety education or advice is unnecessary. Indeed the opposite is true. General food safety education and specific training for people in the food industry and general food hygiene education for the public are as important as education about nutrition.

Essential though food legislation may be, laws usually lay down only the minimum standards below which something cannot fall.

Recognising this, many food businesses set company standards that are in excess of the legal minimum – something that you may wish to consider doing too.

Chasing profits

Like every other commercial operation, food companies need to make a profit to survive. Even food organisations in non-profit-making sectors still need to keep within their budgets, so many of the issues involved in profit chasing are just as relevant to them. In the last three chapters we looked at how the need to stay in business and food safety issues impinge upon each other. In this chapter we take a brief look at some other business matters.

Controlling costs

Every manager knows that one way to increase profit is to lower costs. But the true result of cost-lowering initiatives depends entirely on how those costs are reduced. Suppose that you decide to lower costs by reducing energy consumption. You could do this in a number of ways. However, if you were to pasteurize a product, such as milk or ham, at a temperature that was lower than the legal requirement, there would soon be an *increase* in costs – perhaps because of an outbreak of food-borne illness, or because the reduced shelf life would lead to food being thrown away, or because of a well-publicised court case and the subsequent loss of custom.

More for less

Increasing efficiency is another well-tried way to reduce costs – whether this is achieved through improved management systems, increased staff productivity, better workflow, new equipment or any other means. In the short term this may *increase* costs – for example, as a result of training staff in new ways of working, or improving the risk assessment system. In the long term, however, you should get more benefits for less outlay, so *reducing* your costs.

Waste reduction

Yet another way to decrease costs is to reduce waste. General aspects of waste reduction – for instance, by reducing packaging – are discussed in the CIEH's book *Environmental Management at Work*. However, in food businesses some of the most controllable waste consists of discarded ingredients or products and reworked or recalled products – all arising because of faults or customer complaints.

As you will see in Part 4, an advantage of a HACCP, or a similar, system is that the cost of implementing the system can be outweighed by savings in the time and products that were previously 'wasted' because of faults and customer complaints.

The role of staff

One of your key management roles is likely to be the motivation of staff so that they can all play their full part in food safety. You need to make it clear that food safety is every individual's responsibility whether he or she is a buyer, production worker, chef, kitchen porter, quality manager, shelf-stacker, sandwich-filler, cleaner, maintenance engineer or any other jobholder in a food business. Developing a sense of individual and team responsibility should help to raise overall standards of food safety and may also reduce the need for supervision, as staff may help to supervise one another.

Competitiveness

How many companies use their food safety systems and good food safety record as a marketing tool? In fact, quite a number do just that, particularly those in the manufacturing and processing sectors. If a customer or a client company (one that buys food from you but is not the consumer) is seeking a product and Company A can offer a tried and tested food safety system while Company B can offer only a wing and a prayer, who do you think is most likely to get the business?

Making it easier for others

- Discuss the factors of importance to food safety that help to make a profit for the business.

- Make it clear that staff should not attempt to cut corners on anything to do with food safety.

- Point out that high standards of food safety help the company to stay in business and remain an employer.

3. What do we need to manage?

What do we need to manage?

'Waiter! There's a fly in my soup!' wails the disgruntled diner in a time-honoured British joke. 'Shh. Keep your voice down, sir,' replies the waiter promptly, 'or everybody will want one.'

Even if this ludicrous scenario fails to make you smile, it certainly draws attention to the consumer expectation that the food they buy is safe to eat and that nothing about its appearance, smell, taste or ingredients will put them off eating it.

Food safety legislation supports such consumer views, insisting that all food intended for human consumption should be uncontaminated, safe to eat (so that it does not injure health) and of the nature, substance or quality that the consumer demands.

Food hazards and legal requirements are the main issues you need to manage if you are to secure the safety of the food and legal compliance. Part 3 looks at them in detail, providing the underlying knowledge for good management practice that is discussed in Part 4.

It is particularly important to understand thoroughly all the key points in Part 3 and to feel confident in using the key words listed in both sections. All these terms are explained in the relevant chapter and can also be found in the Glossary.

Hazards

Key points

Hazards in context

What hazards are.

The significance of food hazards in contemporary food safety practices.

Types of food hazard.

Biological and microbiological hazards

The significance of microbiological hazards to the management of food safety.

Types of microbiological hazard.

Bacteria

Categories of bacteria, defined by their impact on humans.

Characteristics of bacteria.

Bacterial reproduction, including factors influencing multiplication and the optimal conditions.

The role of toxins and their impact on health.

The significance of spore formation to food safety.

Sampling and monitoring techniques and their limitations.

Bacterial food-borne illness

Categorisations of bacterial illnesses linked to food.

Differences between food poisoning and food-borne infections.

Types of food-borne micro-organism and the illnesses they cause.

Sources of contamination and the foods most commonly involved.

Vehicles and routes of contamination.

Transmission of illness, onset, symptoms and carrier status.

The principles of control.

Viruses

Characteristics of viruses.

Sources of contamination, vehicles and routes of contamination.

Transmission of illness, onset, symptoms and carrier status.

The principles of control.

Parasites

Characteristics and life cycles of parasites.

Foods most commonly implicated in parasitic infection.

Transmission of illness, onset, symptoms and carrier status.

Control methods.

Fungi

Characteristics of fungi.

Sources and routes of contamination.

Illness from fungi.

Mould and yeast spoilage.

Control methods.

Chemical hazards

Causes and sources of food-borne chemical illnesses.

Characteristics of illnesses caused by chemicals.

Control measures throughout the food chain.

Categorisations of chemicals.

The chemical hazards that can adversely affect the safety of food.

Typical symptoms and consequences of food-borne chemical poisoning.

The differences between acute and chronic chemical food-borne illness.

Naturally occurring chemicals

Sources of naturally occurring chemicals.

Symptoms of illness.

Mycotoxins

The categorisation of mycotoxins and their implications for human health.

Symptoms of illness.

The conditions in which mycotoxin-producing moulds thrive.

Problems with preservation techniques.

Controls at the farm and purchasing policies.

General controls.

Introduced chemicals

Typical introduced chemicals implicated in food poisoning.

Characteristics of illnesses caused by introduced chemicals.

The consequences of chemical accumulation and carry over.

Physical hazards

The scope of physical hazards.

Common physical contaminants and their sources.

Health implications of physical contaminants.

Disgust – implications under the law and for customer relationships.

Intrinsic and extrinsic contamination.

Allergen hazards

The differences between a food allergy and a food intolerance.

Typical symptoms.

Anaphylactic shock.

Foods commonly implicated in food allergy and intolerance.

Key words

Acid/acidic
A pH of less than 7.0.

Acute disease
An illness in which symptoms develop rapidly after infection.

Acute poisoning
The effect of eating food containing a high level of a toxic substance over a short time.

Aerobe
An organism requiring oxygen.

Alkali/alkaline
A pH of more than 7.0.

Allergen
A substance, usually a protein, in food that makes certain people ill, even though the food is harmless to others.

Allergic reaction
Symptoms of illness caused by an allergy.

Allergy
An adverse response by the body's immune system to an allergen.

Anaerobe
An organism that does not require oxygen.

Anaphylaxis/anaphylactic shock
An extreme response of the body's immune system that can be life threatening.

Antibody
A natural protective chemical produced by the body.

At risk group
People at greatest risk from food-borne pathogens, including pregnant women and unborn children, breast-fed babies, the very young, the elderly, people who are ill or convalescing and people who have weakened immunity to disease.

a_w (or water activity)
The moisture available to an organism.

Bacterial growth curve
The changes in the size of a bacterial colony, as recorded on a graph. The development of the population of an organism.

Bacterium (plural: bacteria)
A single-celled micro-organism. Some are harmful, causing illness or spoiling food. Others are beneficial and are needed to make foods such as cheese and bread.

Base/basic
Another word for alkaline.

Binary fission
Reproduction by splitting in two – the way in which most bacteria multiply.

Carrier
A person who is infected by a pathogen and can pass it on to others, but who does not experience symptoms.

Carry-over effect
The accumulation and transmission of a chemical.

Chronic disease
An illness in which symptoms last a relatively long time and may take some time to develop after infection.

Chronic poisoning
The effect of eating food containing a low level of a toxic substance over a long period.

Ciguatera
The most common type of poisoning from fish, caused by eating fish that have been contaminated by toxic algae.

Commensal
A biological relationship in which one organism gains benefits without harming another; a form of symbiosis.

Contaminant
Any unwanted material, object or substance in food.

Contamination
Any unwanted matter in food. The presence in food, or the process of transferring to food, any unwanted material, object or substance.

Core temperature
The temperature at the centre, or in the thickest part, of food.

Critical limit
In HACCP, the border between safe and unsafe.

Cross-contamination
The transfer of a contaminant from one contaminated product, such as raw meat, to another previously uncontaminated product, such as a ready-to-eat food.

Danger zone
Temperatures from 5°C to 63°C at which most food-borne pathogens multiply easily. The temperature range to be avoided for high-risk foods.

Death (or decline) phase
The final stage of the bacterial growth curve.

Definitive (or primary) host
The host on or in which a parasite carries out its sexual stage.

Denature
A structural change in protein or nucleic acid caused by heat, chemicals or high or low pH.

DNA (deoxyribonucleic acid)
The genetic material inside every cell of an organism.

Ectoparasite
A parasite living on a host's body surface.

Endoparasite
A parasite living in the organs, inner tissues or blood circulation system of a host.

Endospore
A survival form, or stage, of some bacteria. Usually shortened to 'spore'.

Endotoxin
A toxin in a bacterial cell which is released when the cell dies.

Enterotoxin
A toxin affecting the intestine.

Enzyme
A type of protein that can trigger chemical reactions in an organism without itself undergoing any change.

Exotoxin
A toxin released from a living bacterium into its surroundings.

Extrinsic contamination
Contamination from sources other than the raw food itself.

Extrinsic factor
An external factor, such as temperature and atmosphere, that influences the growth and survival of a micro-organism.

Facultative
A description for a microbe that can live in a variety of conditions – for instance, in the presence or the absence of oxygen.

Faecal coliform
An organism, such as *E. coli*, the presence of which indicates faecal contamination.

Flora (microbial)/microflora
The microbial species normally found in a particular habitat, such as the intestine.

Food-borne disease/illness
A general description of any illness from contaminated food. In this book the phrase covers all types of food-related illness from food or water.

Food-borne infection
An infection caused by pathogens that are carried by food but are not dependent upon it.

Food poisoning
An illness, caused by pathogens living on food or by chemicals, that occurs after contaminated food has been eaten. Sometimes also used as a simple general term for all kinds of illness related to food.

Fungus (plural: fungi)
Mushrooms/toadstools, moulds and yeasts.

Gene
The smallest unit of heredity. A segment of DNA.

Genus (plural: genera)
A classification of organisms. A large group of related, or similar, species sharing many characteristics.

Germination
Sprouting, reproducing.

Halophile
A salt-loving or salt-tolerant micro-organism.

Hazard (food)
A source of danger: any thing, condition or circumstance that could cause harm (injury or illness) to the consumer. Any biological, chemical or physical agent in, or condition of, food with the potential to cause an adverse health effect.

High-risk food
A food that easily supports the multiplication of pathogenic micro-organisms and so requires time and temperature control to stay safe to eat.

Host
An organism supporting a parasite on or in its body.

Incubation
Another term for 'onset'.

Infection
The presence and multiplication in the body of a pathogen that produces a disease.

Infective dose
The number of micro-organisms that have to be present to cause a disease.

Inherent
Inbuilt.

Intermediate (or secondary) host
The host in which the larval stages of endoparasites develop.

Intoxication
The process or symptoms of poisoning.

Intrinsic contamination
Contamination associated with the food itself.

Intrinsic factor
Inbuilt factors, such as pH, a_w and nutrients, that influence the growth of micro-organisms.

Lag phase
The first stage of bacterial growth in which an organism adapts to its surroundings and does not reproduce.

Log (or logarithmic) phase
The stage of rapid bacterial multiplication.

Log scale
The curve on a graph of bacterial growth.

Mesophile
An organism preferring temperatures between 10°C and 55°C.

Microaerophile
An organism that does not need very much oxygen.

Micro-organism/microbe
An extremely small (micro) organism.

Nitrite
A chemical used as a food preservative. In unsafe quantities it may cause food poisoning.

Nitrosamine
A chemical compound that can cause food poisoning.

Obligate

Obliged to do something. A description for a microbe that is obliged to live in particular conditions to survive – for instance, an obligate aerobe must have oxygen, while an obligate anaerobe must live in oxygen-free conditions.

Onset (or incubation)

The time between infection and the first symptoms of disease.

Organism

An independent life form.

Potable

Safe to drink. Generally used to describe water treated for use as drinking water.

Serotyping

A method to identify bacteria through specific antigen/antibody reactions.

Spoilage

Any undesirable change in food that makes it unacceptable for eating. The natural processes of ageing, deterioration, decay or 'going off'.

Spore

A reproductive cell – for instance, of fungi. A shortened version of 'endospore', the dormant, survival form of some bacteria.

Sporulation

Spore production.

Stationary phase

The stage of bacterial growth when the population has reached its maximum.

Supplier's certificate

A supplier's guarantee of the wholesomeness of a product based on criteria set by the purchasing company.

Thermophile

Heat-loving micro-organisms that thrive at between 40°C and 80°C.

Toxic

Poisonous.

Toxin

A poisonous substance produced by some bacteria and fungi.

Vegetative cell

Living, reproducing cell.

Vehicle of contamination

Any substance, object or living being that carries contamination from one point to another.

Virus

An extremely small infective organism that can multiply only within living cells.

Water activity

See a_w.

Xerophile

An organism that likes dry conditions and can survive low a_w values.

Hazards in context

Hazards and risk are central to contemporary thinking about effective food safety management. Since the 1990s all food businesses in the UK have been obliged by law to identify the food hazards in their type of work and to take steps to deal with them. Where a hazard cannot be eliminated, businesses must control the level of risk from that hazard.

Good management
The identification and control of hazards underlie best practice in food safety management.

Part 3 looks in detail at what constitutes a food hazard – under the categories of microbiological, physical and chemical hazards – and at the main features of food safety legislation. Before reading these crucial chapters you may wish to take a brief look at what *hazards* mean in the food industry in general and how an understanding of hazards lays a foundation for applying the best possible methods to the management of food safety.

What are hazards?

We are all familiar with the everyday conversational use of the word hazard to indicate a threat, or possibility, of danger. In Parts 1 and 2 we described food hazards simply as being any situation, thing or condition that could cause harm to the consumer. If we wanted to be more specific, we could say that a hazard is anything biological, microbiological, chemical or physical that might cause harm to the consumer, or 'that is reasonably likely to cause illness or injury in the absence of its control' (*HACCP Principles and Application Guidelines*, National Advisory Committee on Microbiological Criteria for Foods, USA).

Food hazard
A biological, chemical or physical agent in, or condition of, food with the potential to cause an adverse health effect.

European legislation defines a hazard as being 'a biological, chemical or physical agent in, or condition of, food with the potential to cause an adverse health effect' (Regulation (EC) No 178/2002). A more scientific definition, by the International Commission on Microbiological Specifications for Foods (ICMSF), explains a hazard as 'the unacceptable contamination, unacceptable growth and/or unacceptable survival by micro-organisms of concern to safety or spoilage and/or the unacceptable production or persistence in foods of products of microbiological metabolism'.

The last definition is of course restricted to microbiological hazards and ignores physical and chemical hazards. However, as you well know, there are many opportunities along the food flow from farm to fork for contamination by physical objects (sometimes called *foreign bodies*) and by chemicals as well as by micro-organisms.

What is clear from all these definitions, and from others we could quote, is that a hazard represents the potential for harm. As a food safety manager, you need to stop the *possibility* of harm from becoming *actual* harm, whether that harm is in the form of illness, injury or simply disgust at an objectionable extra ingredient in food.

Types of hazard

There are many *potential* food hazards – including micro-organisms such as bacteria; chemicals such as cleaning products; and physical objects such as hair, metal staples or insects. Even so, they are *actual* hazards only when they are on food – when they have contaminated food.

All forms of food contamination are undesirable and may cause harm to consumers. If you are to prevent illness or injury from food, you need to prevent or reduce contamination.

From hazard to illness
Microbiological hazards include microbiological contamination, microbiological multiplication and microbiological survival. Physical hazards come from physical contamination, while chemical hazards come from chemical contamination.

With micro-organisms the possibility of harm does not stop at contamination, because the multiplication and *survival* of micro-organisms also constitute food hazards. As you can see from the diagram below, microbiological hazards occur in more ways than do physical or chemical hazards. Microbiological hazards include microbiological contamination, microbiological multiplication and microbiological survival, while physical hazards are simply physical contamination and chemical hazards are simply chemical contamination.

Contamination, multiplication and survival

Biological and microbiological hazards

Most biological hazards to food are *micro*biological – they are too small to be seen without a powerful microscope. Microbiological hazards include pathogenic and spoilage bacteria, fungi and many microscopic parasites – other parasites are big enough to be seen without a microscope. Viruses are also included under this heading.

Biological hazards become a threat to food safety through contamination and by multiplication and survival.

Contamination

Contamination can happen at many stages in the food flow including growth, harvesting, slaughtering, storage, processing, warehousing, transport, retail display, preparation and service. Food contaminated by micro-organisms creates the *possibility* of a food safety problem. To stop the problem arising, you need to prevent or reduce contamination.

Multiplication

Some micro-organisms, particularly the food poisoning bacteria, cause illness because they have experienced the right conditions in which to multiply on the food after the initial contamination. To stop this, you need to control the conditions in which the bacteria can multiply. So, another type of microbiological hazard is the *multiplication* of micro-organisms. The foods that provide the ideal conditions for multiplication and known as high-risk foods.

Survival

Some processes, such as heating, are designed to kill micro-organisms. If, for whatever reason, the process fails to work properly, some or all of the pathogens may survive. To prevent survival, you must ensure that such processes are effective. So, a third type of microbiological hazard is the *survival* of micro-organisms or spores.

Chemical hazards

Many types of chemical can cause problems, including agricultural and industrial chemicals, cleaning products and cooking equipment. As with microbiological hazards, undesirable chemicals are a hazard only if they are *in* our food, and it is this that you need to control.

Chemicals do not multiply, nor are there heat processes designed to kill them, so chemical contamination is the only type of chemical hazard.

Physical hazards

Naturally occurring materials, such as twigs, and introduced materials, such as splinters of wood from pallets, could be a hazard if found in food. It is simpler to consider the hazard not as a piece of wood but as physical contamination which needs to be controlled. Physical contamination is the only type of physical hazard.

Managing hazards

There is more information about managing hazards throughout Part 4, particularly in the section 'Preventing food contamination' and in the chapters 'Controlling time and temperature' and 'Hazard Analysis and Critical Control Point'.

Biological and microbiological hazards

Biology is the study of organisms – independent life forms, which are sometimes referred to as 'creatures'. Organisms are divided into various categories (or 'kingdoms') such as plants; fungi, bacteria and animals – the category that includes humans.

Biology is a wide-ranging subject that incorporates many different disciplines. For example, bacteriology deals with bacteria, mycology deals with fungi (mushrooms, moulds and yeasts) and there are also other specialist areas of study, for example for protozoa (microscopic single-celled organisms).

Some of the smallest organisms on Earth cause some of the greatest headaches for food safety. They include bacteria, fungi and many parasites. These extremely small (micro) life forms can be seen only with the help of a powerful microscope, so come under the heading of microbiology – the study of micro-organisms, or microbes for short. For convenience, viruses are also usually included in this group, and we do so throughout this book.

Although micro-organisms (including viruses) form a very large and varied group, most of them are:

- extremely small – 'invisible' to the naked eye

- relatively simple in structure

- extremely adaptable to different conditions

- ubiquitous – they occur everywhere.

What they also have in common is their potential to cause either food safety problems or spoilage, or both, whatever the type of food business.

Microbes
The study of micro-organisms helps food managers to produce safe food and prevent spoilage.

Microbiology underlies many of the things that your business needs to do to ensure that the food it produces is safe to eat and has an acceptable shelf life. So, it is the foundation for many of the main principles of food handling and for the management policies you need to develop and implement.

It goes without saying that you also need to give your full attention to other aspects of food safety management, such as the prevention and control of physical and chemical hazards, but microbiological hazards are the foremost problem for food safety. Micro-organisms are responsible for most cases of food-borne disease worldwide.

Practical value
The following five chapters are designed to give you a far greater understanding of why micro-organisms can cause so many problems and why good hygiene practice is essential to prevent outbreaks of food-borne illness.

Bacteria, the main cause of food-related illnesses, are discussed first with a separate chapter about the illnesses they can cause. These are followed by chapters about the non-bacterial organisms – viruses, parasites and fungi. Problems caused by mycotoxins, certain poisons caused by moulds and yeasts, are discussed under chemical hazards on pages 126 to 130.

In Part 4 various chapters discuss effective methods to prevent microbes and other organisms from causing illness and the consequent loss of business reputation and profit.

Step-by-step approach

Don't worry if you do not have a scientific background. Everything is explained in simple terms, sometimes with additional, more detailed information for those who already have a grasp of biochemistry.

In some management positions in some sectors – such as in food processing, food packaging and the development of novel foods – you may need to know a great deal more about microbiology than is covered in these chapters. If so, speak with a training adviser about additional courses of study. Sources of additional information are suggested in the 'Sources of further help' on pages 415 to 424.

Bacteria

There is hardly a place on Earth that is not inhabited by bacteria. These tiny organisms are literally all around us and are a natural, integral part of our own bodies. In fact, we cannot do without them. They help to create the air we breathe and the plants we eat. They enable us to digest food, they break down bodily waste products and they are responsible for foods such as cheese and yoghurt and medicinal drugs such as some antibiotics.

Even so, we can have trouble living with some bacteria because they can cause debilitating and life-threatening diseases. To make this love-hate relationship more complicated, some types of bacteria can be both beneficial and harmful to humans.

This chapter introduces the main bacterial characteristics of significance to food safety, while the next chapter considers specific bacteria and the illnesses they can cause. As a contrast, the feature on pages 113 to 114 takes a brief look at some of the benefits to be gained from harnessing the power of various types of microbes.

Classifying by the impact upon humans

As you can see, bacteria are far from being just the germs or the 'bugs' of everyday conversation. One of the most convenient ways to classify them is by their impact upon humans and human activity:

- pathogenic bacteria are responsible for causing disease
- spoilage bacteria are responsible for the degradation of food (and other substances)
- commensal bacteria are usually harmless, may be positively beneficial – for example, for agriculture, medicine, food production and many other processes – and live in harmony with people and other host organisms.

When considering food safety we need to concentrate on *pathogenic* bacteria, because they are responsible for most cases of food-borne illness, and on *spoilage* bacteria because they can damage food and cost thousands of pounds in waste and lost business.

Some bacteria belong to more than one group, being harmless or even beneficial commensals in some contexts, but damaging pathogenic or spoilage organisms in others. For example, *Lactobacilli* are essential for the fermenting processes that produce yoghurt, certain cheeses, sausages and sauerkraut (a traditional German dish of pickled cabbage). If they get into the 'wrong' foods such as beverages, however, they may cause unwanted effects such as unpleasant, odd, or 'off', flavours. *Staphylococcus aureus* bacteria live harmlessly and normally as commensals in nasal mucus, but once they are transferred to food, they can have pathogenic characteristics.

Characteristics of bacteria

While humans have trillions of cells in their bodies which perform many tasks, bacteria each have a single cell. Just one little machine (the cell) is responsible for all the functions needed to stay alive, including metabolism (all the chemical changes, including combining and breaking down substances), growth and reproduction. This makes bacteria both very simple and very complicated.

Bacteria tend to be *heterotrophs* – they depend, as do humans, on consuming organic matter to continue living, growing and multiplying. In contrast, plants are *autotrophs* and make their own food by converting sunlight into energy, a process known as *photosynthesis*.

Scientists describe bacteria according to:

- morphology – the shape of the bacterial cell and other features seen under a microscope, such as the existence of organs for moving about and the way bacteria aggregate (clump together)

- anatomy – the microscopic structure of the individual bacterial cell

- physiology – the metabolism of the bacterium and the conditions that particular species favour.

We need to focus on physiology, but to understand how this impacts upon food safety, we first need to take a quick look at the morphology and anatomy of bacteria.

Morphology – shaping up

A typical bacterial cell measures between 1μm and 2μm. The symbol μ stands for micro and μm is a micrometre (or micron). This is one millionth of a metre, or 10^{-6}m. (See Reference for guidance on figures expressed to the power of ten.)

The point of this pin is magnified 175 times, making it is easy to see how many bacteria can exist in a very small area.

It is hard to imagine 1μm or 2μm until you see the tip of the point of an ordinary household pin in this greatly magnified (x175) scanning electron micrograph. One million bacteria would fit on there quite easily!

Bacteria are tiny and colourless, so, before examining them under the microscope, scientists may stain them with a dye (see below). They also employ a range of other tests (see page 67 to 69) that assist them in describing and classifying bacteria.

Gram staining

The Gram-staining technique is named after the Danish physician Hans C J Gram who developed it in 1884. The technique involves the use of crystal violet dye, iodine and alcohol (or acetone) to distinguish two groups of bacteria. The Gram reaction, or Gram stain, detects differences in the composition of the bacterial cell wall. Bacteria that stay the violet colour of the dye, such as staphylococci, are described as being Gram-positive, often written as Gram(+) or Gram+ve. Bacteria that go a pinkish colour, such as salmonellae, are described as being Gram-negative, often written Gram(-) or Gram-ve.

There are a number of differences between the two categories of bacteria, such as the anatomy of the cell wall and the kinds of toxin they produce.

E. coli are rod-shaped bacteria.

Shape

Although each bacterium merely consists of a single cell, some types can clump together, either in random clusters or in geometrical aggregates such as pairs, chains and shamrocks.

Both the individual cell shape and the characteristic grouping patterns provide scientists with important clues to the identity of the bacteria in a food sample.

Rods (bacilli)

Some, such as *Salmonella* species (see pictures on pages 24 and 54) are longer than they are broad.

Others, such as *E. coli* (shown above left in a human intestine), can sometimes appear so short that they look almost spherical. Bacilli include Gram-positive and Gram-negative genera.

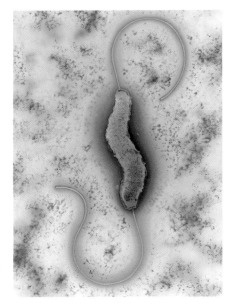

There are bacteria, such as *Campylobacter jejuni*, that are spirally curved.

Spiral (helical)

These look like twisted bacilli and may, like *Campylobacter jejuni* (shown left), be a spirally curved rod.

Some bacteria appear like a tiny teardrop or a comma and are referred to as vibrios – for instance, *Vibrio parahaemolyticus* and *Vibrio cholerae* (see page 83).

Spherical cells (cocci)

Bacteria such as *Staphylococcus aureus* (shown bottom left) have a tendency to form clusters. Almost all cocci are Gram-positive.

Other shapes

Some bacteria, such as actinomycetes, have a branching form that looks rather like a tree with different branches, even though they are still single cells. Even square bacteria are known to exist!

Anatomy – physical strengths and weaknesses

Close examination of bacterial anatomy has enabled scientists to discover weak points and develop methods, such as disinfection, that can disable or destroy bacteria.

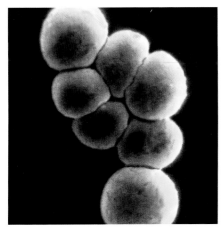

Some bacteria, such as *Staphylococcus aureus*, can form clusters.

The structure of a bacterium

The *cell wall* is a strong, rigid structure that determines the characteristic shapes of particular species of bacteria. The cell wall is permeable so that the bacterium can exchange substances with the surrounding environment, allowing nutrients and waste material to pass through. The composition of the cell wall is responsible for the Gram reaction (see page 50).

Between the cell wall and the inner part of the cell is the *cell membrane*, which is also known as the *plasma membrane*. Together, the cell wall and membrane create a double organ that acts rather like a security barrier between the vital contents of the inner cell and the bacterium's immediate local environment (sometimes called the *surrounding medium*). The cell membrane is selectively permeable in both directions – it allows nutrients to pass into the cell and waste products to pass out of the cell. If the membrane is damaged – for instance, by chemical disinfectants or antibiotics – the cell is likely to die.

Some bacteria, including certain spoilage types, have a gel-like extra layer, called the *capsule*, outside the cell wall. When these bacteria contaminate food, the surface of the food becomes slimy or sticky. Chemical disinfectants can desiccate (dry out) the capsule, often damaging the cell wall and causing the bacterium to die.

Inside the cell is the *cytoplasm*, a semi-liquid containing enzymes (proteins that spark off other biochemical reactions), *metabolites* (proteins, fats and other products of digestion), waste products and so on.

The cytoplasm surrounds essential structures such as *storage granules* (stored proteins for later use) and ribosomes (where genes – units of inheritance – are replicated). The genes are on a linear chromosome consisting of a strand of deoxyribonucleic acid, better known as DNA. The DNA determines the individual and species characteristics of the bacterium – its preferences for food and environment, for example, as well as its rate of reproduction and resilience in adverse conditions.

You might find it helpful to consider DNA as the organism's personal User's Guide to Life which contains all the information and do-it-yourself tools needed for existence, growth and reproduction. If the DNA is damaged or destroyed, the organism cannot read and follow the instructions in its User's Guide and the cell cannot function properly.

Nucleus free
Unlike many other life forms, bacteria do not have a cell nucleus.

In most life forms every cell has a *nucleus* – a structure inside the cell that protects the genetic material. But bacteria do things differently. Instead of having a nucleus, they store most of their genetic material on a circular macro-molecule (a ring-chromosome, which looks a little like a loop of the coiled cable to a landline telephone handset). Small pieces of DNA may form extra rings known as plasmids.

Some bacteria have an external organ called a *flagellum* (plural: *flagella*), from the Latin for lash or whip, which acts rather like a boat's outboard motor, propelling them along.

Bacteria can have one, two or more flagella to move around. Other external organs, called *pili*, are hair-like projections that help the bacterial cell to adhere to surfaces such as those of the human intestine.

Some bacterial structures, such as the capsule, parts of the cell wall, the flagella and the pili, have *antigenic* qualities. This means that they prompt the immune system of the host to start defending itself by producing *antibodies*. Antibodies can be detected in blood, providing a useful hint about the cause of an infection.

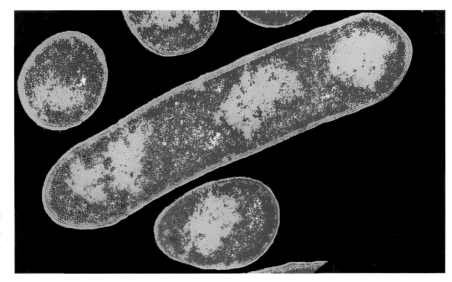

Highly magnified and false-coloured micrograph of *Clostridium botulinum* bacteria.

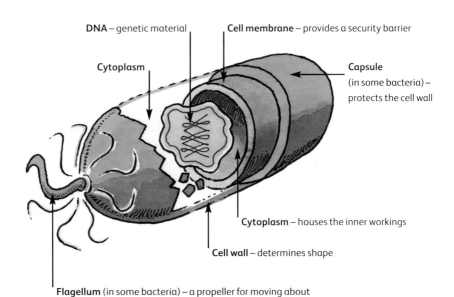

DNA – genetic material

Cell membrane – provides a security barrier

Cytoplasm

Capsule (in some bacteria) – protects the cell wall

Cytoplasm – houses the inner workings

Cell wall – determines shape

Flagellum (in some bacteria) – a propeller for moving about

Inside a bacterium

Unless you have a highly trained eye, it can be difficult to distinguish the parts of a bacterium even in a highly magnified and coloured micrograph such as the one of a *Clostridium botulinum* (top). The illustration above therefore exaggerates some key features to make them a little easier to understand. You'll see that the illustration includes a flagellum, which is not present on *C. botulinum*, but you can see a micrograph on page 25 of a *Salmonella* Typhimurium that does include this structure.

Physiology – beyond the microscope

However diligently scientists examine bacteria under the microscope, they cannot discover everything in this way. Other techniques are needed to confirm identity, especially when it comes to distinguishing particular strains of a species.

Physiological tests, also called biochemical tests, are essential when the full identity of an organism has to be established beyond doubt – for example, when it is intended for use in food processing or must be eliminated to prevent food-borne disease. Physiological testing aims to identify an organism's preferred nutrients, waste products and enzyme activities.

Two immunological tests are also used:

- serotyping, based on the interaction between the bacterium and host antibodies
- phagetyping, based on identifying viruses that attack the bacterium.

For details of these and other tests see pages 67 to 69.

Bacterial reproduction

The bacterial mother cell matures. (The DNA size and shape are exaggerated here.)

The DNA is replicated.

The septum, a separating wall, is drawn in. (This is the stage shown in the micrograph below.)

There are now two separate identical cells which can repeat the process if conditions are favourable. The 'sister' cells of some species do not separate completely after fission but create cell clusters after repeated divisions.

This *Salmonella* Typhimurium bacterium is in the process of binary fission. The DNA has been replicated and the septum has been drawn in, so that two identical cells can be formed.

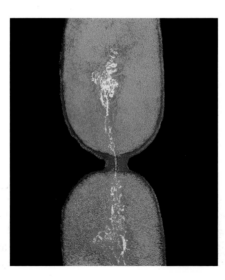

Understanding the way in which bacteria reproduce and the time they take to do so has helped the food industry to develop simple but effective ways to prevent food poisoning and to keep food safe and appetising to eat.

Binary fission

Bacteria can reproduce asexually. This means not only that they do not have sex, but also that they can reproduce without exchanging and recombining their DNA. Instead, bacteria multiply by a process called binary fission – which means splitting in two. As you can see from the greatly simplified diagram above, one 'mother' cell divides into two genetically identical

Bacterial growth curve

| Lag phase | Log phase | Stationary phase | Decline phase |

Log number of bacterial cells (y-axis)

Time/hours (x-axis)

'daughter' cells and the 'mother' cell itself then ceases to exist. Under favourable conditions, binary fission is repeated many times, doubling the numbers every generation and creating large populations very quickly. The rate of multiplication varies from species to species, but the rule of thumb is that each cell divides in two every 10 to 20 minutes. There are other forms of asexual reproduction (see the micrograph of yeast budding on page 109), but cell division is the only asexual bacterial method.

The bacterial growth curve

The growth rate of a bacterial population varies from species to species. It also depends on how favourable the environment is for the particular species. There is, however, a general growth pattern that bacterial populations follow. This pattern is best shown as a graph (see above), which is known as the bacterial growth curve. The x-axis (horizontal) is used to represent time and the y-axis (vertical) to show the number of viable cells. The curve is known as the log scale. To understand what happens, imagine that:

- there are a few bacteria on a high-risk food left in a food preparation area
- the environmental conditions of the room stay pretty much the same throughout the period we are concerned with – about five hours.

The phases of growth

At first there is a period, called the lag phase, in which nothing seems to happen. This apparent delay (or lag) is in fact a time for adjustment, while the bacteria get used to their surroundings. There is no bacterial multiplication at this stage. It may help to imagine swimmers who wade cautiously into the water and need to adjust to the temperature before starting to swim off. The duration of the lag phase depends on the species, the initial number of the bacteria and the environmental conditions in which they find themselves.

The next phase, called the log phase or logarithmic phase, is one of rapid reproduction and a steadily mounting growth curve (assuming conditions are favourable). It is as if the swimmers are gaining speed. Only a few bacteria die at this time, so the population virtually doubles every generation.

The rate of increase, represented by the steepness of the curve, depends on the particular species. You can think of different species as being different classes of swimmers, the advanced class racing along and the beginners striking out more slowly.

The third stage is the stationary phase, which, at first sight, resembles the lag phase because nothing seems to happen. In fact, the population of bacteria has reached its maximum. It is as if the swimmers have reached top speed and cannot accelerate any more. Bacteria still multiply in this phase, but the increase in numbers is balanced by cell mortality (the number of bacteria that die).

The change from the log to the stationary phase happens because of the depletion of nutrients – rather as if our swimmers were using up their last reserves of energy – and the accumulation of bacterial waste products.

The final stage shows a more or less steady decline towards zero on the y-axis. The total population decreases rapidly as more and more cells die, while fewer and fewer new cells are produced. This is called the death phase or decline phase. Our swimmers become increasingly exhausted and drown.

A clue to controlling food-borne disease?

So, can an understanding of the bacterial growth curve help you to manage food safety? It may be tempting to think, if only for a moment, that the only precaution a food handler needs to take is to wait until the bacterial population has exhausted itself and died. Even if it were possible to know exactly when the food was contaminated, so that you could calculate the decline phase, the food would have lost all its nutritional value in this period. What's more, it would now also contain poisonous by-products from all the bacterial activity.

The growth curve does, however, point us towards three possible ways to help to guarantee that food is safe – we can:

- interrupt the log curve at any point by creating lethal conditions – for example, by boiling the food

- prolong the lag phase by creating inhibitory conditions – for example, by refrigerating the food, altering the pH (see page 62), removing moisture (see pages 61) or adding preservatives (see pages 341 to 343)

- serve high-risk food as soon as possible after preparation while any pathogenic bacteria are still in the lag phase.

A typical pattern of population development

1 cell	becomes	2 cells	after 20 minutes	(1st generation)
2 cells	become	4 cells	after 40 minutes	(2nd generation)
4 cells	become	8 cells	after 60 minutes	(3rd generation)
8 cells	become	16 cells	after 80 minutes	(4th generation)

Bacterial spores – a survival strategy

Some bacteria have the ability to produce endospores, often called spores for short. They should not be confused with *fungal spores* (see page 109) which are a form of propagation. Endospores are a dormant stage, or form, that a bacterium takes to enable it to survive adverse conditions. In fact, bacterial spores are one of the most resistant forms of living cell. They can survive chemical treatment, drying, freezing, normal cooking temperatures and high and low pH conditions. Only two bacterial genera produce spores – *Bacillus* and *Clostridium*. Both genera include spoilage bacteria, such as *Clostridium acetobutyricum* and *Bacillus stearothermophilus*, as well as food-borne pathogens such as *Clostridium botulinum* and *Bacillus cereus*.

When the going gets tough

When conditions become unfavourable for bacteria, those that cannot form spores start to die, while *Bacillus* and *Clostridium* species start sporulation, the process of forming spores (see the micrograph below).

The vegetative cell (living, reproducing cell) begins to form a hard case *inside* itself. The case contains all the vital ingredients, such as its DNA, needed to continue life once the harsh conditions have passed. In the false-coloured electron micrograph (left) a

In this greatly magnified and false-coloured electron micrograph a *Clostridium perfringens* bacterium is towards the end of forming a spore. The green structure with a red membrane in the lower part of the bacterium is the spore. When complete, the rest of the bacterium will dissolve, leaving a hardy survival 'capsule'.

Clostridium perfringens bacterium is completing spore formation. The spore, coloured green with a red membrane, is visible in the bottom part of the picture.

When the spore is complete, the rest of the cell degenerates, releasing a microscopic, dried-up bundle that can stay dormant, without absorbing nutrients, for many years. Spores have been detected in archaeological excavations of sites that are at least 2,000 years old, but there is considerable scientific debate about the length of time that a spore can remain viable (able to come back to life).

When conditions are favourable once more, the endospore becomes active again. It absorbs water, splits and releases a vegetative cell that restarts the normal cycle of bacterial growth and reproduction. This process of coming back to life is called germination.

The threat from spores

As bacteria in spore form can withstand harsh conditions and do not need water, oxygen, heat or nutrients, they can survive in almost any environment. They may be carried into food premises by various forms of 'transport', including soil on vegetables, other raw ingredients and unprocessed foods, and on air-borne dust and dirt, particularly where windows, skylights and doors are open and not screened.

It is important to understand that there is not a significant risk to human health from consuming the spores themselves, except in the case of babies or infants who can become ill from swallowing spores of *Clostridium botulinum*. The examples on page 58 show that the real danger is from spores that germinate and multiply, leading to new populations of harmful bacteria in the food that can cause illness.

Example

Endospores consumed in food

Food is cooked thoroughly right the way through for sufficient time at an appropriate temperature. All the bacteria that cannot form spores are killed, while the spore-forming organisms turn into their resistant dormant form. If the food is consumed immediately after cooking, nothing happens: no symptoms of illness develop and there is no threat to health.

Endospores germinate and multiply, then food is consumed

If food is cooked in the same way but left at room temperature for some time after cooking, conditions develop that are favourable to bacterial multiplication and the spores germinate, releasing active vegetative cells. These vegetative cells reproduce rapidly, without competition from non-spore-forming bacteria that have been killed by the heat. By the time that the food is eaten it may contain dangerous levels of pathogenic bacteria or bacterial toxins, making food poisoning very likely.

Control

Spores are very difficult to destroy so normal heat treatment, such as cooking, does not kill them. The time and temperature criteria used in canning processes (see page 338 to 340) and in autoclaving (the sterilization of medical and laboratory materials) are designed to kill them. Irradiation also destroys spores – see pages 67 and 345 to 346

Toxins – by-products of bacterial life

Toxins are poisonous substances produced by living organisms such as bacteria and some fungi and algae. They are usually complex enzymes, types of protein, and they attack other essential proteins in our bodies. The following paragraphs focus on bacterial toxins, the direct cause of most cases of food-borne disease. You'll find information about fungal toxins (mycotoxins) on see pages 126 to 130.

Types of toxin

There are two sorts of bacterial toxin:

Poisoned arrow
The word toxin is based on words for poisoned arrows and derives ultimately from the Greek for bow.

- endotoxins, which exist within the cell

- exotoxins, which are secreted as waste products.

Some bacteria, such as *Bacillus cereus*, can produce both types of toxin.

Toxins can also be classified by their effects:

- enterotoxins affect the intestinal system

- neurotoxins affect nerve functions.

You may come across a description of a bacterium that combines the type and effect of its toxin. For example, *Staphylococcus aureus* could be described as an exogenic enterotoxin-producer.

Toxins
In everyday speech when we say that something is toxic we just mean that it is poisonous. But in biology toxin has a specific meaning and refers only to poisons produced by living organisms such as bacteria and fungi.

Endotoxins

Endotoxins are normally sealed in the bacterial cell and released only when the bacterium dies or sporulates. This may be either before or after the food is consumed. *Clostridium perfringens*, for example, can sporulate in the intestine.

Exotoxins

Exotoxins are poisonous substances secreted by some bacteria, either during binary fission or as digestive waste products. This means that they can contaminate food before it is eaten. Even if the bacteria themselves are killed – say by cooking – the exotoxin will still be present and able to cause illness.

Enterotoxins

Toxins that affect the intestines are known as enterotoxins. They are virulently poisonous: about 500µg per kg of body-weight of the plant poison strychnine would kill someone, but just 0.1µg per kg of body-weight of a bacterial enterotoxin would be lethal.

Neurotoxins

These poisons attack the nervous system and are the most dangerous biotoxins on Earth. The most deadly is the toxin produced by *Clostridium botulinum*. The lethal dose is just 0.0003µg per kg of body-weight.

How bacterial toxins make you ill

Bacterial toxins may give rise to many symptoms. The most typical are vomiting and diarrhoea. Others include chronic poisoning and the destruction of vital organs and the nervous system.

The nature of the symptoms may give a useful hint about the likely causative organism. As soon as our bodies perceive traces of unwanted matter, the intestinal system tries to get rid of them as quickly as possible. Exotoxins are usually detected early on, in the stomach. The stomach collapses and sends the food back by the quickest route – a process we call vomiting.

Endotoxins are generally detected only in the intestines. Many bacteria that produce endotoxins, such as species of *Salmonella*, would not normally survive the acidity of the stomach on their own. However, when they contaminate food, the food serves as a protective shield that allows them to pass through into the small intestine. Here they find near-neutral conditions that suit them. By then it is too late for the body to send anything back by vomiting, so our system defends itself by turning the usually slow and controlled movement of the gut (the intestinal peristalsis) into an uncontrolled, forceful process – diarrhoea.

What bacteria need to survive

When we first teach staff about illnesses linked to food, we usually tell them simply that bacteria depend upon a favourable combination of food, moisture, warmth and time. Later on, we might expand this list to include conditions such as atmosphere (oxygen and other gases) and pH (the acid-alkali scale). Whatever our choice of words, we explain that the basic conditions for bacterial survival and multiplication depend upon the presence of favourable conditions and the absence of inhibitory factors. These are really two sides of the same coin.

As you can imagine, the biochemistry behind bacterial requirements is fairly complicated. You are not expected to study microbiology in depth but, as a manager, you need to understand the principles of the factors that affect the growth of bacterial populations.

This will help you to appreciate how preventive measures work and, in turn, will help you to plan and monitor controls that are appropriate to your workplace:

- preventing bacteria from multiplying

- killing pathogenic and spoilage bacteria.

Essential bacterial requirements

A bacterial population grows in direct relation to the presence of favourable conditions. These conditions, or factors, can be divided into two groups – intrinsic and extrinsic.

Intrinsic factors are attributes inherent in the food and include:

- the nutrient content of the food

- moisture, expressed as water activity (a_w)

- acidity or alkalinity, expressed as hydrogen-ion concentration (pH).

Extrinsic factors are conditions of the environment and include:

- temperature

- time

- atmosphere.

Competition between micro-organisms also affects the population growth.

The next few pages look in detail at how each of these factors affects bacteria.

Intrinsic factors

These are characteristics that are part and parcel of the food itself.

Nutrient content

High risk
Foods rich in protein and moisture can easily support microbial multiplication and are known as high-risk foods.

All foods suitable for humans also suit micro-organisms. Food-borne microbes show a marked preference for foods that are rich in protein and high in moisture. Such foods, which are known as high-risk foods, are particularly vulnerable to microbial multiplication and need to be refrigerated. The smallest quantities of these foods can support very large bacterial populations – a good reason for cleaning and disinfecting work surfaces, equipment and utensils thoroughly.

Some bacteria are relatively unfussy about their choice of nutrients, while others target particular foods like milk products, seafood or cereals. Some depend on the presence of certain vitamins – for example, *Staphylococcus aureus* needs thiamine (part of the vitamin B group).

Some foods contain antimicrobial substances, like etheric oils, that have an inhibitory effect on bacterial growth. Other foods have biological barriers, or protective layers, against microbial growth – lobster and mussel shells, for example. The risk of bacterial contamination increases as soon as the protective layer is removed or destroyed.

The surface of meat is likely to be contaminated, so a single cut into the muscular layer increases the risk of bacterial contamination throughout the meat because microbes are transferred by the knife from the surface. The more the meat is chopped or minced, the greater the risk of bacterial contamination throughout.

High-risk foods

High-risk foods easily support microbial multiplication. Such foods tend to be rich in protein and fairly moist. They include meats and meat products, such as pies and sausages; poultry; stocks, gravies, stews and sauces; all kinds of seafood (fish and shellfish); milk, cream and dairy products; and eggs and egg products.

Moisture

Like all living creatures, micro-organisms need water. Bacteria prefer moist foods such as meat, fish and liquid and semi-liquid products.

Water activity
Moist foods have a high water activity (a_w), meaning that the water in the food is readily available to bacteria (and other micro-organisms).

However, most foods do, in fact, contain quite a lot of water even when we perceive them to be 'dry' products. Items such as bread and biscuits may contain enough water to support bacterial growth. On the other hand, some foods such as jam seem to be very moist but are not high-risk foods because the water is bound by dissolved agents. In other words, ingredients like salt and sugar make the moisture unavailable to bacteria.

To support bacterial multiplication, the water in the product must be actively available – there for the taking. The availability of water is known as water activity (a_w). It is the a_w that tells us just how likely particular foods are to support bacterial growth.

(You might see water activity expressed as $a_w = P/P_o$. The 'P' represents the vapour pressure of the food and the 'P_o' represents the vapour pressure of water at the same ambient temperature. Don't worry if this kind of information makes your eyes glaze over: the important point is to know which foods have high water activity – see below.)

The a_w of pure water is 1.0, so all foods other than water have a value below 1.0. Most fresh foods have an a_w around 0.99.

The tolerance range of individual micro-organisms to a_w varies greatly, but most bacteria reach optimal growth at a high a_w (values at above 0.95). Pathogenic and spoilage organisms grow fastest at around 0.98. If the a_w in food is too low for bacterial growth, most bacteria become dormant. If the dry conditions are prolonged, the cells eventually die.

Optimal growth
Bacteria generally prefer water activity above 0.95 and grow best at about a_w 0.98. Gram-positive bacteria generally survive well with low a_w, but Gram-negative types usually do not.

Gram-negative bacteria, such as *Salmonella*, are particularly vulnerable when water activity is low. Exceptions include salt-tolerant bacteria (known as halophiles, from the Greek for salt loving) such as *Vibrio parahaemolyticus*.

Gram-positive bacteria generally tolerate low water activity more easily, so the typical flora in cured meats is usually Gram-positive. Organisms growing at a low a_w are

Examples of the a_w of foods

Meat (fresh)	0.95-0.99
Meat (cured)	0.87-0.95
Fruit & vegetables	0.94
Bread	0.94-0.97
Cheese (hard)	0.90
Jam	0.67-0.87
Flour	0.2

xerophiles (from the Greek for something that loves dry conditions). A lot of fungi are also xerophiles and this is why mould can spoil 'dry' foods that are not usually at risk from pathogenic contamination.

There are various techniques for lowering the water activity of food. They include:

- reducing the overall water content (dehydration)
- increasing the concentration of *electrolytes* – for example, by salting
- adding solutes such as sugar to bind water
- combining some of the methods mentioned above, as in pickling.

Hydrogen-ion concentration (pH)

The acidity or alkalinity of food is the key intrinsic factor in bacterial growth. The measure of whether something is acid or alkali (often called basic) is the pH scale. It runs from 0 to 14, with 7 as the neutral point (see below). A pH below 7 is acidic, while above 7 is alkaline or basic.

Neutral choice
Bacteria generally prefer a fairly neutral pH from about 6 to 8. As most foods fall within this range, most things we eat are vulnerable to bacterial multiplication.

Most foods have a pH between 7 and 4, so they are neutral or slightly acidic. Only egg white is truly alkaline, measuring at around 8. Microbial growth is possible within a broad range of pH values, but most bacteria grow best at or near neutral (pH 6-8). This means that most foods can support bacterial multiplication.

High and low pH values both inhibit bacterial growth. Processing and storage usually lower the pH of food, so reducing bacterial growth. However, some other microbial growth, such as mould, may still occur at low pH. Sometimes this has the effect of increasing the pH of the food and therefore of increasing the risk of bacterial growth once more.

Bacterial spores survive at *any* pH level, but germinate only at above pH 4.5.

From a food safety point of view, pH needs to be considered in combination with other factors such as temperature. The genus *Salmonella* is a good example of how pH and other factors together affect the behaviour of pathogenic bacteria:

- *Salmonella* will usually multiply at pH as low as 4.1 if all other conditions are optimal
- at lower temperatures (below 10°C) *Salmonella* will not multiply below pH 5
- added inhibitors, such as salt and preservatives, stop *Salmonella* from multiplying below pH 5.6.

Approximate pH values for some foods and other items

Acid			
	Lemon juice	1	Gastric juices
		2	Battery acid
	Vinegar	3	
	Orange/ tomato juice	4	
	Black coffee	5	Acid rain Human skin
		6	Saliva
Neutral	Milk	7	Pure water
	Egg white	8	Soap
	Baking soda	9	
		10	Detergent
		11	Milk of magnesia
		12	
		13	Caustic soda Household bleach
Alkali (or base)		14	

The acid test

Puzzling over ways to test and control the quality of beer as it matured, Danish chemist Søren Peter Lauritz Sørensen devised a way in 1909 of measuring

acidity – the pH scale. Today the scale has innumerable applications both inside and outside brewing and the food industry, including medicine, agriculture, geology, chemistry and biology.

The 'p' stands for potenz, which means strength in Danish and the 'H' is the scientific symbol for hydrogen. So pH describes the concentration ('strength') of free hydrogen ions in a solution. Most solutions are within the scale of 0 to 14, with 7 as neutral, but values outside the range are also possible. Acidic foods with a pH below 4.0, such as soft drinks, fruit such as grapefruit, (left) vinegar and wine, are usually safe from bacterial multiplication (although they may be vulnerable to fungal growth) and have a long shelf life.

Extrinsic factors

Things that are not part of the food itself but that influence the development of microbial flora during food storage and processing are known as extrinsic factors.

Temperature

Kill or stop
High temperatures can kill bacteria, while low temperatures can suspend multiplication.

All microbial activities depend on the temperature of the environment. This is perhaps the most important extrinsic factor. Each species has only a limited temperature range within which it can grow. Within this range, there is an optimal (most favourable) temperature for multiplication. At temperatures *above* the maximum for their growth range, bacteria experience thermal injury and die. At temperatures *below* their minimum, the growth of the population stops, although individual bacteria survive and may resume multiplication when the temperature rises again.

Most micro-organisms are found at temperatures between -15°C and 80°C. However, pathogenic and spoilage bacteria are more limited in their growth range. According to their temperature requirements we distinguish three groups:

- psychrophiles (from the Greek for love of the cold)

- mesophiles (from the Greek for love of an intermediate temperature)

- thermophiles (from the Greek for love of heat).

Between the psychrophiles and the mesophiles some scientists distinguish another group – psychrotrophs (from the Greek, meaning that they can grow in the cold).

Most food pathogens are mesophiles – they grow best at room temperature. It is unfortunate for food safety that their optimal temperature is almost our average body temperature of 37°C. The recommended refrigeration temperature of below 5°C stops

Temperature category	Range	Optimum
Psychrophiles	-5°C to 20°C	10°C
Psychrotrophs	0°C to 35°C	25°C
Mesophiles	10°C to 55°C	35°C
Thermophiles	40°C to 80°C	50°C

mesophiles from multiplying but does not stop psychrophiles and psychrotrophs. Bacteria of the genus *Listeria* are psychrotrophs and can therefore multiply in refrigerated food. Both the mesophile and the psychrophile groups contain many spoilage organisms.

As you know, the temperature range from 5°C to 63°C is often called the temperature danger zone – a temperature range in which most pathogens and spoilage organisms thrive. *Most* pathogenic bacteria do not multiply at temperatures below 5°C, as this is outside the danger zone. All vegetative bacteria are killed by temperatures above 63°C, which is also outside the danger zone. However, spores and certain toxins might not be destroyed by heat.

Do bear in mind that most of the daily routine of food preparation takes place at an ambient temperature within the danger zone which provides ideal conditions for microbial growth. This means that high-risk foods (see page 61) should never be allowed to stand at room temperatures for longer than absolutely necessary.

Time
The control of time is even more crucial when it is difficult to control temperature – particularly during thawing and cooling. If these processes are allowed to take a long time, bacteria have time to multiply in the food. Remember that time determines the growth rate of a bacterial population (see pages 55 to 56).

The control of time is also important during heat treatment. For example, food may reach a 'safe' temperature on the outside but, if it is not cooked for long enough, the core temperature may not be high enough to kill pathogens. The rule of thumb is that bacteria provided with sufficient food, moisture and warmth divide every 20 minutes. Some species multiply much faster than the average – *Clostridium perfringens* can multiply every 9.5 minutes under favourable conditions, while *Vibrio parahaemolyticus* needs only 7 minutes.

The chart below shows what happens to a sample of food with 100,000 typical bacteria when the food is at different temperatures for different periods. (For guidance on numbers expressed to the power of ten, see page 378).

Every raw product carries its own microflora, which includes spoilage bacteria as well as pathogenic bacteria. Most pathogenic bacteria do not cause food poising unless they have multiplied to a considerable number (10^5 to 10^6 per gram of food). In raw products the

Temperature	After 1hr	3 hr	6 hr	8 hr	Effect
4°C	100,000	100,000	100,000	<100,000	hardly any increase
22°C*	200,000	800,000	$6x10^6$	$25x10^6$	division every hour
37°C**	800,000	$50x10^6$	$25x10^9$	$16x10^{10}$	division every 20 min

* typical room temperature
** average body temperature

number is not usually great enough to be a direct threat to health. The danger comes from keeping the food in conditions that allow the bacteria to multiply to a high concentration. Given enough time and the right environmental conditions, just one bacterium can lead to the production of one million bacteria in less than four hours – and you always have more than one bacterium on a raw product!

Atmosphere

The composition of the air – known as the atmosphere – also affects bacterial growth. Different types of bacteria have different requirements for oxygen. Some species exist only where there is oxygen. Others survive only in its absence. Yet another group is flexible and has the option to live with or without oxygen.

Microbiologists usually distinguish between:

- obligate aerobes, which must have oxygen

- microaerophiles – aerobic bacteria, such as *Lactobacillus* and *Campylobacter*, which grow better where there is a *reduced* concentration of oxygen

- obligate anaerobes, which must have an oxygen-free environment

- facultative organisms, which can survive with or without oxygen.

Each category includes pathogens and spoilage types.

Like water, oxygen may be either free or bound to other molecules. Aerobes need free oxygen (O_2) to survive, and this is present in most unprocessed foods.

Preservation techniques such as canning and vacuum-packing have the effect of removing free oxygen. This kills all obligate aerobes and slows down facultative organisms, leaving perfect conditions for anaerobes. This is why it is necessary to refrigerate vacuum-packed food to inhibit the remaining microflora. Carbon dioxide (CO_2) and ozone (O_3) slow down the growth of aerobes. Both atmospheres are used in packaging to extend the shelf life of foods such as meat and fish.

Microbial competition

Most bacteria are influenced by the presence and activities of other microbes. There are some organisms that produce substances that inhibit the actions of, or even kill, other organisms, but there are others that merely compete for nutrients and space. Either way, they are in competition, and the competition among them helps to prevent any one species taking over.

The following analogy may help: imagine the microbes as various hostile armies trying to conquer the same city (say, a morsel of food).

As long as the armies fight among themselves and use up their energy in trying to defeat each other, the city has a fair chance of survival. But if one army starts to gain over the others, the situation

Oxygen requirements Aerobes need oxygen to survive. Anaerobes cannot survive in the presence of oxygen. Some microbes are 'obligate' and are obliged to live with or without oxygen. Others are 'facultative' and have the flexibility to live in either type of environment.

becomes a lot more dangerous for the city. Eventually the weaker armies are destroyed and the victorious troops can launch an all-out assault on the city.

Basically, this means that it is not just the number of bacteria in food that we need to worry about, but whether or not they are all of the same kind. It is safer to have competing populations of different species than just one strong colony. When one group of micro-organisms is destroyed or inhibited by others in the same environment, it is called *microbial interference*. When two or more groups inhibit each other, we say that there are *antagonisms* between them.

Antagonisms occur in various ways. *Staphylococcus* does not multiply in the presence of *Pseudomonas*, *E. coli* or *Streptococcus* because they consume the amino acids it needs. Aerobic bacteria suppress the growth of *Clostridium botulinum* in fresh meat by altering the pH of the food. Lactic acid bacteria create acidic conditions that inhibit or kill many pathogenic and spoilage organisms. The inhibitory effect of species, such as *Lactobacillus reuteri*, can be used to *preserve* food but they are also added to a food product as *protective* cultures.

Putting intrinsic and extrinsic factors to work

Food technologists manipulate the factors that are essential for bacterial survival and multiplication in order to keep food safe to eat and to prolong its shelf life. The basic idea is to put 'barriers' in the way of the bacteria by combining several unfavourable intrinsic and extrinsic conditions that slow down their growth. This is known as *hurdle technology* which you'll encounter in Part 4 in 'Preservation – maintaining quality over time'. For now, it is worth taking a brief look at the methods that actually destroy bacteria.

Workplace weapons

In most instances food businesses can only *inhibit* bacterial multiplication because there are just a few ways to *destroy* bacteria:

- heat treatment
- chemical treatment
- irradiation.

Heat treatment
High temperatures (those above the temperature danger zone of 5°C to 63°C) can kill bacteria and this thermal destruction is one of the reasons for cooking, or treating, food at high temperatures. The length of time needed at a specific temperature depends on a number of factors that you will read more about in Part 4. Thermal death is rarely instantaneous and the period involved varies with every species. Survival rates depend upon the combination of time and temperature and on the initial bacterial load – the number of bacteria on a food.

Chemical treatment
While most chemicals used for preservation purposes only *inhibit* the multiplication of bacteria and *delay* microbial spoilage, many cleaning chemicals are bactericidal, meaning they actually *destroy* bacteria in the environment. These strong chemicals cannot of course be used on food itself, but they are an essential tool in maintaining clean premises

and a bacteria-unfriendly environment. The way in which the bacteria are destroyed depends on the type of chemical used. Typical lethal damage includes breaching the cell wall, coagulating the cytoplasm, disrupting the permeability of the membrane or reacting with cell constituents, such as essential proteins.

Irradiation

Electromagnetic irradiation causes cell death by destroying the genetic material (DNA) of the cell. In 1976 the World Health Organization (WHO) gave its blessing to the unrestricted use of irradiation for potatoes, wheat, various fruits and vegetables and poultry.

In European Union countries government licences must be obtained to irradiate food. Only one licence has been granted in Britain, and that is for spices. There is more information about the use of irradiation as a form of preservation in Part 4.

Bacterial monitoring and its limitations

Bacterial monitoring is essential in many branches of the food industry. Food packagers and processors in particular run bacteria-identifying tests regularly, both to prevent the outbreak of disease and to identify the presence of beneficial bacteria.

Identifying pathogenic and spoilage bacteria can be both time-consuming and complicated. Suspect food has to be sampled and organisms from it grown under laboratory conditions – a process that can take several days. While you are waiting for the test results, you may have to keep suspect food 'in quarantine'. You should also postpone decisions about changing or retaining food preparation and cleaning practices until test results are known.

Even then, remember that the *type* of bacterium is just one of the factors to be considered and, as microbes are rarely distributed evenly on food, the result is valid only for that particular sample that has been tested.

To date, none of the common methods can determine exactly how many microbes a product contains. However, they can be used to discover:

- the general amount of contamination of surfaces, equipment and utensils

- the potential contamination of food and the organisms involved

- the possibility of spoilage

- the potential shelf life of the product.

Testing methods

You need specialist advice or training to choose the right testing methods for your workplace and you need to consider:

- which foods, products and processes you deal with

- what kind of information would be the most useful

- which micro-organisms you suspect are present.

Biological techniques

These rely on being able to grow in the laboratory the microbes that are present in the sample.

Contact (or swabbing) technique

This is the oldest and most widely used method for checking food-contact surfaces. The surface is swabbed and a colony of micro-organisms grown from the swab sample.

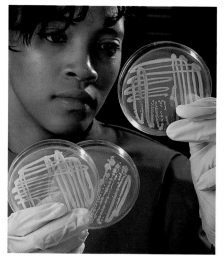

In the laboratory samples of bacteria obtained by swabbing are smeared onto a growth medium and allowed to multiply. Identification of the types and numbers of bacteria can then be carried out.

The organisms are then identified by standard methods of counting or microscopic examination, often following staining (see page 50) which makes them more visible. Swabbing is particularly useful for demonstrating the importance of food safety to staff because the micro-organisms are then visible to everybody.

Most probable number (MPN) method

This relatively simple method is useful for determining the density of faecal coliform bacteria, such as *E. coli*. The microbial growth in a sequence of dilutions of food samples is compared against standard MPN tables to estimate the original number of organisms.

Biochemical methods

These techniques look for indicator substances or metabolic products that show the presence of bacterial enzyme activities.

ATP bioluminescence

This method measures the emission of light by living organisms – the light emitted when a particular enzyme (luciferase) is in the presence of adenosine triphosphate (ATP), which is the main source of cellular energy in living organisms. Although this is a very sensitive method, it can be used in food premises and the results can be obtained within 15 minutes without the use of laboratory cultures. However, as food also contains ATP, the accurate interpretation of levels of contamination may be difficult. This method is best used to demonstrate the effectiveness of cleaning methods or the total level of micro-organisms in raw materials.

MUG test

Some bacteria, such as certain strains of *E. coli* and *Salmonella*, have a particular enzyme that splits the nutrient methyl-umbelliferyl-glucuronide (MUG). The MUG test detects and measures this reaction.

Physical methods

These methods use physical properties to detect bacteria.

The impedance method

Electrical resistance is used to determine the presence of bacteria. The more micro-organisms there are, the more metabolic products and the higher the electrical resistance. This method has the advantage of being quite fast, but it is unspecific about the nature of the organisms.

Microcalorimetry

This method detects the temperature change caused by microbes breaking down food.

Radiometry

This measures the speed of ingestion, usually of radioactive glucose introduced into the culture medium. The time required is inversely related to the number of micro-organisms in the sample – the fewer the organisms, the slower the process.

Immunological methods

These methods use immune responses in host cells to identify micro-organisms. Two of the most common such techniques are serotyping and phagetyping.

Serotyping

Serotyping uses known antibodies to identify unknown bacteria. Antibodies are part of a mammal's automatic defence system. They are special proteins formed in response to an invasion by foreign particles with antigenic qualities (see page 52). Antibodies react with only one component of the antigen so that when a reaction occurs it gives a clue as to which type of bacteria are present.

The test involves mixing antisera – kits of known antibodies – with bacterial samples. The results are visible, either through physical changes in affected samples on agar plates, or through colour changes of the enzymes of susceptible bacteria. The latter method is known as an ELISA (enzyme-linked immunosorbant assay) test.

Phagetyping

This test uses bacteriophages – viruses that attack bacteria. Many of these viruses attack only one bacterial strain, so that when a reaction occurs the bacterium is decisively identified. Strains identified in this way are called phagetypes.

Genetic methods

These use strands of genetic material, either DNA or ribonucleic acid (RNA), to make the identification.

The PCR (polymerase chain reaction) test

This test depends on the activity of a particular enzyme involved in genetic replication and is extremely specific and expensive to carry out. It may be used more in the future because of rapid advances in molecular genetics.

Making it easier for others

- Emphasise that we cannot see, taste or smell pathogenic ('harmful') bacteria when they have contaminated food, so staff must follow some simple rules, such as keeping food out of the danger zone, in order to keep food safe to eat.

- Make sure that all food handlers know which are the high-risk foods used in your premises and how they should take care of them.

- Link all the basic-level underlying knowledge about bacteria (and the other micro-organisms) to workplace rules and best practice.

Feature

Putting microbes in writing

The proper names for microbes can appear a little daunting at first, but there are good reasons why they are named as they are.

With so many creatures on Earth, we need a clear way of distinguishing one from another. So all living things have a two-part scientific name, such as *Salmonella enterica* (a bacterium commonly responsible for food-borne illness) or *Homo sapiens* (modern humans).

All the names for organisms are Latinised. This may seem odd as Latin is a 'dead' language, but in the eighteenth century, when the system was developed, Latin was the common language of science.

Even the inventor of the system, the Swedish naturalist and physician Carl von Linné, was known then, as he is today, by the Latin form of his name – Carolus Linnaeus.

His taxonomy (system of classifying organisms), referred to today as 'the Linnaeus system' or 'binomial nomenclature', has stayed in use ever since.

This helps to avoid confusion as everyone uses the same two-part Latin name throughout the world, whatever their own everyday language.

The first part of an organism's name – such as *Salmonella* – refers to the genus. This is a large group of related life forms to which the organism belongs. The second part of the name – *enterica* – refers to the species, which identifies a particular type of even more closely related organisms within the genus.

When referring to the species, you must always use the full two-part designation. Express it in *italics* or, if you are writing by hand or using a typewriter without italics, underline it instead.

The genus always takes a capital letter, the species does not. You can abbreviate the genus name – for example, *S. enterica* – after giving the name in full at least once and where there is no chance of confusion with another bacterium, such as *Staphylococcus*, that starts with an 'S'.

As scientific knowledge has increased it has become possible to make finer and finer distinctions within species. Some of these subdivisions include varieties, strains, phagetypes and serotypes, also called serovars.

Rapid developments in molecular genetic techniques have also made it possible to establish even clearer relationships between species. As a result, the classifications of some micro-organisms have been revised.

The parasitic roundworm *Trichina spiralis*, for example, was previously known as *Trichinella spiralis* (see page 106) and *Salmonella* is now recognised as having just two species, *S. enterica* and *S. bongori*.

These are then divided into nearly 3,000 serotypes or serovars (subdivisions distinguished by their chemical or immunological attributes), which are commonly named after the place where they were identified or the disease they cause.

One bacterium responsible for causing food poisoning was previously styled as *Salmonella typhimurium*. It is now designated as *Salmonella enterica* serovar Typhimurium.

The species name – *Salmonella enterica* – is in italics. The serovar name – serovar Typhimurium – is in plain text, with Typhimurium beginning with a capital letter.

This can all become rather unwieldy, so there is an accepted shorter version for serovar names – for example *Salmonella* Typhimurium. We use this simpler style in the book.

For the purposes of day-to-day food safety, the changes in nomenclature probably make little difference to you.

However, as revisions to classifications are continuing, you should expect to come across other name changes as scientists gather more information using molecular techniques.

Bacterial food-borne illness

There are many ways of classifying illnesses caused by pathogenic bacteria and their toxins. When talking about food-related symptoms, it is common to divide the illnesses and the bacteria that cause them into two broad categories – those caused directly by the invasion of the body by bacteria (an infection) and those caused by bacterial toxins produced either directly on the food, or produced in the body after ingestion (an intoxication).

Other classifications frequently used in the UK are food-borne infection and food poisoning and it is these that we use in this book and describe in detail on the following pages.

Reminder
In this book we use 'food-borne illness' or 'food-borne disease' to describe *all* the categories of food-related illness.

Avoiding confusion

Rather in the way that you are advised to use *either* imperial *or* metric measures when cooking (but not both), we strongly advise you to use just one pair of the categories – either use food-borne infection together with food poisoning, as we do in this book, or use infection together with intoxication.

In the past, you may have been accustomed to describing food-borne infection as 'food-borne disease'. There is no issue of right or wrong in this: it is simply a matter of being consistent.

Two groupings of categories of common food-borne bacteria

Either (as used in this book)…	Or…
Food poisoning *Aeromonas hydrophila* *Bacillus cereus* *Clostridium botulinum* *Clostridium perfringens* *Escherichia coli* *Salmonella* species (except *S*. Typhi and *S*. Paratyphi) *Staphylococcus aureus* *Streptococcus* species *Vibrio parahaemolyticus* *Yersinia enterocolitica*	**Intoxication** *Bacillus cereus* *Clostridium botulinum* *Clostridium perfringens* *Escherichia coli* *Escherichia coli* O157 *Shigella dysenteriae* *Staphylococcus aureus*
Food-borne infection *Brucella abortus* *Brucella melitensis* *Campylobacter jejuni* *Escherichia coli* O157 *Listeria monocytogenes* *Mycobacterium bovis* *Mycobacterium tuberculosis* *Salmonella* Paratyphi *Salmonella* Typhi *Shigella dysenteriae*	**Infection** *Aeromonas hydrophila* *Brucella abortus* *Brucella melitensis* *Campylobacter jejuni* *Listeria monocytogenes* *Mycobacterium bovis* *Mycobacterium tuberculosis* *Salmonella* species (including *S*. Typhi and *S*. Paratyphi) *Vibrio parahaemolyticus* *Yersinia enterocolitica*

Poisoning or intoxication – why the difference?

If you are comfortable using one or other of the paired categories suggested on page above, you may prefer to skip to the bottom of page 73. However, if you were slightly bemused by some of the differences in categorisation and wish to know a little more about the reasons why, take a look at the explanations below.

Intoxication versus food poisoning

Intoxication simply means affected by a toxin (or poison) so it is a reasonable assumption that an intoxication is the same as food poisoning. Unfortunately this is *not* the case. As you can see from the table on the previous page, some food poisonings are infections and some food-borne infections are intoxications.

In the past

The reasons for the different categories are largely a matter of convention. The first food-related illnesses to be recognised were true cases of poisoning, such as botulism. As other conditions were recognised that were being caused by bacteria that were growing on food, they were also classed as food poisoning, whether they were intoxications or infections. The important issue was that they seemed to require food for multiplication to the point where there were enough of them to cause an infection or to produce sufficient toxin to cause an intoxication.

When it was discovered that some other diseases were also related to food, because transmission could be via food, another name had to be found for them. They were generally called food-borne infections. From this arose the curious situation where some infections are in a group called 'food poisoning' and some intoxications are in a group called 'infection'.

Category confusion

The criteria for classifications are often a compromise in the first place. Before long it is found that not everything fits neatly, so further compromises are made. As a result we can end up with classifications that are not totally logical but by now are comfortably familiar. Perhaps the good news is that modern usage tends to collect all categories together as food-borne illness (or food-borne disease)!

Distinctions – why bother?

So why bother with any categories at all? Of course, you need to recognise the terms when you read about them elsewhere. More importantly, it is useful to know which organisms fall under which group because it may help you to decide on control measures – some bacteria need to live on food before they become a food safety problem, while others use food only as a means of transport.

In the end, the most important thing to remember is that you need measures in place to stop microbes getting onto food. That way, you minimise the chance of any category of food-related illness!

Appropriate usage
In everyday conversation the expression 'food poisoning' is often used to describe all types of illness from contaminated food. You may prefer to use this expression when making food safety easier for some of your colleagues. The choice of term is simply a matter of *general* or appropriate *specialist* use. (See also 'Making it easier for others' on page 93.)

Bacterial food poisoning and food-borne infection

The main differences between bacterial food poisoning and food-borne infection can be summed up as the distinctions between the:

- number of bacteria necessary to cause symptoms of illness
- onset of symptoms
- part food plays in the whole scenario.

Food poisoning

With just a few exceptions (such as *Clostridium botulinum*), food poisoning occurs only after a very large number of bacteria (10^5 to 10^6 per gram) or a large quantity of bacterial toxin has been ingested. Bacteria reach such high numbers by using food as the medium for multiplication. Some bacteria, such as *Staphylococcus aureus*, can start toxin formation on the food even before it is eaten (although it takes more than one million of them to produce enough toxin to cause illness).

Most food poisoning symptoms affect the gastro-intestinal system and typical symptoms are abdominal pain, diarrhoea and vomiting. Fever, malaise and general weakness may be among other symptoms experienced. The incubation period is relatively short: depending on the organism, people may become ill after only a few hours or days. The number of bacteria in the food influences the incubation period and the onset of symptoms is rapid if the bacteria have had time to multiply on the food. So, controlling the length of time that high-risk food is left in the danger zone is essential. Most illnesses (*C. botulinum* is an exception) typically last from about six hours up to about seven days.

Food-borne infection

In sharp contrast to food poisoning, food-borne infection is caused by relatively few organisms which develop in the body of the victim over a fairly long time (days and weeks compared to the hours and days of food poisoning bacteria). With the infective dose being very small, these bacteria need not necessarily multiply in food – they are only *transmitted* or *carried* by the food. Typically they are carried by water, and this is often the source of epidemics like typhoid and cholera following a natural disaster, such as an earthquake or flood, when the supply of drinking water is one of the first things affected.

Bacteria that cause food-borne infections are also readily carried by other vehicles of contamination (things which pick up and move bacteria), such as hands and soil, and by air as air-borne droplets.

As bacterial multiplication does not take place on the food, the time before contaminated food is eaten is not a significant factor in the onset of illness. The symptoms can be severe, such as kidney disease, because the organism often enters the bloodstream.

Common food-borne bacteria

Details of common bacteria implicated in food poisoning and food-borne infection are given later in the chapter (and summarised in Reference), together with information about some bacteria that may be of significance in the future. First, however, we look at the most common factors behind food-borne illness.

Factors leading to illness

Food-borne illness is preventable but there is so much of it worldwide that we are forced to conclude that many things are going wrong, whether the ultimate blame is laid at the door of ineffective management, inadequate staff training, poor staff and process supervision, patchy legal enforcement, apathy, carelessness, negligence or a combination of these.

The results of research by the US Centers for Disease Control and Prevention (CDC) in Atlanta, USA, into the causal factors of food poisoning in the USA, Canada and the UK are shown opposite. The figures show the percentage of instances in which an identified factor was at least partly responsible for an outbreak of illness. The figures do not total a hundred per cent because there are often multiple causes identified for an outbreak.

Main factors leading to food poisoning

63 %	Inadequate cooling and cold holding
29 %	Preparing food ahead of planned service
27 %	Inadequate hot holding
26 %	Poor personal hygiene/infected persons
25 %	Inadequate reheating
9 %	Inadequate cleaning of equipment
7 %	Use of left-over food
6 %	Cross-contamination
5 %	Inadequate prime cooking or heat processing
4 %	Toxic chemical contamination from containers
2 %	Contaminated raw ingredients
2 %	Intentional chemical additives
1 %	Incidental chemical additives
1 %	Unsafe sources

Most common reasons for food-borne illness

Let's look at the top five factors identified. What do they have in common? With the exception of one category (poor personal hygiene and infected persons), they are all to do with temperature control.

Getting on for two-thirds (63 per cent) of outbreaks involved inadequate cooling and cold holding. We need to ask why the time and temperature control was inadequate.

Was it because of the food handlers' lack of awareness, apathy, negligence or carelessness? Or had the managers failed to supply and maintain the correct equipment; provide enough refrigerators, chillers or cold cabinets; or train or supervise the staff adequately? Alternatively, had the managers accepted business that was in excess of the company's ability (equipment, premises or personnel) to deal with?

A total of 29 per cent of outbreaks was caused by preparing food too far ahead of planned service. It is highly likely that the food was left at an ambient temperature or within the temperature danger zone.

Were the staff unaware of the likelihood of multiplication of food poisoning bacteria, or were they lazy or careless? Or did the managers fail to provide sufficient equipment to store prepared food, organise enough staff to work at that period, allow poor workflow or accept an order which was beyond the company's ability to fulfil?

It is impossible to give answers here for each case, but the questions highlight just how much food-borne illness is a management issue.

Perhaps you should ask yourself frequently: have I provided sufficient trained staff and sufficient suitable equipment and working space for the job in hand, and can I say that none of the issues listed above will happen in my company because of poor management?

Most vulnerable

Anyone could become ill with a food-borne disease after eating contaminated food, but some people are especially vulnerable if they do become ill and may even die as a result. Those in this **at risk group** include the elderly; the very young; people who are ill, convalescing or who have weakened immune systems; and pregnant women, unborn children and breast-fed babies.

Pathogenic food-borne bacteria

Examples of the bacteria responsible for causing food-borne illnesses are given in alphabetical order on the following pages. Food poisoning bacteria are given first, with food-borne infection bacteria starting on page 84.

Bacteria responsible for food poisoning

These bacteria cause food poisoning when they have multiplied in food to high levels or have produced a lot of bacterial toxin and the food is then eaten.

Bacillus cereus

This organism has been associated with food-borne illness in Europe since the early twentieth century. Much research was carried out in the 1950s but it was not until the early 1970s that the first reported outbreak occurred in the UK.

B. cereus
Forms spores.
Two types of toxin can be formed – one in the body, the other in food.

Bacillus cereus is an aerobic, Gram-positive, spore-forming rod. While widely distributed in nature, it is typically found in soil, dust and vegetation. This bacterium can grow between 7°C and 48°C, but its optimum is between 28°C and 35°C. It has a pH tolerance between 4.9 and 9.3, although some strains can tolerate down to 4.35, and its preferred a_w is 0.912.

B. cereus produces two toxins, one of which gives rise to the *diarrhoeal syndrome* and the other to the *emetic syndrome*.

Diarrhoeal syndrome

The incubation period is normally 8 to 16 hours and the symptoms of diarrhoea, abdominal pain, nausea and some vomiting (although this is rare) usually last for one or two days. The illness is caused by the production of a toxin in the intestine, which explains why diarrhoea is a more likely symptom than vomiting and why the incubation period is longer than that for the emetic syndrome.

Emetic syndrome

This is more severe and acute than the diarrhoeal syndrome. After an incubation period of one to five hours, the symptoms may include vomiting, abdominal pains and sometimes a little diarrhoea. The symptoms last for six to 24 hours.

The illness is caused by ingestion of a toxin that has already been produced on the food. As a consequence, there is a shorter incubation time than that of the diarrhoeal syndrome and the toxin acts on the upper gastro-intestinal tract, causing symptoms (mainly vomiting) that are associated with the stomach rather than the intestine.

Foods implicated

As the species name *cereus* suggests, foods commonly involved in outbreaks include cereals and grains. Rice and rice-based items, cereals, soya beans and soy products, meat, fish, milk, vegetables, pasta and tofu are common sources of *B. cereus*, although it is possible to isolate it from many other foods.

A common route of infection is the cooking of boiled rice that is then stored at an ambient temperature which, given enough time, allows spores to germinate and produce a toxin. Subsequent heating of the rice will not destroy the toxin. In the case of fried rice, flash frying is insufficient to destroy either the toxin or all of the vegetative cells.

Control

Control measures are strict control of time and temperature – including cooking, cooling, storing and reheating (if reheating really must be carried out) – and the prevention of cross-contamination.

Clostridium botulinum

The name *botulinum* derives from the Latin word *botulus*, meaning sausage, and from the German word *Botulismus* which originally meant sausage poisoning.

The earliest references to botulism come from Württemberg in Germany in the late eighteenth and early nineteenth centuries when outbreaks of sausage poisoning from blood-sausages caused illness and death. Originally the sausages were par-boiled, then smoked. Then it was discovered that if the sausage casings were filled loosely so that pockets of air were left, and if the sausages were boiled thoroughly, then they did not become toxic.

Without realising it, the sausage producers had established that *Clostridium botulinum* bacterium is an anaerobe.

Found in soil and water, this bacterium is an anaerobic, Gram-positive, spore-forming rod. Seven types have been identified, classified according to their toxins: five types cause disease in humans while the other two types are associated with animals. The human infection route is through raw food contaminated with spores. Following germination of the spores, the multiplying bacteria produce an exotoxin. The illness is caused by the ingestion of the toxin in the food.

Extremely dangerous toxin

The toxin produced by *C. botulinum* is a neurotoxin. This accounts for some of the symptoms being different to those caused by other food poisoning bacteria. The symptoms can include double vision, difficulty in speaking and swallowing, headache, nausea, fatigue, constipation, vomiting, dizziness and muscle paralysis leading to respiratory failure and death. The incubation period is eight to 72 hours, with 12 to 36 hours being typical.

The illness normally lasts one to ten days, although there are reports of it lasting for much longer periods. Death can occur unless an antitoxin is given fairly early in the course of the illness. The mortality rate varies between 30 and 60 per cent and seems to be lower in Europe than in North America. There is no known carrier status for the organism.

Preferred conditions

Fortunately *C. botulinum* appears to be a poor competitor and cannot grow or produce toxin in the presence of large numbers of other micro-organisms.

C. botulinum
Common in the environment.
Forms spores.
Produces a neurotoxin.
Almost one-third to over a half of cases lead to death.
Temperature needed for spore destruction determines a standard canning temperature.

The temperature range for growth varies slightly depending on the type, but 3°C is about the lowest for the types with which we are most concerned. The upper range is 50°C with an optimum between 20°C and 30°C. The spores are very heat resistant so a temperature of 121°C for three minutes is required to destroy them – hence the temperature of a 'botulinum cook' (see pages 338 to 340). The toxin, however, is not very heat stable and so can be destroyed by thorough cooking. This bacterium is not thought to grow at a pH of below 4.5 and this is another main determining factor in a botulinum cook. The a_w depends on the type: two types are inhibited at under 0.93 and the others at around 0.97.

Foods implicated

Outbreaks commonly arise in countries where home canning is popular. Canned meat, fish or vegetables which have not been heated sufficiently are typically involved. There have also been outbreaks and some deaths from commercially produced foods. Inadequately processed low-acid foods, herbs in oil and vacuum-packed products were implicated. Chopped garlic in oil, which was stored for many months at an ambient temperature, was responsible for outbreaks in the Netherlands, Canada and America in 1985. The largest outbreak in the UK was in 1989 when 27 people became ill and one died after eating hazelnut yoghurt made with contaminated cans of hazelnut puree.

You may come across references to 'temperature-abused baked potatoes'. These generally describe cases of botulism in America from baked potatoes that were wrapped in foil and kept unrefrigerated for several days before use.

Control

Adequate time and temperature controls are essential, especially in canning, bottling and vacuum-packing.

Infant botulism

This is a condition in infants under one year old. While an adult's intestine is not a favourable environment for spore germination, it seems that some botulinum spores can germinate in the intestine of the very young and can produce sufficient toxin to cause illness. While the symptoms in some infants are fairly mild, in others the condition is severe. Although fatalities are rare, the first and most common symptom is constipation. Other symptoms include generalised weakness, a weak cry, poor sucking reflex, lack of facial expression and poor head control.

The illness is widespread in the USA, particularly in some of the western states where there is believed to be a high incidence of botulinum spores in the soil. There are between 60 and 90 cases a year, normally associated with honey. It is therefore not recommended for food safety reasons to feed honey to children under one year old.

Clostridium perfringens

The first detailed description of the illness associated with this pathogen was by Betty C. Hobbs and others in the UK in the early 1950s (when the bacterium was named *C. welchii*), although the illness and its association with the bacterium were probably well known for at least a decade previously.

Clostridium perfringens (shown in a micrograph on page 57) is an anaerobic, Gram-positive, spore-forming rod and is widely distributed in nature. Five types are recognised: Type A is normally associated with food-borne illness, although Type C can cause a non-food-related disease. Sources are the human and animal intestine, soil, dust and spices.

The illness is caused by an enterotoxin which is produced when large numbers of the bacterium (usually about 10^6) sporulate in the intestine – almost always as a consequence of bad food-preparation practices. Typically, bacterial spores form because of a survival response to the 'threat' from the heat while the food is cooking. When the food starts to cool, especially if this happens slowly, the spores can germinate and bacterial multiplication can then occur. When the food, which is now heavily contaminated, is eaten the bacteria encounter unfavourable conditions in the intestine. They protect themselves once again by forming spores, in the process releasing the enterotoxin which causes illness.

C. perfringens
Forms spores.
Toxin released during sporulation in the intestine.
Poor temperature control is a common cause of problems.

The symptoms are diarrhoea and abdominal pain, which last for up to two days. Vomiting is rare. The incubation period can be six to 24 hours with the norm being around eight to 18 hours. Fatalities are rare but do occur in the elderly and in people with compromised immune systems.

It is believed that the toxin can sometimes be produced on the food itself, which would account for the shorter onset times that are sometimes encountered.

Preferred conditions
C. perfringens is a mesophile, growing at between 20°C and 50°C, with 37°C to 45°C as the optimum. The ideal pH is between 5.5 and 8.0. The a_w for spore germination and growth has been reported at as low as 0.93, with spore formation requiring a higher value.

Foods implicated
Foods commonly implicated include foods and ingredients that have been cooled too slowly after cooking is complete, such as cooked meat and poultry, gravy, sauces and spices.

Control
Measures include strict time and temperature control in cooking, cooling and reheating; only reheating once (if absolutely necessary); separation of cooked and raw foods; and thorough cleaning and disinfection routines.

Escherichia coli
This bacterium is a normal inhabitant of healthy human and animal intestines where it lives in large populations as a harmless commensal. In fact, most strains of this aerobic rod-shaped bacterium are harmless, but certain strains are pathogenic and can cause severe abdominal pains and diarrhoea, the latter being especially dangerous and even fatal for young children.

The serotype ETEC (enterotoxic *E. coli*) is the causative agent for traveller's diarrhoea (also known by a range of more colourful names, including Montezuma's revenge and la tourista) because the bacterial strains involved are not usually found in the traveller's home country and are, in a sense, in the wrong place at the wrong time. The strain of *E. coli* that has been in the news for several years – *E. coli* O157 – is classed as a food-borne infection (see page 86).

Food poisoning from *E. coli* is caused by an enterotoxin and usually starts between 12 and 72 hours after eating contaminated food. The symptoms usually include abdominal pain, fever, diarrhoea and vomiting and last from one to 14 days.

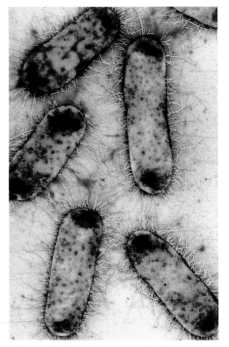

Symptoms of food poisoning from *Escherichia coli* usually start 12 to 72 hours after eating contaminated food.

Sources and foods implicated
Human and animal intestines are the major source of *E. coli*, together with meat and sewage. As large numbers of the bacterium inevitably end up in sewage, it has long been used as an indicator organism for faecal contamination (faecal coliform) of food or water. Meat is sometimes contaminated by *E. coli* during slaughter. Foods commonly involved are raw meat, undercooked meat products, gravy and raw milk.

Preferred conditions
This Gram-negative mesophile can multiply at temperatures as low as 7°C to 10°C. Research suggests that it may even be able to multiply at a temperature as low as 4°C as it can survive refrigeration. Its optimal multiplication temperature is around 37°C – average human body temperature. It needs a minimum a_w of 0.95 and prefers a neutral pH, although multiplication is possible as low as 4.4.

Control
The safe disposal of sewage is essential, together with the strict separation of raw and cooked foods, adequate cooking and effective personal hygiene.

Salmonella species
Salmonella is the organism which most clearly demonstrates that bacterial evolution is continuing. Not only are new strains identified and described every year, but the bacterium also reveals how a relatively harmless initial inhabitant of the gut has developed new and dangerous representatives and occupied new niches, such as the ovaries of poultry.

As with some other pathogenic bacteria, *Salmonella* have also developed strains that are antibiotic-resistant.

Named after Daniel Elmer Salmon, an American vet who lived in the late nineteenth and early twentieth centuries, *Salmonella* is a genus of facultative anaerobic, Gram-negative rods which are widely distributed in the environment. The main reservoirs are humans and animals. In terms of severity their effects can vary from mild discomfort to death.

Categorising the bacterium

With nearly 3,000 known serotypes, not all of which are true food poisoning organisms, the *Salmonella* bacteria are in a league of their own – and their taxonomy (biological classification) is complicated and often revised (see page 70). For epidemiological purposes (the study of the causes and spread of disease), they can be divided into three groups:

Salmonella
Multiply in food.
Eggs, poultry, raw milk
and raw meat are
commonly implicated.

- those that infect humans only and can be transmitted by food, such as *Salmonella* Typhi and *Salmonella* Paratyphi (previously *S. typhi* and *S. paratyphi*)

- host-adapted strains, some of which – for example, *S*. Dublin (formerly *S. dublin*) in cattle – are human pathogens and can be transmitted by food

- strains with no preferred host, which can be pathogenic for humans and animals – this group contains most of the strains responsible for food-borne illnesses.

Salmonella Typhimurium (formerly *S. typhimurium*) – pictured on pages 24 and 54 – and *Salmonella* Enteritidis (formerly *S. enteritidis*) are the most common causes of salmonella food poisoning. The illness is caused by the invasion of the body by a large number of bacteria, which have multiplied on the food. The infective dose is thought to be about 105 per gram. The incubation period is between six and 96 hours, typically 12 to 48 hours.

Carrier
Someone who is
infected by a particular
pathogen, does not
develop symptoms of
the illness but can pass
on the pathogen to
others.

The symptoms of salmonellosis are diarrhoea, vomiting, fever and abdominal pain, which usually last up to seven days. The mortality rate varies according to the age of the person affected, with high rates among the 'at risk group' (see page 76). The serotype reported to have the highest mortality rate is *Salmonella* Choleraesuis (formerly *S. choleraesuis*). Normally the intestine is clear of the organism fairly quickly after the symptoms disappear, but up to five per cent of patients become carriers.

Preferred conditions

Salmonella multiply quite readily between 7°C and 45°C. Their minimum pH tolerance is between 4.05 and 5.5 depending on the *type* of acid in a food. The optimal growth range is between 6.6 and 8.2. The a_w tolerance depends on the pH, but multiplication is believed to be inhibited at about 0.94 when pH is neutral.

Sources and foods implicated

The primary sources of *Salmonella* are human and animal intestinal tracts and faeces. The infection route is via raw animal products such as raw meat, eggs and egg products, milk and poultry. Another infection route is via faeces and fertilisers, for example, on vegetables. Insects, birds, pets, rodents, terrapins, sewage and water can also be sources. Foods commonly involved in outbreaks include meat and meat products, poultry, raw milk, eggs and egg products, dairy products and seafood.

Control

High standards of personal hygiene, avoidance of cross-contamination, thorough cleaning and disinfection routines, effective pest management and strict control of time and temperature are the main weapons against this bacterium.

Staphylococcus aureus

This bacterium and its associated illness were first studied at the end of the eighteenth century but its full mechanisms were not fully understood for some considerable time. *Staphylococcus aureus* bacteria are facultative anaerobic, Gram-positive cocci and are mostly resident in humans. They are found in the nose, throat and hair and on skin and hands, as well as in boils, pimples, sties, septic lesions, burns and wounds. In moist habitats,

Normal inhabitants of the human gut can include *Streptococcus* (the spherical bacteria) and *Escherichia coli*.

such as the nose, the numbers per square centimetre can be as high as 10^3 to 10^6. They can also be found in animals – for example in cows or goats with mastitis – and can lead to a direct infection in humans as a result of drinking raw milk.

Staphylococcus aureus is an exotoxin producer, but not every bacterium produces toxin. There need to be about 10^6 (one million) bacteria for there to be enough toxin-producers present to produce sufficient toxin in the food to cause illness when the food is eaten. The toxin is fairly heat resistant and can survive for 30 minutes at 100°C.

The symptoms of illness include diarrhoea, acute vomiting, nausea, abdominal pain and sometimes collapse. A fall in body temperature may sometimes occur. The onset time is one to six hours and about four hours is typical. Symptoms normally last for 12 to 48 hours. The mortality rate is very low.

S. aureus
Found on the human body and in the throat, nose and boils and cuts.
Short onset and duration.
Toxin-producer.
Toxin fairly heat resistant.
Grows at low a_w.

Preferred conditions
The growth range is usually between 7°C and 48°C, with toxin being produced at between 10°C and 46°C. While the bacterium can grow over a pH range of 4.0 to 9.8, its optimal range is 6.0 to 7.0. Even though it is not salt tolerant, *S. aureus* can grow at the rather low a_w of 0.83, but 0.86 is regarded as typical.

Sources and foods implicated
Foods commonly involved in outbreaks include ham, poultry, egg products, dairy products, potato salads and raw milk from cows and goats.

The infection route is via humans and bad hygiene practices and, on occasion, from raw milk. The contamination results from any one or a combination of factors: infected food handlers contaminating the food as a result of bad personal hygiene; poor temperature control; preparation of food too far in advance of serving; inadequate heating and so on.

Control
Control measures are strict personal hygiene, especially with regard to hand washing, 'excluding' food handlers with skin infections or colds (see page 275 to 277), effective temperature control and avoiding the use of raw milk.

Vibrio parahaemolyticus

Vibrio parahaemolyticus
Aquatic.
Illness usually associated with fish or seafood.

Vibrio parahaemolyticus is unique among pathogens connected to food because its source is almost exclusively fish or seafood. Identified in the early 1950s in Japan, it remains the major food poisoning problem in that country. A Gram-positive, facultative anaerobe, the bacterium is a halophile found in coastal sea waters.

Illness is caused by the invasion of the body by a large number of this bacterium. The infective dose is not accurately known but is thought to be about 10^4 per gram. Carrier status is possible. The symptoms are diarrhoea, vomiting, abdominal pain, fever and dehydration and can last for up to seven days. The onset time is four to 96 hours with 12 to 24 hours being typical. The infection can be fatal to those in the 'at risk group'.

Preferred conditions

Multiplication is possible between 10°C and 44°C, with the optimum being 37°C. The organism is pH tolerant between 4.8 and 11.0 with an optimal growth range of 7.6 to 8.6. The a_w is 0.99.

Foods implicated

The primary sources are fish and seafood, especially those from warmer waters or polluted water, although cross-contamination can cause a problem in other foods.

Foods commonly involved in outbreaks include clams, oysters, crabs, shrimps and lobsters.

Control

Measures are buying seafood only from known and approved sources, strict time and temperature controls and avoiding the serving of raw or lightly cooked seafood to 'at risk groups'.

An ugly death

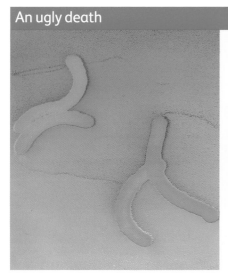

A mid-nineteenth century illustration depicts cholera as a sinister shrouded figure rising from a river while the figure of Science, shown as a Roman soldier, nods off to sleep. The micrograph (left) is the bacterium now known to be responsible for cholera, *Vibrio cholerae*, which is often water borne. Death can follow rapidly after violent vomiting, diarrhoea, muscle spasms and dehydration, which can make the victim's face look black. There were epidemics in Peru and in most countries of South and central America in 1991. More than a thousand people died from the disease in eastern India and Bangladesh in 1992.

Yersinia enterocolitica
Multiplies under refrigeration. Often spread by faecal-oral routes.

Yersinia enterocolitica

Yersinia enterocolitica is from a family of facultative anaerobic, Gram-negative rods with 11 species that include *Yersinia pestis*, the organism responsible for outbreaks of plague, such as the Black Death (1348) in Britain and The Great Plague of London (1665-6). The genus is named in honour of the pioneering Swiss bacteriologist Alexandre Yersin who produced an antiserum and cured several plague victims in Hong Kong in 1896.

The symptoms of *Yersinia enterocolitica* are mainly diarrhoea, fever, headache and abdominal pain, but it has been associated with much more serious conditions such as reactive arthritis, mesenteric lymphadenitis, terminal ileitis and pseudo-appendicitis.

The incubation period is usually one to 14 days and the bacterium can persist in the patient's stools for some considerable time. The infective dose has not yet been confirmed.

Preferred conditions

Widely distributed in the environment, both on land and in water, *Y. enterocolitica* can multiply at temperatures as low as 0°C or as high as 44°C, but its optimal range is between

32°C and 34°C. Its pH range is from 4.6 to 9.0 with an optimum between 7.0 and 8.0. Of particular concern is the ability of this bacterium to multiply at refrigerator temperatures.

Foods implicated

Milk, milk products, egg products, raw meat (especially raw pork), poultry and vegetables are implicated. The route of infection is faecal-oral and contaminated food or water.

Control

Control measures include proper heat treatment.

Emerging food poisoning pathogens

Streptococcus viridans and S. faecalis have been suspected of involvement in food poisoning but as yet no firm evidence has been established.

Aeromonas hydrophila is an aquatic organism associated with fish and frogs. It is a facultative anaerobic, Gram-negative rod and is a toxin producer. As well as diarrhoea, it has also been associated with endocarditis, meningitis, soft tissue infections and bacteraemia.

Bacteria responsible for food-borne infections

Although food poisoning bacteria are probably the best known pathogens in the food industry, it is the bacteria which cause food-borne infections that often have the most dangerous consequences. In many cases – for instance, *E. coli* O157 – scientists and food handlers have had to develop new strategies to fight these constantly developing sources of microbiological hazard.

You will also find under this heading some bacteria that rarely cause infection through the food-borne route: tuberculosis (TB) is a case in point. Pasteurization, the heating process for milk, was originally based on the destruction of the bacteria *Mycobacterium tuberculosis* (responsible for TB) and *Brucella abortus* and it is often forgotten that this method was designed to combat one of the main scourges of humans that still causes deaths in many parts of the world. Information about tuberculosis and brucellosis is included in this book because they are still prevalent food-borne infections in many places. (TB is also re-emerging via routes other than food, but these are not discussed here.)

General controls

Establishing a *general* preventive approach to food-borne infection through your company's HACCP system will help, even though some *special* measures may be needed to deal with particular organisms. A combination of the following methods will help you to control almost all bacteria implicated in food-borne infections:

- use only potable water for food preparation, as an ingredient and for cleaning tasks

- make certain that sewage is disposed of safely

- take special care that milk and milk products, including ice-cream, are subject to the correct and appropriate heat treatment, such as pasteurization

- do not use or sell shellfish from polluted waters

- train staff in all aspects of food hygiene

- supervise staff to maintain the highest possible standards of personal hygiene

- identify suspected carriers (see page 276)

- supervise and monitor standards of hygiene through all stages of production, storage, distribution and placing on the market

- avoid contact with animals: if contact is necessary, make sure that staff observe strict personal hygiene

- maintain effective systems of pest control.

Brucella

Brucellosis is a typical zoonosis – an illness that can be transmitted from animal to human and from human to animal. It is known under many names, including undulant fever, Malta fever (*Brucella melitensis*), Mediterranean fever or Bang's disease (*B. abortus*).

The natural reservoirs are sheep, goats and cattle but the bacteria may also be found in deer, caribou and dogs. The sources of infection vary according to the geographic area – the disease occurs worldwide but especially in Mediterranean countries, central and South America and central Asia. Sporadic outbreaks often occur following the consumption of raw cow's, sheep's or goat's milk or products made from the milk.

The common hosts of *B. melitensis* are sheep and goats in Mediterranean countries and in Mexico and central America where up to 90 per cent of herds of goats can be infected. As a consequence, Malta fever is largely an occupational disease. The name of *B. abortus* hints that the bacterium is often responsible for stillborn calves.

Brucella
Transmitted by raw milk, contact with animal tissue or blood, or by airborne droplets.

One mode of transmission is by contact with animal tissue or blood, so the people most at risk are those working with infected animals or their hides and tissues, such as farm workers, abattoir workers, shepherds and vets. There is also the possibility of air-borne (droplet) transmission by both animals and humans, for example by inhaling *Brucella*-infected dust from manure. The bacteria multiply only in the host but can persist for long periods in dried dung or tissue. Laboratory personnel dealing with *Brucella* must take special safety precautions.

The symptoms include fever, headache, weakness, depression and generalised aching after an incubation period of between five and 30 days.

Brucella in raw milk survive in milk products which are not heat treated. The cream of the infected milk is usually more heavily affected than the other components. The organism is not heat tolerant and will die at standard pasteurization temperatures. The deliberate souring of milk inhibits the organism but does not eliminate it. Brucella can tolerate pH levels of 4 to 5.

Control

The control of milk-borne brucellosis depends on its eradication from dairy animals, which may involve slaughtering every animal in the infected herd or flock, and on adequate heat treatment of milk and dairy products. Other necessary preventive measures are thorough hygiene measures in the slaughterhouse and throughout the food flow, including strict personal hygiene after dealing with farm animals.

Campylobacter jejuni

The name *Campylobacter* comes from the Greek word *campyle*, meaning crosier or Bishop's crook, and under the microscope the bacterium appears as a spirally curved rod (see page 51). *Campylobacter jejuni and C. coli* are the main two species involved in illness from food. *Campylobacter* is the most common identified cause of food-borne disease in

England and Wales and the main cause of diarrhoeal illness worldwide. The World Health Organization (WHO) says that *Campylobacter* bacteria cause more cases of diarrhoea around the world than, for example, *Salmonella* in food. In developing countries, children under two years are often affected and may die from the illness. The WHO says that the incidence of human campylobacter infections has been steadily increasing for several years in almost all developed countries, but the reasons for this are unknown.

C. jejuni
Can survive vacuum-packing. Destroyed by normal cooking temperatures.

Campylobacter are micro-aerophillic Gram-negative bacteria that can survive vacuum-packing. The genus contains about 14 different species.

Before the 1970s it was implicated in abortion in cattle and sheep and reduced fertility in cattle – it was originally named *Vibrio foetus* – as well as with a multitude of different clinical symptoms in animals. For a long time the human pathogenic potential of the genus was of no interest, but it is now of special concern to the food industry. The infective dose can be under 500 cells.

Symptoms and duration
Campylobacter jejuni is the most commonly reported species and causes sporadic gastro-enteritis and acute infectious bacterial diarrhoea. The symptoms also include headache, fever, abdominal pain and nausea.

The usual onset time is between two and five days, but is sometimes longer. The normal duration of illness is between two and seven days, but a subsequent stage can follow.

The potential complications are meningitis or septicaemia. Occasionally, *C. jejuni* is implicated in serious conditions that can follow the food-borne infection. These include Reiter's syndrome (polyarthritis enterica), Guillain-Barré syndrome (a form of acute polyneuritis) and Miller-Fisher syndrome (ophthalmoplegia; face paralysis).

Patients are typically aged from 10 to 29 years, but predisposition plays a special part – for example, the incidence of infection among AIDS patients is almost 40 times as high as that in the general population.

Sources and foods implicated
Wild birds, such as seagulls, crows and feral pigeons, are a natural reservoir and often contaminate surface water. Poultry, sheep, pigs and cattle can also harbour the organism in their intestines, so turning farm animals into potential carriers. *C. jejuni* is commonly found in raw poultry, raw meat, raw milk, offal and sewage. Transmission from people to pets and from pets to people is common, while person-to-person transmission is probably of minor significance. The optimum temperature for *C. jejuni* multiplication and maximum toxin production is 42°C. The heat-labile (changeable) enterotoxin can be destroyed, along with the *Campylobacter* bacteria themselves, by normal cooking temperatures.

Control
The major causative factors are undercooking by time or temperature, or both, and contact with animals. Correct pasteurization temperatures and the prevention of cross-contamination are major tools to control the organism.

Escherichia coli O157
This is an extremely tough organism. It has been shown to survive for 60 days on a stainless steel surface and can persist for a long time in the environment – in cattle dung, contaminated water and soil. So far it has been detected in cattle, pigs and sheep. Its full name is *Escherichia coli* serotype O157:H7. This may be shortened to the more

Using a letter
Serotypes start with a capital letter, so write O157 with a capital letter 'o' and not with a zero.

manageable *E. coli* O157. You may also find references to this serotype as VTEC or EHEC – abbreviations that refer to their pathogenic characteristics.

Symptoms and duration

The infective dose is even lower than that for *Campylobacter* and fewer than ten organisms can cause symptoms. The onset of symptoms varies widely, but 48 hours is typical. The illness can last for one to eight days.

The bacterium produces a dangerous toxin that has been likened to the Shiga toxin (see page 92). Infection is accompanied by bloody diarrhoea (haemorrhagic colitis) and haemolytic uraemic syndrome (HUS), the latter resulting in kidney failure. About two per cent of cases result in death.

Foods implicated

Serotype O157
Toxin producer. Associated with undercooked meat and meat products.

The serotype has been recognised since 1982 when it became established in Canada and the USA. It is sometimes known as 'barbecue disease', or similar nicknames, because of its association with undercooked beefburgers. As well as undercooked beefburgers, foods linked to the bacterium include raw meat, gravy, raw and incorrectly pasteurized milk, some raw fish and unpasteurized apple cider.

The two worst outbreaks in Britain were in November 1996, the same year in which there was a serious outbreak in Japan, and in September 2005 (see panel below).

Control

The separation of raw and cooked foods and strict personal hygiene are among the current control measures. New controls may become evident as knowledge increases of this relatively new threat to public health.

Lanarkshire and South Wales *E. coli* O157 outbreaks

A delivery of meat products for a senior citizens' event in Lanarkshire, Scotland, was at the centre of an outbreak of *E. coli* O157 in 1996. Twenty-one people died and about 500 became ill, many of them seriously.

The outbreak prompted public calls for stricter food safety controls and the government appointed an eminent professor to investigate. His findings, popularly known as the Pennington Report, made many recommendations, particularly for butchers shops, including the strict separation of raw and cooked products. The report also highlighted the need for food handler training about food hazards and for continual management control of all aspects of food safety.

In September 2005 there was an outbreak in South Wales affecting mainly schoolchildren. There were 158 cases and one young boy died. A review of the outbreak was published in January 2006 and The National Assembly for Wales has asked Professor Pennington to chair an inquiry into the outbreak.

Listeria monocytogenes

The genus *Listeria* consists of six species of Gram-positive, facultative anaerobic rods. *Listeria* and the resulting illness, listeriosis, have been well documented for many decades. The species of major concern in food safety is *L. monocytogenes* which is widely distributed in the environment in soil, water and sewage. It can be excreted by human and animal carriers and there are many cases of cross-infection. Any product of animal or plant origin may harbour the bacterium.

Listeria bacteria are often found in chilled or delicatessen products – hence the common nickname 'the delicatessen bug' – such as soft cheeses made from raw (unpasteurized) milk, pâté, cook-chill meals, coleslaw, sausages, sliced meats, prepared salads and sandwiches, but it has also been detected on fruits and vegetables.

Characteristics and preferred conditions
Although it does not form spores, *L. monocytogenes* is an exemplary survivor: it is a halophile (copes with salt), tolerates an a_w of 0.93 and can multiply at a pH level between 5.0 and 9.5.

More importantly, the bacterium is psychrotrophic and can grow and multiply at cool temperatures, between 1°C and 3°C. This poses special problems for food handling and storage because standard refrigeration temperatures do not inhibit multiplication and the cells can survive for long periods in conditions that are unfavourable for most other bacteria. A combination of extrinsic factors suitable for listerial multiplication are usually found during the manufacture and storage of soft cheeses.

Symptoms and duration

Listeria monocytogenes
Grows under refrigeration.
Often fatal for those in the 'at risk group'.
High rate of premature births and stillborn babies.
Newborns might have meningitis.

The incubation period is from just one day up to 70 days, with an average typical onset period of up to 21 days. Symptoms include fever, septicaemia and meningitis. *Listeria monocytogenes* invades both body tissue and the bloodstream, producing the substance listeriolysin which prompts changes in the red blood cells. In response, the body increases its production of monocytes. These are white blood cells that fight 'foreign' or antigenic bodies. The increased level of monocytes is conspicuous in the blood samples of those infected and gives the species its name.

Most healthy adults who are not pregnant are highly resistant to listeriosis and may only suffer from mild flu-like symptoms after becoming infected. However, people in the 'at risk group' are far more vulnerable. When pregnant women are infected, for example, listeriosis may result in premature birth or stillbirth, or the baby may be born with meningitis. The duration of the mother's illness depends upon the symptoms and the predisposition of the victim. Since 2001 there has been a sharp increase in the number of cases affecting people over 60 years old in the UK, other European countries and America, but the reason for this is still unclear. People with suppressed immune systems, such as those recovering from illness and those with AIDS, diabetes or alcoholism, are also in the 'at risk group'.

Control
In the USA it is estimated that the financial damage attributable to *Listeria monocytogenes* is approximately $500 million each year! Many American states have issued special restrictions on the 'acceptable' level of the bacterium in food by declaring it 'an adulterant' and there must be no *L. monocytogenes* in any 25g sample of food. This means that ready-to-eat foods containing the organism are considered 'adulterated' – in other words, not fit for human consumption.

In the UK, however, where unpasteurized soft cheeses, for example, carry a health warning for those in the 'at risk group', the presence of *L. monocytogenes* may not always be regarded as a measure of unfitness. In the mid-1990s a Scottish court ruled that a particular cheese was fit for human consumption, even though more than one laboratory reported that the cheese had high levels of the bacterium.

Given the symptoms, thorough hygiene measures are nonetheless essential from primary production (slaughterhouse, dairy) to the very last process step. As a psychrotrophic organism, *Listeria* is a special hazard for every product stored under refrigerated conditions for long periods (for instance, many dairy products).

The best general methods of control take particular account of the risk for specific groups of people as well as time and temperature. Avoid serving raw (unpasteurized) milk and milk products, such as some soft cheeses, to those in the 'at risk group'. Make certain that milk is correctly pasteurized (see page 331 to 332) and cook thoroughly foods that are implicated in *Listeria* infections. Where foods are served raw, such as some vegetables and salad ingredients, ensure that they are washed thoroughly.

Recalls and epidemics

When *L. monocytogenes* bacteria were detected in a raw milk product – a soft cheese of the Vacherin Mont d'Or brand – a massive product recall started that stretched from 1983 to 1987. In that period there were 122 cases and 34 deaths associated with the cheese.

Vacuum-packed ham and pâté were the subject of product recalls in Britain between 1989 and 1990 when high levels of the bacterium were revealed. After a government warning to pregnant women to avoid soft cheeses, the number of cases of listeriosis decreased in England and Wales.

Contaminated coleslaw killed 15 unborn or newborn babies in Canada in 1981. Raw milk and cheese caused an outbreak in the USA between 1983 and 1985 in which there were 142 cases and 48 deaths.

Mycobacterium
Milk-borne.
Controlled by heat
treatment.

Mycobacterium tuberculosis and Mycobacterium bovis

Tuberculosis (TB) is a chronic bacterial disease caused either by *Mycobacterium tuberculosis* or by *M. bovis* . The infection is detected by special tuberculin testing – the tuberculin sensitivity appears after a few weeks and usually the initial infection goes unnoticed.

The primary reservoir is now humans but there is also a variety of animal hosts, particularly cattle, which gives *M. bovis* its species name, from the Latin word *bovis* meaning cattle. In the UK the badger is reported to be a host. In New Zealand this niche is occupied by the possum and in the USA (among other countries) it has been reported in wild deer. Because of its ability to jump species, bovine TB could theoretically find almost any animal species to be a suitable host.

The occurrence is worldwide, and infants, children and adolescents are most at risk. The transmission is often air-borne (droplet infection), via direct contact (direct invasion through the skin) or food-borne (especially raw milk and dairy products).

Symptoms and long-term consequences

The average incubation period is between four and 12 weeks. Young children are highly susceptible, but it usually takes a high dose of the organism (more than 10^6) to infect healthy adults, the exception being direct infection of the lung which can be caused by inhaling only a few bacterial cells.

Tuberculosis is a progressive disease characterised by the permanent destruction of lung tissue. Chemotherapy (chemical treatment) is usually necessary for one to two years as the organism is able to encyst in human lungs and survive for many decades. This bacterial survival ability caused problems before chemotherapy was available: in many cases a cured person still harboured the organism and unwittingly infected other people or cattle many years after convalescence, so that *Mycobacterium* became active again.

Mycobacterium bovis infection (primarily from cattle) is slightly milder in human beings than is *M. tuberculosis* and spontaneous healing processes are possible. The transmission route works mainly via raw milk as well as via milk infected by cattle manure.

Control

The main preventive measure for food-borne transmission is the correct heat treatment of milk and dairy products.

Typhoid fever
Human-specific with carrier status.
Long incubation.
High mortality rate.

Salmonella Typhi and Salmonella Paratyphi

Typhoid fever

Typhoid fever (also called typhoid, enteric fever or *Typhus abdominalis*, but *not* typhus) is caused by *Salmonella* Typhi (formerly *S. typhi*). It is the most severe of all the diseases caused by the *Salmonella* species. It occurs worldwide and some strains have become multi-resistant to standard antibiotics. It is human-specific and has carrier status. *S.* Typhi holds the record among the food-borne infections: it has the longest incubation time (from three to 56 days), produces the highest body temperature and causes the highest mortality rate.

Foods implicated and routes of infection

Water and milk are typical foods that are affected by this bacterium, which can be transmitted by food or sewage-contaminated water. Drinking water can be contaminated by sewage, or polluted water can contaminate food. Shellfish taken from beds contaminated by sewage, as well as raw fruits, vegetables, milk and milk products contaminated by carriers are important vehicles of contamination. Flies are also thought to be significant in the spread of the disease because they can easily transmit the organism from faeces onto food.

The organism is excreted in the faeces of patients and carriers. Up to five per cent of people affected become permanent carriers, a symptom which is also typical for many other *Salmonella* species.

Symptoms and impact

The incubation period depends on the number of bacteria on the food, but it is usually between 12 and 20 days. The symptoms include fever, spleen enlargement, rose-coloured spots on the body and severe diarrhoea. Relapses are likely to occur. Typhoid fever is fatal in two to ten per cent of cases.

Paratyphoid

Paratyphoid, caused by *Salmonella* Paratyphi (formerly *S. paratyphi*) is less severe than typhoid fever and, unlike *S.* Typhi which is human specific, can also affect animals. While the two illnesses are clinically similar, fatalities from paratyphoid are fewer than for typhoid fever and the occurrence is sporadic or in limited outbreaks.

Control

The preventive measures for both *S.* Typhi and *S.* Paratyphi are:

- ensuring that water used in all food processes is potable and that used water is disposed of safely

- avoiding cross-contamination between potable water supplies and sewer systems

- disposing of human faeces properly

- maintaining high standards of personal hygiene

- achieving high standards of cleanliness in handling and preparing food (for example, cleaning surfaces and equipment thoroughly)

- controlling time and temperature throughout all processes and stages

- obtaining shellfish only from an approved source

- 'excluding' infected persons from handling food (see pages 275 to 276)

- ensuring effective pest control.

Remember that apart from their typical symptoms and that they use food only as a vehicle, S. Typhi and S. Paratyphi are just like other species of *Salmonella* and the control measures depend on the same intrinsic and extrinsic factors.

Typhoid Mary

Early in the twentieth century an American army doctor, Major George Roper, investigated an outbreak of typhoid in the New York area. Six of the eleven members of a household were ill at the summer residence of a wealthy New York banker.

Roper discovered that the family's cook, Mary Mallon, had joined the household a couple of weeks before the outbreak and left shortly afterwards. He then linked her to seven other outbreaks in eight of the families for whom she had worked in the previous decade.

By the time the authorities caught up with her, she was linked to even more outbreaks of illness. Mary was a classic typhoid carrier.

As a public health measure, Mary was forcibly held in state hospitals for a number of years – while the public viewed her either as a poisoner or as an ageing woman unjustly persecuted by the authorities.

She was eventually released and, after changing her name to gain work, caused further outbreaks.

Mary was described as being uncommunicative but a superb cook who loved cooking. It was never established whether she really understood the danger she posed or whether she was driven to ignore it because of her need to earn a living.

Whichever was correct, Mary was forced to live out the rest of her life in a state hospital – a perfectly healthy, inadvertent biological weapon.

Shigella dysenteriae (bacillary dysentery)

Dysentery
This is a general term for bloody diarrhoea.

The genus *Shigella* consists of four species – *S. dysenteriae*, *S. sonnei*, *S. flexneri* and *S. boydii* – all of which are human pathogens. Unlike the closely related *Salmonella* and *Escherichia* bacteria, the *Shigellae* have no known animal reservoir. Infection is usually by the route of human-to-human transmission, with outbreaks therefore caused by human carriers. Food and water can, however, be vehicles of contamination and may play an important part in the chain of infection.

Of the four species, *S. dysenteriae* causes the most serious symptoms – the fatality rate among hospitalised cases has been recorded at as high as 20 per cent. A total of two-thirds of cases are infants and children under ten years. The occurrence is worldwide and typical outbreaks occur under conditions of poor hygiene and sanitation.

Preferred conditions
These Gram-negative rods easily tolerate a low pH: in one case lasting for an entire week in stewed fruit with a pH level of 3.2. The organism grows and multiplies best at between 10°C and 48°C. The survival rate correlates with the ambient temperature. For example, *S. sonnei* and *S. flexneri* can survive in flour, milk, eggs and seafood at 25°C for 50 days: at a lower temperature they can live for even longer.

Infection and impact
The infection is initiated by very low doses (just 10 to 100) of the pathogen and this may account for the fact that the organism is hard to detect in foods that have caused illness. The incubation time varies between one and three days.

The cause of illness from *Shigella dysenteriae*, *S. sonnei* and *S. boydii* is the Shiga toxin (named after Kiyoshi Shiga, the Japanese bacteriologist who first isolated it). The toxin is a bacterial enzyme that inhibits protein synthesis in the victim's body. (*S. flexneri* lacks the Shiga toxin, but behaves rather like the ETEC strains of *E. coli*.)

Shigella
Low infective dose.
Tolerates low pH.
High fatality rate.

Shigellosis, which is also known as dysentery, is spread through the faecal-oral route of an infected person or by the consumption of contaminated food. Food handlers primarily responsible for transmission are often those who do not pay enough attention to washing their hands properly.

After infection, the bacterial cells penetrate the mucous membrane of the victim's colon where they start to multiply, causing parts of the tissue to die and resulting in severe diarrhoea. The stools often contain blood and mucus and the symptoms also involve fever and sometimes vomiting.

Dysentery often occurs in countries with poor or insufficient water sanitation. Transmission by cockroaches and flies may also occur as a result of direct faecal contamination.

Foods implicated
Food-borne infections caused by *S. dysenteriae* have involved milk, water, vegetables, fruits and shellfish as well as salads and egg dishes.

Control

The preventive measures are the same as those listed under *Salmonella* Typhi, especially:

- good personal hygiene and training

- controlled water supplies and disposal

- good sanitary hygiene

- avoiding direct or indirect faecal contamination (for example, flies).

Making it easier for others

- It is *not* crucial for beginners to know the difference between food poisoning and food-borne infections, although it can often be helpful for managers to distinguish them when considering control measures.

- You may also find it useful to characterise individual genera or species of bacteria to make them more interesting and easier to remember. For example, *Salmonella* – the ubiquitous one (it is found almost everywhere and often), *Listeria* – likes it cold, *Bacillus cereus* – the two-faced one (because it produces two sorts of illness), or *Yersinia* – the one with a sting in the tail (because it may cause dangerous side-effects such as arthritis).

- Make sure that all food handlers have a good idea of the most typical transmission routes and the typical symptoms of illness (such as abdominal pain, nausea, vomiting and diarrhoea).

- Emphasise the measures that food handlers should take every day to stop or reduce the likelihood of causing illness.

- Remind food handlers of the unpleasantness of food-borne illness and that some pathogens are life threatening.

- Emphasise the benefits to them, their colleagues, consumers and the general public of high standards of food safety.

Viruses

Extremely small and highly infectious, **viruses** defy easy categorisation. They do not have a complete cell structure and they cannot reproduce themselves independently. Some scientists have even questioned whether they can be described as being truly alive and some do not list them among the micro-organisms (tiny independent life forms). What is certain, however, is that viruses are responsible for causing increasing numbers of cases of illness linked to food.

About 2,000 cases were reported through official channels in the UK in 1999, but research funded by the Department of Health suggests that, as the illnesses caused by viruses often last only a day or so, most cases go unreported. The researchers estimate that the true figure may be far closer to three million cases a year! Food-borne illnesses from viruses also receive far less publicity than those from bacteria, but, as you can see, they are a more serious and prevalent problem than was previously thought.

Even so, only three viruses or viral groups have been shown to be significantly associated with food for human consumption. These are Hepatitis A, Norovirus and Rotavirus which are discussed in this chapter. We do not discuss those viruses, such as the one responsible for foot and mouth disease (FMD), that are not *food*-borne human health problems.

Foods implicated

Viruses are typical examples of a cause of food-borne disease – illnesses caused by infectious agents that are *carried* by food or water, rather than living in it or needing it to multiply. Theoretically any food could be involved in carrying and transmitting a virus, but in practice viruses are typically water-borne, so they may affect shellfish from polluted waters. Raw foods, including milk and vegetables, are also common viral carriers.

Characteristics of viruses

Viruses are measured in nanometres (nm) – one billionth of a metre – and are between 20nm and 300nm in diameter. This makes them about one-hundredth to one-third the size of bacteria! Their structure is very simple: a single strand of nucleic acid (genetic material) is surrounded by a protein coat which acts as a protective shell and enables them to link to the surface of a host cell. Host cells are needed because viruses can reproduce only *within* living cells – they do so by hijacking the cells of bacteria, animals and plants.

Reproduction

As soon as the surface of the virus's protein coat becomes linked to the surface of the host cell, rather like a lock and key, the viral nucleic acid is injected into the host cell. Here the viral material immediately starts using the host's nucleic material to prompt the formation of new virus particles. New viruses are released gradually from the host cell, which may then go back to its normal cellular functions. Viral illness occurs when infected host cells do *not* perform their normal functions.

Bacterial hosts
Viruses are obligate
parasites. Those which
infect bacteria are
known as
bacteriophages.

As viruses can reproduce only in living tissue, the virus-contaminated food we eat must be regarded as a form of transport into the human body. The food carries the virus but the virus does not need the food as nutrition.

Contamination and general controls

Viral contamination can occur in two ways:

- at source – foods intended to be eaten raw, such as oysters

- by handling.

The first route of contamination indicates the need for an integrated approach to food safety, from primary production right through to consumption – for example, strict control of sewage emissions, control of irrigation water and the testing of water from which shellfish are harvested (see 'Testing' on page 96).

The general bacterial control measures of time and temperature are also effective against viruses because viruses can be destroyed by normal cooking processes. This helps to explain why viruses are generally associated with *raw* foods such as salads and uncooked seafood. Viruses can, however, withstand a number of chemical disinfectants.

The second route of contamination can be controlled by effective personal hygiene, as with other forms of microbiological contamination.

Viral food-borne illness

It may take only one virus to turn a host cell into a virus-producing factory, so the infective dose is usually very small. Viral infections are highly contagious and person-to-person spread is common among family members, close friends or employees working in the same workplace. The spread of a virus often occurs by the faecal-oral route where personal hygiene standards are poor. The onset of illness is often 'explosive', with projectile vomiting and diarrhoea.

Hepatitis A (HAV)

This organism, which belongs to the genus *Hepatovirus*, has only one serotype. If you are infected by it, you gain life-long immunity. To date it is the only food-borne virus for which a vaccine is available.

The symptoms of HAV infection are fever, nausea, vomiting, abdominal pain, liver disease and jaundice and can last from seven days to several months. The incubation period can be 15 to 50 days, although patients tend to be infectious for a week before the symptoms show. The routes of infection are often difficult to ascertain, but it is generally accepted that the faecal-oral route is significant. The human intestinal tract is the usual source, although urine and blood may also be infected.

Foods commonly involved are sewage-contaminated water, raw shellfish, raw vegetables, salads and any foods, such as sandwiches, that are prepared by bare hand.

Highly magnified
micrograph of
Hepatitis A virus

In 2003 about 600 people became ill with the disease and three died after eating contaminated food at a restaurant near Pittsburgh, USA.

Testing

Shellfish are usually infected after being too close to a sewage outlet and it is difficult, if not impossible, to cleanse the shellfish by *depuration*. (This involves keeping shellfish in clean (unpolluted) water for several days. The shellfish will flush out any bacterial contamination but cannot cleanse themselves of viruses.) Although the European Union shellfish directive requires all sorts of control on *bacterial* contamination of water, it ignores viruses which are, arguably, the greater cause of problems. In the case of raw vegetables, the contamination comes from irrigation by contaminated water. Inadequate hand washing can lead to the infection of food that is prepared by bare hand.

Control

Control measures include adequate hand washing, correct heat treatment, ensuring that irrigation water is free from contamination and buying shellfish from reliable sources – that is from classified waters. (In fact, it is a legal requirement to use shellfish only from classified waters.)

Norovirus

Norovirus – previously known as Norwalk, Norwalk-like virus or small round structured virus (srsv) – is named after an outbreak in Norwalk, USA, in 1968. The virus was first described by the American paediatrician Zahorsky in 1929 as being associated with 'winter vomiting disease'.

The source is the human intestinal tract and water contaminated by sewage. The foods most commonly involved are raw shellfish, raw vegetables, sandwiches and water. Person-to-person spread is commonly involved, especially where people are living, or spending time, close to one another – for example, on cruise ships, in military camps and in establishments such as schools, hospitals and residential homes.

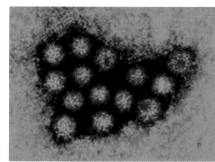

Highly magnified micrograph of a cluster of Noroviruses.

The Health Protection Agency estimates that this virus affects between 600,000 and one million people in Britain a year in 130 to 250 outbreaks.

In 1980 one quarter of the population of Bramham, North Yorkshire, became ill when a leaking sewage pipe contaminated the local water supply. A decade later 229 people were affected in Riding Mill, Northumberland, when contaminated river water somehow became connected to the drinking water supply.

Norovirus is involved in many highly publicised outbreaks on board cruise liners worldwide. Significant outbreaks also occurred in New Orleans following Hurricane Katrina in 2005, in Iraq and Afghanistan in 2002 (involving several thousand military personnel) and in Japan where new strains of the virus produced in children more serious symptoms than usual.

The typical incubation period is one to two days and the illness usually lasts between one and three days. The symptoms are nausea, vomiting, diarrhoea and abdominal pain, although fever and headaches are also possible.

Control

As with Hepatitis A, the control measures are scrupulous hand washing, correct heat treatment, buying shellfish from reliable sources and ensuring the wholesomeness of irrigation water. Anecdotal evidence suggests that the military authorities quickly controlled the outbreak in Afghanistan by positioning Military Police at every hand washing station to ensure that all personnel washed their hands. After an outbreak enclosed spaces are usually disinfected by 'fogging' – very low volume spraying that creates a fog.

Rotavirus

Rotaviruses cause between 500,000 and one million deaths worldwide each year. They cause several types of gastro-enteritis and frequently cause severe diarrhoea in young children which can lead to serious dehydration. The source is humans and sewage-contaminated water and the symptoms are diarrhoea, vomiting and some fever.

Highly magnified micrograph of Rotaviruses.

The onset period is one to three days and the duration is four to eight days. As with the other viruses, the foods most commonly involved are raw shellfish, raw vegetables, salads and infected waters.

Control

Again, the control measures are hand washing, correct heat treatment, buying shellfish from reliable sources and ensuring that irrigation water is free from contamination.

Making it easier for others

Explaining the points listed below may help staff to understand why personal hygiene, especially hand washing, is so important.

- Viruses are food-borne but do not need food as nutrition. They reproduce only within living cells and this means that viruses need other living organisms in order to continue.

- The infective dose is usually very small because it takes only one virus to turn a host cell into a virus-producing factory.

- Viral infections are highly contagious and person-to-person spread is common, especially among family or staff members or where people are in close proximity.

- The spread of the virus often occurs by the faecal-oral route when general hygiene rules – especially hand washing – are not obeyed properly.

- Some viruses can be transmitted by water and food. The typical high-risk products are shellfish from polluted waters and raw foods such as unpasteurized milk and uncooked vegetables.

- Viruses can be destroyed by normal cooking processes.

Parasites

There are many close relationships in nature where two species profit from living together. This is known as symbiosis. Parasitism, in contrast, is an exploitative relationship.

The parasitic organism, which may be a micro-organism, plant or animal, lives on or inside another organism – the host – at the host's expense. It may be a little like having inconsiderate, illegal tenants in occupation. Although parasites can cause injury to, or even the death of, their host, this is a rare and accidental consequence of everyday parasitic activity. After all, why would a parasite aim to destroy its home and food store? Sometimes a host dies simply because a developing stage of a parasite, which usually has a complicated life cycle involving moving home several times, ends up in the wrong host.

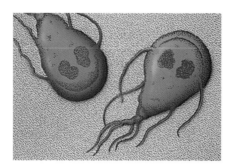

Sewage-polluted water often carries parasites, such as this protozoan *Giardia lamblia*, that become uninvited guests in the human body.

A problem worldwide

Many of our foodstuffs enable a variety of 'unwanted guests' to take up human occupation. Foods of animal origin, such as beef, lamb, pork, fish and shellfish, are most frequently involved, but leafy vegetables can also become contaminated by the infective forms of parasites. Dealing with them can require specialist training, but all managers and chefs throughout the food industry need to know something about parasites, particularly as some, such as *Clonorchis sinensis*, are listed by the World Health Organization as a cause for increasing concern (see pages 24 to 27).

Making a practical difference

It has to be acknowledged that the life cycles of many parasites can seem a bit complicated at first. However, unless you work in a sector of the food industry where specialist knowledge is essential, it is not usually necessary to memorise the names of all the different stages of parasitic life cycles. Just concentrate on how contamination occurs, which foods or products are most affected and suitable preventive methods. Use the summary charts in the Reference section as a reminder.

Complicated specialists

For the purposes of nourishment and propagation, parasites are selective specialists living permanently or temporarily on or in another organism:

- ectoparasites live on the surface of the host's body
- endoparasites live in the inner organs, tissue or blood circulation system of the host.

Ectoparasites, which include fleas and lice, are outside the scope of this book, but endoparasites include three groups of food-borne organism that can infect humans and so are significant to the management of food safety. They are:

- protozoa
- flatworms, including tapeworms and flukes
- roundworms.

Characteristics of parasites

Parasites do not live and reproduce themselves on foodstuffs. They always need a *living* host where they can develop from the 'egg' stage into a mature adult form. Development usually takes place in several stages and may involve one or more intermediate host which may be potential human food sources, such as cattle and pigs. The definitive host (sometimes known as the *primary* host) is the one in which the adult parasite carries out its sexual cycle.

The development cycle

Before you read about the life cycles of a number of parasites, you may find it helpful to obtain a general view of the stages involved in just one life cycle, in this case, *Taenia saginata* – the beef tapeworm.

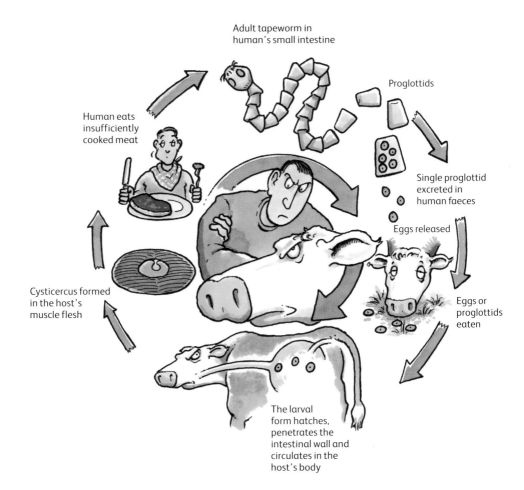

Adult tapeworm in human's small intestine

Proglottids

Human eats insufficiently cooked meat

Single proglottid excreted in human faeces

Eggs released

Cysticercus formed in the host's muscle flesh

Eggs or proglottids eaten

The larval form hatches, penetrates the intestinal wall and circulates in the host's body

Life cycles and illnesses

Protozoa

The name protozoa (singular: protozoan) means first creature and many scientists believe protozoa to have been among the first organisms on Earth.

They are unicellular (single-celled), as are bacteria. However, they have a cell nucleus to protect their genetic material (DNA), so in this respect protozoa are more like microscopic animals than like bacteria. Many protozoa have highly developed organs, such as flagella, lashes and undulating membranes, to help them to move. Some types can form cysts – tough, inactive forms which can survive without food.

On the right are *Cryptosporidium parvum* oocysts. On the left are hatching vegetative organisms, the sporozoites.

Cryptosporidium parvum

This protozoan has a two-stage life cycle in one host. The first stage is in the form of thick-walled *oocysts* (types of cyst) which start the infection when ingested. The second stage is in the form of *sporozoites* (active, mobile cysts) which invade the host's body cells and produce new oocysts which are excreted in the host's faeces. Oocysts are found in environmental water, such as rivers, lakes, ponds and even puddles, and they can survive chlorination, one of the purification processes involved in making water safe to drink (potable). The transmission of cysts is usually by drinking untreated water or by drinking water that has become contaminated. They can also be spread by food, animals such as cattle, faecal-oral routes and from person to person.

To date the minimum infective dose has not been established, but it has been known to be as few as ten cysts.

After an onset period of about ten days, symptoms of cryptosporidiosis – the illness from *Cryptosporidium parvum* – appear. They include diarrhoea, vomiting, abdominal pains and loss of weight. Healthy people may get away with a little diarrhoea but those who are immuno-compromised – such as those recovering from debilitating illnesses or with damage to their immune systems (for instance, AIDS patients) – can suffer severely. It often becomes difficult to maintain the balance of body fluids and it has been known for an infected person to lose 17 litres of fluid a day.

Symptoms occur six to 14 days after ingestion and symptoms typically last between about nine and 23 days.

The *Giardia lamblia* trophozoite 'feeds' by absorbing nutrients from the human intestine.

Giardia lamblia

Like *Cryptosporidium parvum*, this flagellated protozoan also exists in environmental water, usually in the form of microscopic, pear-shaped cysts. The cysts reach the water in the faeces of wild animals, such as rats and beavers, or in the faeces of people who have already played host to the parasite. When a human host ingests a cyst, the acidic stomach environment prompts the organism to turn into another form – an active, motile form known as a trophozoite, which means feeding cell. At this stage the cell is aggressive and invades the intestinal tissues where it obtains its nutrients by absorption.

Between about five and 25 days after consuming G. lamblia, a human host usually experiences nausea, foul-smelling and often explosive flatulence and watery diarrhoea. Subsequent weight loss is common. About three to four weeks later the host excretes cysts in his or her stools.

One infected person can shed up to nine hundred million cysts per day and the cysts can survive for up to three months in sewage sludge. As a result, giardiasis, the illness caused by Giardia lamblia, is common in countries, regions and institutions with bad sanitary systems.

Giardia cysts can be transmitted by:

- contaminated water

- vegetables that have been washed or grown in contaminated water

- hands washed in contaminated water

- rodent faeces

- human faeces, via the faecal-oral route of poor personal hygiene

- human sewage

- hand-to-hand contact, via the hand-oral route.

The infective dose is very low – a single cyst can lead to giardiasis – and the illness is highly contagious. Symptoms can last from several months to a year or more.

Preventing giardiasis and cryptosporidiosis

Many of the measures to prevent these illnesses need to be taken at the source of water (for example, by the water supply company) or by the food grower, but you should also ensure, as part of good practice, that your workplace takes the following preventive steps:

- use only potable water supplies: this may mean using portable purification equipment and chemicals for outdoor catering events and military 'field' catering

- alert food handlers to the hazards of using private water sources, such as wells or bore holes

- teach food handlers about symptoms to watch out for after returning to work from taking part in outdoor activities such as wilderness walking and inland boating

- train all food-contact staff (and others whose work could affect food safety) in effective personal hygiene, especially with respect to hand washing

- monitor hand washing

- avoid the possibility of cross-contamination by banning animals from food areas and enforcing strict measures for personal hygiene if your staff have contact with pets, or farm or wild animals

- ensure that an effective pest control programme is carried out (see Part 4)

- make certain that food premises are kept scrupulously clean.

Other food-related protozoa

These include:

- *Entamoeba histolytica*, which causes amoebic dysentery

- *Toxoplasma gondii*, an organism mostly spread by domestic cats

- *Sarcocystis* species, parasites derived from cattle (*S. hominis*) and pigs (*S. suihominis*).

Proper cooking – for example, cooking meat to a minimum core temperature of 70°C – should destroy these organisms. However, freezing may not always help because the oocysts are highly resistant. Undercooked meats present the greatest risk of infection from *Toxoplasma gondii* or *Sarcocystis*, while poor personal hygiene can lead to contamination of foods by *Entamoeba histolytica*.

Flatworms

Flatworms have simple, flattened bodies without blood vessels. They include free-living flatworms and parasitic flukes and tapeworms.

Tapeworms

The tapeworm's taxonomic category is *Cestodes*, from the Greek for girdle, and aptly describes the adult worm which looks like a girdle of many links. This parasite develops in several stages and may have more than one intermediate host.

The adult tapeworm develops in the intestines of its definitive host. Single proglottids, each containing many eggs, are excreted in the faeces of the definitive host.

Back in the natural environment, the released eggs can be taken up by an intermediate host which harbours the development of the larval stages.

The larvae travel through the intestinal layers of the intermediate host into the bloodstream and lymph system, from where they proceed into the muscle tissue or other organs, or both.

A larval cyst is then formed – a form containing several new potential 'buds' from which new tapeworms can emerge. It is the swollen larval cyst that gives immature tapeworms the common name of *bladderworm*, because the cyst looks rather like a miniature worm-filled balloon.

While adult tapeworms are usually easily treated with medicines, the larval cyst can 'hide' in vital human organs and cause serious illness or death.

Food-borne tapeworms of special concern are *Taenia saginata* (beef tapeworm), *Taenia solium* (pork tapeworm), *Diphyllobothrium latum* (fish tapeworm) and *Echinococcus granulosus* (dog tapeworm). The first three of these organisms are named after their intermediate host, even though the definitive hosts are humans.

Taenia saginata

The beef tapeworm is widely distributed throughout the world wherever beef is eaten. The adult worm can reach up to ten metres long! The adult attaches itself to the intestinal wall of the definitive host – humans – and the terminal proglottids, which contain eggs, are passed in the faeces. About eight or nine proglottids are excreted every day, each of them containing up to 80,000 eggs.

The proglottids, or the released eggs they contain, are eaten by grazing cattle (intermediate host). The eggs hatch in the cattle and develop into the first larval form which moves through the body and ends up as a bladderworm in muscle tissue, such as the heart, which may be eaten by humans. The life cycle restarts when the adult form develops in a human (the definitive host) after raw or undercooked infected tissue has been eaten.

Taenia solium

The pork tapeworm also occurs worldwide wherever pork is eaten. The adult superficially resembles *T. saginata* except for the scolex which is armed with a double row of hooklets that provide firm fastening to the intestinal wall.

The life cycle is also very similar except that pigs are the intermediate hosts and harbour the bladderworms which can give pork a speckled appearance, often referred to as 'measly' pork.

Bladderworms (the larval cysts) are found not only in the muscular tissue but also in various organs such as the lungs, liver, heart and brain. Pigs often become infected on land contaminated by outflow from septic tanks, which are common in farming districts, or from faeces of other farm animals.

Metres of worm in the human intestine

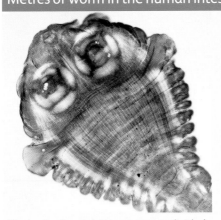

attach themselves firmly to the layers of the intestinal tract. Two of the suckers are visible in the top of this micrograph of a *Taenia saginata* – at this angle they look a little like eyes.

The suckers of a *Taenia solium* (shown at a more conventional angle at the top of the page 104) appear as four circles. The scolex narrows into body-segments (proglottids) which each contain complete 'male' and 'female' sexual apparatus (tapeworms are hermaphrodites).

The body of an adult tapeworm is divided into a head-like structure (the scolex) and thousands of thin, flat body-segments. To think about these parts as head and body is, however, rather misleading as the scolex is mainly a contact organ, the hooks and suckers of which allow tapeworms to

The chain of proglottids can reach several metres, so a host harbouring several tapeworms may have a gut literally stuffed with metres and metres of worm segments! The mature segments, which are the last third of the chain of proglottids, contain thousands of eggs.

It is usual for people harbouring the adult tapeworm (as definitive hosts) to need to undergo chemotherapy treatment.

However, humans can also become the intermediate host if eggs are accidentally ingested (for instance, via hands contaminated by polluted soil). When this happens, the bladderworm can grow in human muscle tissue or in vital organs – a condition known as human cysticercosis. When the brain is infected (cerebral cysticercosis) symptoms similar to those of a brain tumour occur – and the condition is inoperable.

Infection by *Taenia solium* (right and below) can lead to inoperable conditions of the human brain. Cooking meat thoroughly or freezing it can destroy *Taenia* cysts.

The safe collection and treatment of sewage play an important part in the prevention of *Taenia* infections. By law beef and pork are checked for, among other things, traces of tapeworm infection at the abattoir. However, there are important preventive steps that can also be taken farther along the food flow, including cooking pork and beef thoroughly – to a minimum core temperature of 70°C – or freezing the meats, both of which destroy the cysts.

Diphyllobothrium latum

The fish tapeworm lives in the intestines of humans and other mammals such as dogs, cats, pigs and bears. Infection in humans is usually caused by eating raw or underprocessed freshwater fish from sewage-contaminated ponds and lakes. Just three weeks after being ingested, the worm reaches its characteristic final length of ten metres. One fish tapeworm can have as many as 4,000 proglottids and the host's faeces can contain as many as a million eggs.

Diphyllobothrium has at least two intermediate hosts and four stages of development. The first larval form, a free-swimming organism, hatches in water where it is ingested by the first intermediate host, which is usually a crustacean. A second larval stage develops in this first intermediate host.

Then the food chain takes its usual course and the first intermediate host is eaten by a second intermediate host, which is usually a freshwater fish. The third stage of development takes place in the muscle tissue of the fish.

Before it is the turn of humans, the second intermediate host can be devoured by a bigger species. As big fish eat little fish and even bigger fish eat the big fish, the hosting can be repeated several times until this third larval form is eaten by a human or another mammal – the definitive host. Only then does the adult tapeworm develop.

The main control is to avoid serving or selling raw or very lightly cooked fish. Thorough cooking or freezing will kill the organism.

Echinococcus granulosus

Unlike the parasites we have discussed so far, the definitive hosts of *Echinococcus granulosus* are not humans but dogs. However, humans can become infected when they consume vegetables contaminated with dog faeces containing dog tapeworm eggs or when dogs lick humans – just consider for a moment how dogs clean themselves. Once a person is infected, the cyst develops in the inner organs, such as the liver, lungs or brain – often with fatal consequences. Treating a dog regularly with worming treatments minimises the risk, but food handlers should be made aware of the hazards of keeping pet dogs, particularly in or near kitchens or other food areas.

The fox tapeworm (*E. multilocularis*) also has dangerous symptoms: they are similar to those of *E. granulosus*. Foxes can contaminate wild berries, which are often eaten raw.

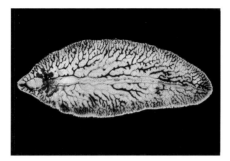

Adult liver fluke, *Fasciola hepatica*, at the stage where it ingests blood and tissue debris from its host's bile duct.

Flukes

Fasciola hepatica

The liver fluke has a complicated life cycle of several stages which may involve more than one intermediate host. It is widely distributed in areas where sheep and cattle are raised. The major definitive hosts of *Fasciola hepatica* are humans, cattle and sheep. It has also been found in goats, pigs and deer.

The adult fluke lives in the definitive host's bile duct (which is reached via the liver), where it causes inflammation. Eggs released by the fluke are passed in the host's faeces, often ending up in environmental water. After a few days in the water, the first larval stage (the miracidium) develops. This motile organism infects its first intermediate host – a water snail. Inside the snail the miracidium turns into a *sporocyst*, which produces a 'mother cell' (the redia). In turn, the redia turns into another free-swimming larval stage (the cercaria) that leaves the snail and attaches to water plants.

The definitive host usually eats the cercaria (the infectious stage) on plants such as watercress or weeds that grow in water. Symptoms occur about 30 days after ingestion and include pain in the area of the liver, loss of appetite and fatigue. It is also possible to develop a throat infection (pharyngeal fascioliasis) from eating raw, or undercooked, infected liver. Painful hoarseness and coughing may lead to difficulty in breathing and swallowing.

Farmers can use antiparasitic medication to treat cattle and sheep. Freezing or cooking meat thoroughly prevents infection. Food businesses should ensure that they buy from reputable sources any vegetables, such as watercress, that are grown in water. Freezing or cooking vegetables will also kill flukes.

Roundworms

Belonging to the taxonomic category of *Nematodes*, roundworms have slender, unsegmented, cylindrical bodies and are found in abundance in soil and water. Many are parasitic.

The dark green oval is a cyst of *Trichina spiralis* in human muscle tissue. The cyst contains one coiled larva, stained in purple.

Trichina spiralis

This roundworm, formerly *Trichinella spiralis*, affects pigs, horses, domestic mammals, rats and more than 40 other species of wild animal around the world. The life cycle is simple: the larvae and adult form live within the same host, although in different organs and tissues. *Trichina* are not hermaphrodite, but have both male and female forms.

When infected muscle tissue from a host animal (such as a pig or rat) is eaten, the larvae, which are in cyst form in the muscle, are released into the host's stomach. They mature in the intestines, often without giving rise to symptoms in the host. The male worms die, while the females each produce up to 2,000 new larvae which travel through the lymphatic system towards the muscles where they encyst, remaining viable and infectious for many years. For further development the encysted larvae need to enter a new host which usually happens when infected muscle tissue is consumed.

When people eat infected pork, the first symptoms are usually nausea, abdominal pain, diarrhoea and sometimes vomiting. These symptoms pass and the next stage – invasion of the muscle tissue – may happen almost unnoticed at first. Serious muscle pain, fever and difficulty with breathing, chewing and swallowing may follow, sometimes leading to death. The muscle pains indicate that 1,000 or more *Trichina* larvae per gram of tissue have been deposited.

Trichinosis (or trichinellosis), the illness cause by *Trichina*, can be prevented by ensuring that pigs are not fed with infected meat, game or uncooked waste food. Pigs are omnivorous and often become infected by feeding on rat carcasses containing the encysted organism.

The disease can be prevented by cooking pork thoroughly to a minimum core temperature of 70°C. The use of microwave ovens for heating pork has been shown to be unreliable, unless steps are taken to ensure that the meat is cooked thoroughly throughout. Freezing pork kills the encysted larvae only after 15 days of frozen storage! Pickling and salting is also a preventive measure, but do note that the meat is safe only *four months* after processing.

Making it easier for others

Emphasise the importance of preventive measures that are appropriate within your sector of the food industry. For instance, if you manage a catering company, stress the importance of proper cooking or freezing to kill parasites.

Feature

Air-borne travellers

For many people the word fungi suggests strange growths on a rotting woodland tree stump or, in a food context, tray after tray of button mushrooms in a supermarket.

But this is like thinking of animals as being only the large furry mammals and forgetting about the birds, fish, insects and other creatures that make up by far the greater number of animal species.

As well as the familiar woodland varieties and edible mushrooms, fungi include *microscopic* organisms – the single-celled yeasts and the thread-like moulds.

Originally considered as part of the plant kingdom, fungi are now recognised as being in a separate biological category of their own.

Unlike plants, fungi cannot make their own food through photosynthesis. Instead they live by absorbing nutrients from their environment, which may be soil, water or – as with the tree stump varieties – dead organic matter.

Fungi also grow on living plants, sometimes causing severe crop damage. A few types can live on humans – for example, athlete's foot and thrush (*Candida albertans*). Fungi that grow on plant and animal matter survive by breaking down the tissue of their host so that they can feed on dissolved nutrients.

As specialists in decomposition, they have both beneficial and harmful effects on our food. The process of fermentation, for instance, which is a specialisation of certain yeasts that can turn carbohydrate into alcohol and carbon dioxide, has given us beer, wine and leavened bread. Without moulds we would have no Camembert, no Stilton, no soya sauce, and not even chocolate.

On the other hand, fungi can destroy living material, spoil food and leave a product that is not of the nature, substance or quality that the consumer expects (see page 158 to 159).

Fungi have a varied repertoire of reproductive techniques but it is often through air-borne spores that they manage to reach food, seemingly out of nowhere.

The first we may know of the presence of a fungus is when we see a mushroom. There is no biological difference between mushrooms and toadstools. They are the fruiting bodies of certain types of fungus.

When you pick a mushroom, you are picking just the fruit, not the whole organism. The main part lives in the soil sending out long fibres that produce mushroom bodies when conditions are favourable.

Anyone who picks or purchases wild mushrooms must learn to identify dangerous varieties, such as the destroying angel and deathcap (see page 120). As moulds can produce spores, even storing toxic varieties with edible ones could lead to illness.

Most yeasts grow as colourful colonies ranging from creamy white to pink to red. The powdery bloom on grapes, plums and other fruit is a form of wild yeast. These fungi will not make you ill but they can spoil food, making it inedible. In fact they are one of the few micro-organisms to affect acidic foods such as pickles.

Yeasts usually reproduce by budding. The round brownish pink structures you can see in the greatly magnified colour scanning micrograph on page 107 are budding yeast cells on the skin of a melon.

Moulds consist of tubular cells called hyphae which collectively form a growth known as a mycelium. The most familiar types are the green-grey growth on stale bread and the white down on fruit and vegetables.

In the micrograph, air-borne mould spores have germinated and penetrated the skin of the melon. The long green structures are mould hyphae, and you can just see the fruiting bodies on the tips of some of them.

Mouldy food should always be thrown away as mould can produce poisonous substances known as mycotoxins (see page 126).

Fungi

Fungi play an important part in our culinary traditions but they can also cause illness and spoil food. Some mushrooms – types of fungus that are visible to the naked eye – are poisonous and these are discussed in 'Chemical hazards'. This chapter discusses the *microscopic* fungi – the yeasts and moulds.

Yeasts

Yeasts are microscopic unicellular fungi. They can be distinguished from bacteria by their larger cell size – from 5μm to 8μm in diameter – and their typical oval or elliptical cell shape.

Most yeast species reproduce by budding. As you can see from the greatly magnified micrograph (right), a small bud gradually grows from the 'mother' cell (the larger structure) of *Saccharomyces cerevisiae*, also known as baker's or brewer's yeast. When the 'daughter' cell is about the same size as the 'mother', it separates as a new, but genetically identical, individual. The circular areas on the 'mother' cell are scars from earlier buds.

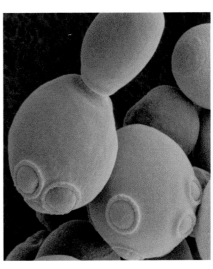

Some yeasts also produce spores, known as ascospores or basidiospores. These should not be confused with bacterial spores (endospores), which are a survival mechanism.

Yeast buds developing from a 'mother' cell.

Yeast spores can spread by many contamination routes, but air-borne contamination is typical. Foods contaminated by yeasts may have a fruity smell.

Preferred conditions

Yeasts are fairly heat resistant and can multiply over a wide temperature range. Many are psychrophilic and can grow at a temperature as low as -15°C. They prefer an a_w range of 0.90 to 0.94 and grow best in slightly acidic conditions, with a pH between 4 and 4.5, in foods with a high sugar content.

A problem of spoilage

Yeasts do *not* cause food poisoning but there are some species that are capable of causing considerable spoilage. As they prefer acidic food with a high sugar content, foods such as fruit, fruit juice, wine and pickled food are especially vulnerable to yeast spoilage.

Yeast cells need a lot of sugar to maintain their adenosine triphosphate (ATP) level (the primary source of energy for living organisms). Fruit contains high amounts of both glucose and fructose (types of sugar) which are broken down by the yeast enzymes. If there is only a little or no oxygen available, the sugars are broken down into alcohol. Yeasts have been hailed as a possible source of cheap, abundant energy in the form of fuel-alcohol for motor vehicles.

Moulds

Moulds are filamentous (thread-like) fungi. Their tubular cells, called hyphae, are about 30µm to 100µm in diameter. They extend, sometimes forming branches, into a mass known as a mycelium. Many moulds reproduce by both asexual and sexually formed spores, and the identification of moulds is based primarily on the structure of these reproductive bodies.

Preferred conditions

Although they prefer neutral conditions, moulds can also tolerate a pH range from 2 to 8, so they have a considerable advantage over most bacteria which have a more limited range of tolerance. Moulds prefer ambient temperatures but, like yeasts, continue to grow at temperatures below 0°C. Some species can tolerate low water activity at below a_w 6.0 and this is why many dry foods such as biscuits, cheeses and nuts may be spoiled by mould.

Moulds are strictly aerobic and will grow only on the *surface* of foods. Food spoilage is often visible as white, black or blue-green mildew.

Making it easier for others

- Explain that mould spores can be carried in the air, can settle anywhere and colonise a wide variety of foods.

- Encourage staff to think of preventive measures as being common sense or plain good housekeeping practices:

  - rotate stock in storage, making sure that food is used before the expiry of *use by* or *best before* date marks

  - check for signs of mould or yeast before using or selling the product

  - store the food in dry conditions

  - keep containers and cupboards clean.

Management matters

At first there may seem to be a lot to learn about microbiology at this level of study. However, knowledge means power when you have to deal with microbes and you could compare this aspect of food safety to military defence. First you need to get to know your enemy as closely as possible by studying the weak and strong points, then you can use that information to make the conditions for your attack as favourable as possible. Armed with this information, you will be in a far stronger position to carry out a hazard analysis, evaluate risk and formulate and implement effective management controls. In short, the information will help you to become a better manager.

A knowledge of intrinsic and extrinsic factors is a key to food safety in general and to food preservation in particular. Sometimes a single factor can control an organism, but most of the time you have to deal with several factors, the most important of which is usually the time and temperature combination.

Distinctions between types of illness

It is necessary to get to grips with the technical differences between food poisoning and food-borne infections, a task not made easy by the different historical, geographical and industrial uses of different terms in the same context. You might find it helpful to use the mnemonic FIN to check the main differences between food poisoning and food-borne infection:

- **f**ood (a medium for multiplication or merely a vehicle of contamination)

- **i**ncubation time (short or long)

- **n**umbers (small or large).

Characteristics of bacterial species

Don't worry if it is difficult at first to remember details like the incubation time, temperature ranges, pH levels and so on for a particular organism: after all, unless you are working with such information every day, it is the kind of thing you can look up when you need to.

If you are following a course of study, your trainer or tutor will give you invaluable guidance about the level of detail you need to remember. Rereading and making notes will help to make things easier, of course, as will the summary charts in the Reference section. You should find that the marginal notes provide useful reminders and they may be a great revision boon if you are about to take an advanced-level examination.

The information about any pathogen is like a logic puzzle – know one or two pieces of information and the rest become apparent by association or by a process of elimination.

For example, think of the symptoms, as they give a clue to the nature of the pathogen. Ask yourself whether vomiting is involved. If so, then the stomach must be affected and therefore the onset time of the illness is probably quick as the stomach is near the beginning of the alimentary tract. Conversely, if vomiting is not involved, then the onset time may be a bit longer. There again, if the onset time is very quick, your first thought should be of toxins as they acutely affect the stomach before the rest of the alimentary tract. This type of exercise can be done for most of the symptoms.

Spores and toxins

It is easy to remember which bacteria are spore-formers or toxin-producers or both.

- *Spore-formers* are all members of the genera *Bacillus* and *Clostridium*. None of the other food poisoning genera are spore-formers.

- All the spore-formers are toxin producers. So too is *Staphylococcus aureus* (which does *not* form spores).

Controls

When you are thinking about how you can apply all this information to your workplace, it may be helpful in the first instance to compare the preventive measures of *protect*, *prevent*, *destroy*, which work against food poisoning organisms, with the options you have for food-borne infections:

- *protect* food from contamination – this works against organisms that cause food poisoning or food-borne infections, and is your first line of defence

- *prevent* multiplication – this is essential for most food poisoning organisms where illness arises from the ingestion of large numbers of bacteria; in contrast, bacteria responsible for food-borne infection can cause disease in very small numbers (sometimes fewer than 100) and *do not* depend on multiplying in the food

- *destroy* bacteria (typically by heat treatment) – this is an important last line of defence against organisms that cause food poisoning or food-borne infections.

What about other control measures? Again, this is fairly easy as almost all of them include proper time and temperature management, good personal hygiene, prevention of cross-contamination, good cleaning, disinfection and so on.

Microbes at our service

When you are in charge of producing safe food it is easy to feel besieged by armies of lethal microbes just waiting to break through your defences and wreak havoc among your customers.

Microbes can indeed be very dangerous, as you have seen in Part 3. But these humble life forms are in fact powerhouses of complex chemical reactions that can be harnessed to promote health and cure disease in dozens of different ways.

Fungi and bacteria have given us antibiotic drugs such as penicillin and streptomycin, used to treat a host of killer diseases, including tuberculosis and septicaemia. Then there are cyclosporin, used against eczema and to prevent the rejection of transplant organs, and gliotoxin, a potential weapon against cancer.

Vitamin C (ascorbic acid) no longer has to be extracted from foods but can be manufactured, thanks to the oxidising properties of the bacterium *Acetobacter suboxydans*.

Vitamin B_2 is produced from yeasts while B_{12}, once extracted from animal liver in order to treat pernicious anaemia, is now created in large quantities by the same bacteria that are used to ferment sewage. Carotene, a close relation of Vitamin A, can be produced industrially from fungi.

Then there is the amazing story of steroids – drugs such as cortisone, used to relieve the crippling pain of arthritis, and progesterone, a key ingredient of the contraceptive pill.

Until the 1950s many steroids could be made only through enormously complex and expensive chemical processing: cortisone initially cost more than £300 a gram and required 37 different steps to create.

Then scientists discovered that a simple mould could do most of the work for them simply by being allowed to grow on the right chemical mixture. Now cortisone is an everyday prescription drug.

These are just a few of the uses to which scientists have put micro-organisms in a bid to improve health, cure illnesses and alleviate symptoms.

There are many other uses, including the production of artificial blood plasma, the creation of antisera (given after exposure to infectious diseases) and the making of vaccines.

Of course, this is not the end of the story. As scientists look for new ways to put these miniature chemical factories to work, the list lengthens on the benefits side of the microbiological balance sheet.

An accidental hero?

The Scottish bacteriologist Alexander Fleming discovered penicillin in 1928, allegedly through sheer untidiness.

He left a culture of bacteria growing uncovered long after he should have disposed of it from the laboratory of St Mary's Hospital, London, where he worked. (The picture shows him there, in the foreground, as a young man in 1909.)

One day Fleming noticed that a colony of the mould *Penicillium notatum* had

started to grow alongside the bacteria – not in itself surprising as mould spores are common in the air.

Around the mould, however, the bacterial culture was dissolving – medicine's first glimpse of the power of antibiotics, strange chemicals that are made by some microbes but destroy others.

By the 1940s antibiotics were in medical use and they now help to save lives every day all around the world.

Chemical hazards

Perhaps there is a curious twist to the way in which chemical threats to food are perceived. On the one hand, the media frequently raise concern about 'chemicals, poisons and toxins' in food. On the other hand, chemical hazards are sometimes nudged aside in professional discussion about food safety management – and may receive scant consideration when a food hazard analysis is carried out. We cannot debate here whether there really is a gap between the genuine and perceived threat from chemicals. Instead, we outline the possible chemical hazards to food so that you can start to consider what *you* should be doing in your workplace to ensure that the food you produce is safe from harmful chemicals. There is more information and advice about managing chemical hazards in Part 4.

The level of risk in your business

Serious contamination of food by chemicals is, as you know, less common than bacterial contamination. What's more, it is not always possible to point to one product as the culprit because some types of poisoning take a considerable time to develop in the body. So, it may be tempting to think that your main forms of control of chemical hazards are suppliers' certificates and the prevention of the careless use of chemicals, such as cleaning products, in your workplace.

Needless to say, these measures are essential, but you also need to manage *all* the food-borne chemicals that put human health at risk. As chemical hazards can arise at *any* stage in the production and sale of food, you also need to be aware of problems that might occur *outside* your premises – including environmental pollution, the use of pesticides and the inclusion of food additives, such as preservatives, in some products.

Practical management

Although chemicals and chemical reactions are complicated – perhaps reason enough for a busy food manager to try to avoid the subject – we focus on the essential, basic information that you need for your work. This and the following three chapters look at particular types of chemical in greater detail, while Part 4 provides additional useful information about eliminating, or reducing the impact from, chemical hazards.

Chemicals as poisons

Before we go any farther, you may wish to check exactly what we mean when we talk about *chemicals* by reading the feature on page 119. Most chemicals are harmless and necessary, while many give our lives considerable benefits. However, just as a few types of bacteria can cause immense human harm, a few food-borne chemicals can also cause illness and even death. For our purposes here, the easiest way to discuss these harmful chemicals is to classify them as *poisons*.

A place in history

The deliberate use of slow gradual poisons earns chronic poisoning its own place in history. During the European Renaissance, for example, poisoning was often chosen as a discreet and effective way to get rid of hostile spouses, political rivals, and those blocking the route to a throne. Symptoms of such poisoning included kidney disease, anaemia and skin discoloration.

Poison

A poison is any substance that harms or kills living organisms. Poisons do not affect inanimate things – you cannot poison a machine or a piece of equipment. If people talk about poisoned containers or utensils, they mean that these objects contain, or are coated with, a substance that is poisonous when it comes into contact with a person or other living thing. Poisonous substances are usually described as being toxic and chemical poisoning arises by means of a *toxic agent* (a chemical poison).

Practical divisions

You will readily appreciate that chemical hazards are a wide-ranging, rather untidy collection of threats to food safety. To make this unwieldy subject a little easier, we have divided them into two main categories – naturally occurring chemicals and introduced chemicals. This division should help you to identify potential *sources* of chemical contamination and the *products* that are most likely to be affected by chemical hazards. Both categories must be taken into account during a hazard analysis (see Part 4).

Naturally occurring chemicals

These are poisonous substances (toxins) that are formed naturally in foods. The toxins are inherent – they are a part of the food. Naturally occurring chemicals include some types of:

- plant

- fungus

- animal, including fish and shellfish.

Some fungi produce poisons known as mycotoxins. As these pose a particular threat to food safety, they are discussed in a chapter of their own (see pages 126 to 130).

Introduced chemicals

This heading covers a wide variety of hazards.

Residues

These are chemicals which are deliberately or accidentally added to, or brought into contact with, the product as it grows. They include:

- veterinary drugs given to animals to treat disease, to improve their resistance to disease or to increase their growth rate

- animal feed additives that can be carried over into human food

- pesticides (herbicides and insecticides) used to treat crops.

Environmental contaminants

These are chemicals that can accumulate in food as a consequence of environmental pollution, such as that caused by leaching (filtering through) from batteries in rubbish tips into the soil and water. Substances involved include:

- heavy metals, such as lead and mercury

- radio nuclides

- by-products of industrial and commercial processes, such as the creation of dioxins when fossil fuels (like coal) or plastics are burned in the presence of chlorine.

Additives

These chemicals are ingredients that are deliberately added to food to enhance its flavour, appearance or shelf life. They include flavourings, colourants and preservatives.

Inappropriate practices

Under this heading comes a wide range of actions, omissions and conditions, including:

■ contact reactions, such as the use of unsuitable containers or packaging

■ careless use of chemicals, such as cleaning products and disinfectants.

Symptoms and consequences

Before we discuss all these different types of chemical hazard in detail in the following chapters, it is important to understand the general effects of poisons on human health.

Acute or chronic

Unlike many cases of bacterial food-borne illness, in which symptoms start within a few hours of eating contaminated food (acute symptoms), the effects of chemical poisoning can be either acute or chronic.

Two types of reaction
Symptoms caused by eating chemically contaminated food can occur immediately after eating or a short time later (acute symptoms), or months or even years later (chronic symptoms).

A food containing a high level of a toxic substance could cause acute poisoning if eaten just once or a few times – for example, symptoms of chemical poisoning usually start between six and 24 hours after eating toadstools containing the toxin amanitin.

In contrast, chronic poisoning develops over a long period as a result of eating food that contains a low level of a toxic substance. Although the intake of the toxic substance may be more or less continuous, the symptoms show only after a considerable time has passed. For example, lead poisoning from old lead water pipes usually takes a long time to develop.

A healthy and fit person can tolerate a higher exposure to a toxic substance than someone who is unfit or weakened by illness. This fact is taken into account in a standard measure – the acceptable daily intake (ADI) – which classifies the toxicity of substances. The ADI represents the amount of a chemical that is believed to be safe to consume every day for a lifetime.

Chemicals in our bodies – various ways to become ill

Dangerous levels of poison in our food can make us ill by:

■ causing symptoms similar to those of food-borne disease

■ overwhelming the body's natural defence mechanisms

■ competing with other similar chemicals that are naturally in our bodies

■ inhibiting some essential body functions

■ exaggerating the effects of chemicals in our bodies

■ causing allergies.

Similar to food poisoning

Some symptoms of chemical poisoning are similar to those of many types of food-borne disease, including vomiting, diarrhoea and stomach pains. The victim may also experience dizziness, headaches and loss of muscular power. The kidneys and liver are often affected.

Overwhelming natural defences

The body's self-defence mechanisms can often be overloaded by poisons. The immune system, which fights 'intruders' that have antigenic properties (see page 52), cannot cope with an overload of chemicals. Instead of fighting off the invading chemicals, the body starts to incorporate and accumulate them. This does not necessarily result in immediate damage because the accumulation of poisons is usually a long-term process. The toxicity of a chemical depends on the state of health of the person who consumes the poison and the impact is increased when someone is undernourished.

Competing with the body's chemicals

Some toxicants can compete with other chemicals in the body and try to replace them. This usually occurs when the poison belongs to the same chemical group as a beneficial compound in the body. In the case of cadmium poisoning, for example, calcium, which is vital for our bone structure, is slowly replaced by cadmium. This leads to a condition known as glass bones in which the skeleton becomes so fragile that bones splinter, sometimes fatally piercing vital body organs.

Inhibiting and exaggerating body functions

Some poisons inhibit the body's usual absorption of essential nutrients, others amplify the effects of various chemicals which occur naturally in the body.

Making it easier for others

- Discuss the potential chemical hazards that could be encountered in your type of food operation.

- Ensure that staff understand the steps they should take to prevent chemical food poisoning.

Living with chemicals

We all recognise cleaning products and pesticides as chemicals, but we might not immediately think of substances such as sugar, salt, fats, perfume and even alcohol as chemicals.

It is also easy to forget that there are chemical reactions going on inside our bodies all the time and that these are perfectly natural and necessary processes. So what exactly are chemicals?

Most definitions relate to something that is a part of, related to, or made by chemistry. So, to understand what a chemical is, we need to understand a little about the study of chemistry.

The science is divided into organic and inorganic chemistry. Organic chemistry deals with carbon compounds (which form the basis of all living things), whether natural or synthesised, while inorganic chemistry deals with elements other than carbon.

Chemistry deals with the *composition* of substances, their *combinations* and their *changes* under various conditions – how one substance can be generated or transformed into another.

A familiar example makes the point. When water (H_2O) turns to steam or ice, these are *physical* reactions (the water is still water but in a different state). Water that turns into a *different* substance – for instance, in the formation of alcohols – is however a *chemical* process.

So, physical criteria deal with alterations or variations in the *state* of a substance, while chemical criteria deal mainly with the *structure* of compounds and *changes* in compounds or elements.

For simplicity, we could just say that a chemical is a substance involved in a chemical process. This process is generated or produced by the interaction between different factors – in the environment, inside a living organism (such as a bacterium, protozoan, plant, fungus, animal or human) or in a laboratory or factory.

Naturally occurring chemicals

People have learnt from painful experience to differentiate between the plants, fungi and animals that are safe to eat and those which are not. Even so, many people throughout the world are harmed or killed each year by eating foods that are poisonous to humans.

The natural toxins in some plants, fungi and animals are so dangerous that the food should *never* be eaten. But there are also foods containing natural toxins that can be eaten without any ill effect, provided they are prepared in a way that eliminates the hazard.

Poisonous plants and fungi

With increased public interest in food from the wild and 'naturally' grown produce, it is possible that cases of food poisoning could increase if people accidentally eat toxic plants and mushrooms.

Cases of mistaken identity

Children are often attracted by the berries or berry-like seed coverings of a wide range of poisonous plants, including yew, holly, lily-of-the-valley and members of the nightshade family. However, even adults poison themselves by mistaking an edible food for a toxic one – typically wild mushrooms. Most cases of mistaken identity are, of course, a matter of public awareness and outside your control, but you should consider the possibility of contaminated supplies when you undertake a hazard analysis (see Part 4).

Wild mushrooms

Looking a little like the field mushroom *(Agaricus campestris)* to the unwary, these death cap mushrooms *(Amanita phalloides)* live up to their common name. Every part of the mushroom, including its spores, is extremely toxic and often causes death.

Eating just one small part of the death cap mushroom *Amanita phalloides* can cause death and it is responsible for up to 95 per cent of deaths from mushrooms. Death cap has some close cousins, such as the destroying angel *A. virosa*, that are also highly toxic.

The toxic agent responsible, amanitin, binds rapidly to body tissue and about 12 to 24 hours after eating the mushroom, severe nausea and vomiting start.

Diarrhoea, headache, mental confusion and jaundice follow. The liver, kidneys, brain and heart are particularly affected. Although treatment with penicillin has reduced the death rate, about half of all people poisoned do die from the symptoms.

The striking red and white spotted mushroom fly agaric *(Amanita muscaria)* is not necessarily deadly, but contains substances which cause narcosis, convulsions and hallucinations.

Sometimes referred to as the witches' mushroom and frequently depicted in children's book illustrations, the fungus has long been associated with magic, shamanistic rituals and the hallucinogenic sensation of flying.

Examples of toxic plants

Some parts of the plant toxic
Boxwood leaves and twigs; cherry kernels and leaves; daffodil bulbs; elderberry leaves, shoots, bark and roots; holly berries; hyacinth bulbs; iris roots; laburnum leaves, pods and seeds; locust/false acacia seeds; poinsettia leaves, stem and sap; privet berries and leaves.

All parts of the plant toxic
Calla lily, bleeding heart, buttercup, Christmas rose, daphne, goldenrod, laurel, lily-of-the-valley, marsh marigold, mistletoe, oleander, rhododendron, wisteria.

Plants

Hemlock (*Conium maculatum*) is a native wild plant that is a member of the carrot and parsley family. It contains several substances that cause muscular paralysis. The symptoms start with nausea, vomiting and fever and proceed to increasing muscular failure followed by respiratory failure and death. This was the plant used to kill Socrates, the ancient Greek philosopher.

Yew (*Taxus baccata*) is an evergreen native tree that can also be used as hedging. All parts are poisonous except for the aril – the fleshy, red cup-like 'fruit' that surrounds the poisonous seed. If the seed is bitten into and swallowed, nausea, abdominal pain and possible heart failure can occur in about six hours. (The whole seed may pass through the body without causing harm.)

The *Solanum* family of plants includes potatoes, tomatoes and nightshades, such as bittersweet (*Solanum dulcamara*), black nightshade (*Solanum nigram*) and deadly nightshade (*Atropa belladonna*). These nightshades grow wild in many parts of Europe. Poisoning usually results from eating the shiny berries, but other parts of the plant are also toxic. As few as three berries of deadly nightshade can be fatal. The symptoms include a dry mouth, rapid heartbeat and pupil dilation.

The castor bean plant (*Ricinus communis*) is often grown for ornamental purposes. Eating just one castor bean can cause fatal poisoning if the bean is chewed. (If the beans are swallowed whole, poisoning is unlikely to occur because the hard seed coat prevents rapid absorption of the toxic agent, ricin.) Symptoms start from two hours to several days after ingestion with a burning sensation in the mouth, nausea, vomiting, diarrhoea, abdominal pain, drowsiness and disorientation, finally leading to circulatory collapse and convulsions.

Prepared for safe eating

Some familiar foods can be poisonous under certain circumstances and food preparation staff need to be clear about the preparation methods they should follow to make such foods safe to eat.

Potatoes

Every day millions of people eat potatoes (the tubers of *Solanum tuberosum*) in one form or another, most of them without knowing that this member of the nightshade family can be toxic.

When potatoes sprout they produce a natural chemical, solanine. If green or sprouting potatoes are eaten without first boiling them, solanine can cause a burning sensation in the mouth and throat, as well as general weakness, nausea, dizziness, delirium and convulsions. The fatal dose is 25mg of solanine for adults: a serving of 100g of green or sprouting potatoes could contain about 8mg of solanine. The chemical is water-soluble, which means that potatoes with partly green skins should be safe after boiling in water, but the water should *not* be consumed, for instance as stock or gravy. The greatest risk is if green or sprouting potatoes are used as jacket potatoes – potatoes baked in their skins – because the solanine is not destroyed.

Red kidney beans

These beans (*Vicia faba*) contain a toxic protein, haemagglutinin, which is heat labile (changeable by heat), so can be destroyed by boiling the beans for about ten minutes. If the beans are eaten without this treatment, they can cause nausea, vomiting, abdominal pain and diarrhoea. Most problems occur when beans are undercooked or when they are cooked slowly – perhaps in a 'slow cooker' – without first boiling them for ten minutes. If red kidney beans are ingredients in products such as vegetable burgers, the beans must still be boiled first. One possible control is to buy canned beans, because the canning process destroys the haemagglutinin.

Rhubarb

The cooked stalks of the rhubarb plant (*Rheum rhaponticum*) are edible, but the leaves and buds are toxic due to their high content of oxalic acid. (Raw stalks also contain very low concentrations and may be toxic.) The symptoms are nausea, vomiting, diarrhoea, abdominal pain and haemorrhages.

Nutmeg

Consumed in small quantities as a flavouring, nutmeg (*Myristica fragrans*) is safe. But eating large quantities can cause hallucinations and delirium accompanied by abdominal pain, headache and dizziness. Several car accidents in America have been attributed to intoxication from eggnogs which have been generously sprinkled with nutmeg. The responsible chemical is myristicine, which is said to produce hallucinatory effects.

Common ink cap

This mushroom (*Coprinus atrementarius*) is poisonous if it is consumed with alcohol or within about 48 hours of drinking alcohol. Fortunately this type of poisoning is not fatal, but you may suffer from severe abdominal pain.

Poisonous animals

Some animals are inherently poisonous to people. Others become poisonous as a result of chemical reactions during decomposition, or because they have eaten substances that are harmless to them but can poison humans – a kind of second-hand poisoning that occurs at the top of the food chain.

Poisonous fish and shellfish

Poisoning from fish mainly affects the peripheral nervous system, those parts of the nervous system that carry information from the sensory organs and carry out involuntary functions such as breathing, digesting and sweating.

Inherently poisonous fish

The roe of some freshwater fish, such as sturgeon and catfish, are toxic during their reproductive season. Eels, sea lampreys and elephant fish are among the fish also known to produce neurotoxins – toxins that affect the nervous system. Symptoms of poisoning have also been recorded from the consumption of shark and ray. Some neurotoxins are destroyed by temperatures above 60°C.

This elegant presentation of the Japanese delicacy of fugu fish has an invisible danger. If the fish has not been prepared properly, toxic poisoning will follow, with a high likelihood of death – about 20 a year. Chefs in Japan must have a special diploma to be permitted to prepare this dish.

Fugu (puffer fish)

In Japan, where puffer fish (*Arothron hispidus*) is known as *fugu*, the fish is eaten raw. As it has tetrodotoxin, a neurotoxin, in its intestines and gonads, all traces of these parts must be removed before the fish is safe to eat.

The effects of the toxin are rapid. Symptoms start 10 to 45 minutes after eating and include unco-ordinated movement, numbness, weakness, nausea, vomiting, diarrhoea, abdominal pain, convulsions and paralysis. The mortality rate is more than 60 per cent!

Tetraodon poisoning (the illness caused by tetrodotoxin) occurs throughout the tropical Pacific, Atlantic and Indian Oceans.

Problems from spoilage – scombroid poisoning

Scombroid poisoning occurs after eating improperly stored dark-fleshed fish such as tuna, mackerel, herring, sardines and bonito. Proteins start to be destroyed by normal ageing processes soon after fish have been caught. If the fish are not refrigerated, frozen, canned or smoked immediately after being caught, spoilage bacteria, such as *Proteus* species, can turn usually harmless chemical compounds in the decaying tissue into highly toxic agents (scombrotoxins).

The toxin is found where there are high levels of histamine present in the fish. (Histamine is a substance released from damaged cells and associated with allergic reactions.)

The histamine is produced by an enzyme reaction (decarboxylase) that converts the amino acid histidine, which is naturally present in the fish, into histamine. The enzyme involved is produced by spoilage bacteria: their multiplication is inhibited by storing the fish on ice or immediate processing. So, although the histamine itself is not the causative agent, controlling its formation seems to prevent the toxin from being produced.

The reaction to scombroid fish poisoning is like an allergic shock. After just a few minutes, symptoms can include a headache, nausea, cramp, vomiting, facial flushing and dryness, and burning sensations in the mouth. Characteristic red and itchy welts may develop. Difficulty in swallowing follows the initial symptoms and death from shock may occur.

Poisonous at the top of the food chain

Many types of marine fish that have fed on certain types of alga and other organisms are poisonous as human food. Some fish such as puffers, trigger fish and parrot fish are poisonous for most of the year, while others, such as moray eel, surgeonfish, moonfish and porcupine fish, are toxic only in certain seasons. Sometimes it depends on the part of the ocean where these fish live – so, poisonous fish living in one locality may be completely harmless elsewhere. More than 300 species have been reported to cause fish poisoning.

Ciguatera poisoning

The most common type of fish poisoning, known as ciguatera, occurs with fish usually considered to be safe, such as mackerel, snapper, sea bass, perch, grouper, surgeonfish, barracuda, pompano and butterfly fish. These fish are not necessarily related but they all live in narrow stretches of coral reef.

Ciguatera is a form of secondary toxicity brought about when algae that are toxic to humans enter the food chain – small fish eat algae, big fish eat small fish and humans eat the big fish. The toxin is mainly concentrated in the viscera (internal organs such as the intestine) and may not be completely removed by evisceration (removal of the organs). The toxin is heat stable and therefore cannot be destroyed by normal cooking processes.

Symptoms of acute poisoning begin between 30 minutes and four hours after ingestion and include numbness, tingling of the face and lips, nausea, vomiting, diarrhoea, dizziness, abdominal pain and muscular weakness.

These symptoms can progress to a second stage of muscular paralysis or convulsions. Death from convulsions or respiratory arrest can occur within one to 24 hours. Patients who survive retain some of the first-stage symptoms for many weeks. They tend to sense temperature in reverse to normal, so that ice feels hot and heat seems cold. Cold objects can cause pain resembling that from an electric shock – a response known as electric shock syndrome.

Poisonous shellfish

Mussels, clams, oysters and other shellfish can become temporarily poisonous during the warm season after feeding on certain *dinoflagellates*, which are small protozoa in plankton. The toxins are thought to be a by-product of the protozoa or bacteria associated with the dinoflagellates. They accumulate in the digestive glands and gills of the shellfish without harming them. However, when people eat the shellfish they may quickly become ill from one of two types of illness, depending on the kind of toxin involved.

PSP – paralytic shellfish poisoning

This illness involves a neurotoxin. The shellfish can have become so poisonous to humans that eating just one contaminated mussel, clam or oyster could result in death. Symptoms start with tingling sensations or numbness in the mouth and spread to the arms and legs within four to six hours. If the patient survives the first 12 hours after eating the contaminated shellfish, recovery is likely. The fatality rate is between one and ten per cent.

DSP – diarrhoeic shellfish poisoning (or diarrhetic in American English)

This illness has symptoms of chills, nausea, abdominal pain, vomiting and diarrhoea within one to two hours.

Toxins associated with shellfish poisoning are usually heat stable, so are not destroyed by cooking. As the limiting growth temperature is between 8°C and 10°C, the usual recommendation is not to eat shellfish in the warm seasons. In the British Isles the rule of thumb is to eat marine shellfish only during months with a letter 'r' in their name – so *not* during the months of May, June, July and August.

Poisonous mammals

Toxic mammals are not usually a problem for the British food industry, but some mammals from cold climates, such as sledge dogs (huskies), sea lions and polar bears, have been reported as being poisonous to humans. Most of the evidence stems from early polar expeditions.

Desperate measures

In 1912, faced with dwindling supplies and a 500km journey to their Antarctic base camp, Australian explorer Dr Douglas Mawson and his Swiss companion Xavier Mertz gritted their teeth against temperatures down to -30°C and winds up to 300km an hour. They were forced to eat their sledge dogs one by one, little knowing that they were slowly poisoning themselves with an excessive intake of vitamin A from the dogs' livers. Mertz did not survive, but Mawson just made it back to camp alive. He was later knighted and is credited with significant discovery, mapping and scientific achievements.

Making it easier for others

- Create clear rules for staff who purchase raw foods and ingredients that might contain naturally occurring chemicals.

- Establish clear rules for staff who deal with such foods.

- Consider banning staff from bringing foods and ingredients into the food premises that have been collected from the wild or obtained from sources other than your approved suppliers.

Mycotoxins

A large number of moulds produce toxic substances – mycotoxins – that can cause a range of serious illnesses and even death. These toxins are from a different chemical group to those produced by mushrooms and are sometimes considered as adulterants rather than as 'naturally occurring poisons'. As far as day-to-day food safety is concerned, it really does not matter how you categorise them and you should not be surprised to come across mycotoxins described as biological hazards rather than as chemical hazards. From a practical point of view and to avoid academic hair-splitting, you may simply prefer to think of mycotoxins as agents of 'non-bacterial food poisoning'.

An underestimated public health hazard

In the past, food contaminated by mould was often regarded as an economic nuisance rather than a health issue and spoiled, or 'rotten', crops were sometimes used as animal feed because they were considered to be harmless. Now, however, it is known that exposure to mould spores or the consumption of mycotoxins can lead to serious illnesses in both people and animals. Cereals (especially rye), nuts and dried fruit are among the foods most likely to be affected.

Although research continues into the degree of risk that mycotoxins pose generally to humans, it is known that mycotoxin-producing moulds can cause food-borne illness and that long-term exposure to mycotoxins can lead to cancer, organ damage and a number of other life-threatening conditions.

Preferred conditions

Beyond bacteria
Moulds that produce mycotoxins can thrive in conditions where bacteria can rarely survive.

Mycotoxin-producing moulds tolerate a wide range of acidic and alkaline conditions and can be found in low pH products, such as fruit juice, in which bacteria have no chance of multiplication. The moulds tolerate low water activity down to 0.80 a_w, so can colonise 'dry' foods, giving them another advantage over bacteria.

Moulds are aerobes and their preferred temperature range is from -7°C to 35°C. However, mycotoxins are heat resistant and can withstand pasteurization and even sterilization.

At the other end of the temperature scale, the ability of mycotoxin-producing moulds to grow at a temperature below 0°C can be observed in many cold-stores and walk-in refrigerators in the form of black patches in moist, inadequately cleaned corners.

General control measures

As many preservation techniques have no significant impact upon mycotoxins, the most effective measures are at source, on the farm, and include preventive measures that minimise or eliminate the growth of mycotoxin-formers, as well as rapid drying processes after harvesting.

Also crucial are storage and transport under controlled anaerobic (sealed) conditions or frozen storage at very low temperatures (such as -18°C). Water activity is best kept at above 0.8 with a pH at below 3 or above 6.5.

There are several electronic sorting and detection methods using fluorescence under ultraviolet light for aflatoxins (see opposite). Any company using foods that are vulnerable to mycotoxin-producing moulds must not overlook them when carrying out a hazard analysis (see Part 4).

Types of mycotoxin

The following examples are likely to be the most significant for food safety in Europe.

Aflatoxins

In 1960 turkeys in a number of flocks in the south and east of England died without apparent reason and the illness was dubbed *turkey X disease*. Investigation showed that the causative agent was peanut meal imported from Brazil. This led to the first identification of mycotoxicosis, the general term for any illness caused by mycotoxins. Subsequently many samples of foodstuffs and peanut meal were tested for toxicity and a considerable number of samples from some 14 peanut-producing countries was found to be contaminated.

The fungus responsible was eventually identified as *Aspergillus flavus* and the type of toxin it produced was named *aflatoxin* after the species name – a(spergillus) fla(vus) toxin. Other types of fungus were also investigated and it was established that several moulds from the genera *Aspergillus* and *Penicillium* produce types of mycotoxin, all of which are referred to as aflatoxins.

Foods implicated

The foods most commonly contaminated by aflatoxins are:

- nuts
- cereals, including rice
- dried fruits.

Carry over

Lurking danger
Mycotoxins can persist throughout the food chain and accumulate in animals used as human food.

Research also shows that cows fed on foods containing aflatoxins excrete toxic milk. This phenomenon, which is typical for mycotoxins in general, is often described as carry over or the carry-over effect.

What happens is that toxins (in this case, aflatoxins) in the primary foodstuff (in this case, cattle feed) are carried over into the next link in the food chain (the cattle). The toxins accumulate in the body fat tissue of the organism (the cattle) and therefore in any food product, such as meat or milk for human consumption, that is gained from the organism.

Every link in the food chain must therefore be regarded as being at risk from a carry-over effect, and there is no technical process to eliminate mycotoxins once they have been ingested and incorporated into body tissue.

Symptoms

Aflatoxins are carcinogenic (can cause cancer tumours) and toxic to the liver. The illnesses that result can be acute or chronic. Acute symptoms include cramp, jaundice-like mucous membranes, loss of appetite and loss of body-weight.

Causes and preventive measures

Aflatoxins often form because of inappropriate food storage conditions and prolonged storage periods. The two most important factors influencing the formation of aflatoxins are high levels of moisture and the temperature.

Patulin

Several fungi of the genera *Aspergillus* and *Penicillium* can produce *patulin* in rotten fruit and other foods. The presence of patulin in food products usually indicates the use of mouldy raw materials.

Foods implicated

The foods most commonly contaminated by patulin are:

- fruit, including apples, bananas, pears, grapes, pineapples and peaches
- fruit juices
- bread.

Symptoms

Patulin is considered to be carcinogenic. High concentrations of patulin (levels as high as 440mg per litre) can cause acute symptoms such as haemorrhage (severe bleeding) and oedema (internal swelling caused by fluid).

Preferred conditions

Some moulds can form the mycotoxin at temperatures below 2°C, so creating a particular risk to fruit and fruit juices kept in chilled storage for prolonged periods.

Ochratoxin

In the 1960s scientists first managed to isolate an unknown mycotoxin from South African cereals and vegetables infested by the organism *Aspergillus ochraceus*. The mycotoxin proved to be highly nephrotoxic (the cause of permanent kidney damage). Since then more than seven closely related substances of the ochratoxin group have been detected, of which Ochratoxin A is the best known and the most toxic.

Hazard to staple foods

Ochratoxin is particularly hazardous to food safety because it can affect so many staple foods (the major foods in the diet of a community), such as cereals, cornflour and bakery products. When ochratoxin is present in animal feed, it has a carry-over effect like that of aflatoxins and accumulates in the animal carcass as well as in animal products.

Some countries have legal limits for levels of ochratoxin. For instance, Denmark declares pork to be unfit for human consumption if pig kidneys contain more than 25mg of ochratoxin per kg of meat.

Foods implicated

This mycotoxin has been found in:

- cereals
- sweetcorn (maize)
- dried beans
- cocoa beans
- coffee beans
- soy (or soya) beans
- citrus fruits
- nuts, such as peanuts
- cured hams and other cured products.

Symptoms

The main symptom is kidney damage.

Control

The best way to deal with ochratoxin is at source, such as quick-drying processes, and by storage under controlled dry conditions.

Ergot

St Anthony's fire was the name given, centuries ago, to symptoms caused by eating bread made from diseased grain. Victims, who suffered fire-like pain from gangrene in the fingers and toes, believed that they would be cured by a pilgrimage to the shrine of St Anthony. Today we know that these symptoms are caused by ergot, a toxin produced by the mould *Claviceps purpurea* which forms a hard black spur on ears of grain. The illness is now called *ergotism*, a form of mycotoxicosis (an illness from a mould toxin).

Ergot-contaminated ears of grain can appear black.

Possession, ritual and midwifery

Perfectly preserved for more than 2,000 years, the body of this man discovered in a peat bog in Grauballe, Denmark, in 1951 revealed that his last meal had included many ergot-contaminated grains. His throat had been cut from ear to ear, suggesting a ritual slaughter that may have included the use of ergot as part of the ritual, or may have been prompted by fear at the man's symptoms – convulsions, or changes in his appearance because of

gangrene. The hallucinogenic properties of ergot may be behind claims of possession and bewitchment in many countries in centuries past, including the events leading to the Salem Witch Trials in Massachusetts in 1692. Often used by medieval midwives in very small doses to ease childbirth, ergot was also used to abort unwanted pregnancies – a practice that probably contributed to the decision to burn many midwives as witches.

Ergotism is caused by a number of *alkaloids* – a group of chemical substances produced by plants and fungi – which are derivatives of lysergic acid, the main ingredient of the hallucinogenic drug LSD.

Some alkaloids – such as caffeine, which is found in tea, coffee and cola-based soft drinks – are relatively harmless. Others have modern medicinal uses – for example, low controlled doses of ergometrine, a constituent of ergot, are often administered towards the end of childbirth. However, some alkaloids – including nicotine, cocaine, morphine, atropine and alkaloids found in nightshades, such as bittersweet and deadly nightshade – can cause serious intoxication or death when digested in high or uncontrolled doses.

In its chronic form ergotism occurred in frequent and widespread epidemics causing many deaths in Europe throughout the Middle Ages. Even scientific advances have not totally eradicated it and an epidemic occurred in England as recently as the 1920s. Ergot is still an economic problem in many areas around the world that grow sorghum (Indian millet or 'Guinea corn') and there were outbreaks of ergot poisoning in the Russian Federation in 1997.

Foods implicated
The foods most commonly contaminated by ergot are:

■ rye

■ other grains.

Symptoms
High doses of ergot cause gangrene, the gradual mortifying (death) of tissue and limbs. Convulsions may also occur.

Preventive measures
Supplier audits and guarantees, together with checks on deliveries of cereals, provide the best controls.

Making it easier for others

It is often easiest to explain a food safety problem, such as that from mycotoxins, by relating it to products that staff are likely to have in their own homes. So, ask staff for suggestions about products that are vulnerable to the growth of mould. They are likely to suggest nuts, cereals, bread, fruit, fruit juices, stewed fruits, cooked vegetables, jams and meat products. Most people have encountered mould on one of these at some time.

■ Remind staff members about the health dangers posed by mycotoxins.

■ Encourage them to consider changing any inappropriate old habits – for example, cutting off the mould 'beard' from bread and cheese or scraping off the mouldy layer of jam before using, serving or selling the rest of the product.

■ Point out the risk to consumers' health of doing such things at work.

■ Remind staff of their legal obligations and emphasise the importance of prevention as the best course of action.

Residual chemicals

Residues of harmful chemicals can accumulate along the food chain. The build-up may start with low levels of chemical contamination of plants that are eaten by cattle, sheep, pigs and poultry. As the chemicals gradually accumulate in the animals' fat tissue and organs, they become even more concentrated in animal-derived foods (such as meat, milk and eggs) that are often eaten by humans.

Although our bodies have detoxifying mechanisms that can deal with some harmful chemical residues, a lifelong exposure to, or intake of, a poisonous chemical increases the number of milligrams of unwanted chemical to each kilogram of body-weight. In the final link of the food chain, a human baby can take in a harmful concentrated dose of chemicals from its mother's breast-milk.

Introduced chemicals

Chemicals used on crops have protected food from attack by fungi and insects while chemicals used on the land have helped to boost the number of harvests and increase their yields. Even so, there is a great deal of public concern about the long-term consequences for the safety of food and the environment from chemicals that were first hailed as wholly beneficial poisons.

Pesticides

Pesticides have helped to control diseases, such as malaria, protect sources of human food (such as the cereal shown here) and increase crop yields, but the overuse, or careless use, of them can poison land, water and the food chain.

The term **pesticide** covers several groups of substances designed to kill pests and weeds and to protect crops and stored products. Pesticides include:

- insecticides – insect control

- acaricides – mite control

- rodenticides – rodent control

- herbicide – plant protection

- fungicides – mainly for mould control.

Pesticides can get into a human food product as a result of controlled and traceable measures, such as treating animal pens with insecticide to eliminate flies, or through less controllable environmental sources, such as water, soil and the air. Some pesticides can accumulate in the environment and join the food chain, becoming increasingly concentrated as they are moved along the links to the top of the chain (see page 131).

Benefit or harm?

Although pesticides have been designed to protect sources of food for humans and the human environment, it should not be forgotten that they are intended to kill living organisms – a purpose which may create dangers to human health.

Many modern pesticides are now in the third or fourth generation of their chemical formulation and the scientists developing them take into account possible close encounters between people and pesticides.

In the past, however, some substances have threatened environmental havoc. The organochloric compound DDT (dichlorodiphenyltrichloroethane), for example, was found in the 1960s to persist and accumulate in the environment and the food chain, threatening to make some species of birds of prey extinct because their eggshells became thinner. This led to worldwide restrictions on the use and distribution of the chemical.

Of course, the potential benefits of applying pesticides need to be weighed against the potential hazards to human health. In most cases, basic precautions and proper applications and doses of the chemical reduce the risk of chemical contamination to a level that is generally considered to be safe.

Public awareness of the possible damage from pesticides in farming may also have helped to curb any excessive or irresponsible use. Nonetheless, 'safe' pesticides can quickly become unsafe if they are stored in an inappropriate way or used in any way other than that specified by the manufacturer, such as spraying crops with an incorrect dilution of the chemical.

Control

An effective integrated pest management programme (see Part 4) should ensure that:

■ pesticides do not come into direct contact with foodstuffs

■ food-contact surfaces that have been contaminated by pesticides must be decontaminated before re-use.

Nitrite, nitrate and nitrosamine

These chemicals are derivatives of nitrogen, which is represented by the chemical symbol N.

The nitrogen cycle

Nitrogen is a vital constituent of life on Earth. While animals obtain the nitrogen they need by eating plants or other animals, plants must extract it from the soil, mainly from derivatives of nitrogen such as ammonia (NH_3) and nitrates. With the help of bacteria – which, for example, release nitrogen from animal waste and from dead animals and plants – nitrogen is continuously recycled and re-used in processes known as the *nitrogen cycle*.

As nitrogen is a key to plant productivity, farmers use various methods to help the nitrogen cycle along, including:

■ leaving fields fallow to enable nature to take its gradual course

■ planting legumes (peas and beans) to provide a suitable habitat for billions of bacteria (such as various species of the genus *Rhizobium*) that live on the roots and 'fix' nitrogen

■ spreading fertilisers to replace nitrogen and other chemicals rapidly.

There are practically no nitrate-free foodstuffs of *plant* origin whereas milk, fresh meat, fresh fish and eggs are *virtually free* of nitrates.

Nitrites and nitrates

Nitrites (NO_2^-) and nitrates (NO_3^-) are ubiquitous and necessary in the environment, but can also occur as environmental contaminants. In the food industry the application of nitrite/nitrate combinations is a long-established method of meat preservation, which helps to retain the colour of meat in pickling and salting processes. The chemicals must be used in controlled measures – the allowable residue of nitrite in food is just 0.01 per cent – because an overdose can result in acute poisoning, with symptoms including a fall in blood pressure, collapse, cyanosis (turning blue), coma and respiratory paralysis. Death follows if emergency measures are not taken. Chronic poisoning depends on the level of exposure.

Nitrates can cause problems in canned products which lead to the breakdown of the lacquer used to coat the inside of the can, so allowing tin to leach into the food. Poisoning can also occur as a result of drinking water from a well where nitrates have leached in. The nitrates in the water can be converted to nitrite by the action of intestinal bacteria. This is especially dangerous if the water is used for reconstituting dried baby milk or baby food.

Nitrosamines

Nitrosamines are highly carcinogenic. They can be formed in foods from reactions between nitrites or nitrates with other compounds, or the presence of certain spices, such as pepper, which react with the nitrate and nitrate salts during the pickling process. With fresh meat of reliable origin and flawless pickling methods (the addition of ascorbic acid to the pickling process counteracts the formation of nitrosamines), there should not be a problem at all. However, in meat which is less than fresh, a degradation of biochemical substances starts and secondary compounds form. If such meat is then pickled, nitrosamines can be formed. Also, if pickled products are exposed to temperatures above 160°C – for example, on a fierce barbecue – nitrosamines can form.

Polyaromatic hydrocarbons

Polyaromatic hydrocarbons (PAHs) are derivatives of phenol which are often used as antiseptics, disinfectants and germicides (you may know these as carbolic acid) and preservatives. Tar and creosotes are mixtures of phenolic compounds and other compounds produced by burning wood or coal – either in uncontrolled conditions, such as forest fires, or in intentional incineration processes, such as metallurgy, or in tobacco smoking.

PAHs are widespread environmental residues. Many polyaromatic hydrocarbons are highly carcinogenic. They can be formed unintentionally when sausages, ham or other meat products are fried, barbecued or smoked, or when the cooking temperature is too high.

Dioxins

The word dioxin covers a group of chemicals that are organochlorine compounds. Among past uses of dioxins were the powerful insecticide DDT (see page 132) and the defoliant spray Agent Orange which was used by the American air force during the Vietnam War and subsequently linked to birth defects. Liver and heart defects, intestinal damage, chloracne (a form of eczema), neurological problems and cancer have all also been attributed to dioxins, while some experimental studies suggest that dioxins may be mutagenic (cause genetic alteration) in humans at extremely low doses.

In an accident at a chemical factory in Seveso, Italy, in 1976 dioxins contaminated a wide area, prompting major health concerns. In the late 1990s there was a scandal in Belgium about levels of dioxins in food when it was alleged, among other things, that chickens were given feed containing high levels of dioxin.

The World Health Organization has defined a level of intake of dioxins considered to be tolerable, and dioxins exist in small quantities in many foods including vegetables, meat, milk, eggs and fish.

Dioxins can be formed when organic substances smoulder or burn in the presence of chlorine. This may happen in the burning of fossil fuels, such as during the production of steel and aluminium, during industrial bleaching of cellulose such as paper production, and also in crematoria.

Metals

Metals are common elements distributed in nature in varying quantities around the Earth. They can enter food by a number of routes – for example, direct contact with unsuitable food containers, industrial pollution of soil used for growing crops and contamination of water from agricultural chemicals.

Heavy

Heavy metals are those with a high atomic mass, such as cadmium, lead, mercury and zinc. They are pure elements that are more likely to combine with other compounds. In low pH environments in particular they pass into their ionized form which prepares them to bind with inorganic or organic substances. They can attach themselves to proteins and change the character of the original compound. If the protein is a functional agent, such as an enzyme, and its original function is altered or blocked, a cascade of toxic reactions can occur. All our food contains tiny traces of metals. Usually this is not a reason for concern, but there is a danger to human health if high levels of heavy metals are present. They have caused some dramatic cases of poisoning, and heavy metals are banned from use as food containers or food-contact surfaces.

Lead

Lead in the environment is almost impossible to avoid. It was used for many years in typesetting, batteries, paint, toys, solder, electric cable covering, pottery glaze, water pipes and brass alloys. Some of these, such as paint, no longer contain lead but there are still other sources, including fumes from motor vehicles, ashes and fumes from burning.

In the past, a common cause of lead poisoning was the action of soft water on lead water pipes. Most lead pipes have now been replaced, but high levels of lead can still get into drinking water if copper water pipes are joined using lead-solder – a practice which is illegal. In 2000 The City of Edinburgh Council issued a leaflet warning people about the possibility of lead in their water and how to minimise the risk.

The most serious toxic effects in humans arise from damage to the brain and the peripheral nervous system. The accumulation of levels of lead in the brain and the liver can be five to ten times the level in blood. Lead is deposited in the skeleton where it accumulates and remains for life. The symptoms are tiredness, loss of appetite, pallor and headaches. Lead poisoning is usually chronic.

Dangers in the food chain

Cattle may be poisoned by lead – for instance, if they feed from contaminated soil or from food or water containers in which red lead (minium) is used as a rust preventative. Minium poisoning leads to acute neurotoxic symptoms. The livestock cannot be used for beef for human consumption because there is no process for reducing the lead content in meats. In 1989 milk from cows on about a thousand British farms was contaminated by lead from feed pellets that had been in contact with lead sulphate during transport.

Food preparation and storage

Lead poisoning can occur through the misuse of ceramic containers glazed with lead oxides. Acute symptoms include a metallic taste remaining in the mouth, abdominal pain, vomiting, diarrhoea and characteristic black stools. There are permitted limits for the lead content of various foods. Precautions can include using meat, and especially offal, only from *young* animals because the lead content accumulates with age.

Cadmium

Cadmium is used for plating metals and in the manufacture of bearing alloys, batteries and silver solders. It can carry yellow and orange pigments, so is widely used in the colour,

Cadmium damages human cells

The toxic potential of cadmium was revealed fully after the investigations into the itai-itai disease in Japan. The Japanese word itai means 'it hurts' or 'ouch'. Farmers and their families had been living for several years on rice which had been grown in waste water from smelting works that was contaminated with cadmium. The victims had pathological alterations to their bone structures, resulting in 'glass bones' and collapsing spines.

varnish and plastics industries. Cadmium plating is soluble in acid foods such as fruit juices and vinegar, and it is banned for food contact under food legislation.

Cadmium can get into the atmosphere, water and soil as smoke created when products containing cadmium are heated above the metal's melting point, for example, during ore smelting or industrial waste disposal. However, cadmium is mainly accumulated in plants. The roots take up the metal from the soil and it spreads into other plant organs. Animals feeding from plants then accumulate the metal in their livers and kidneys and other organs eaten by humans as offal. Wild mushrooms can also absorb high levels of the metal.

Mercury

Mercury and its salts are used in the manufacture of thermometers, felt, cellulose, paints, explosives, lamps, electrical appliances and batteries. The burning of coal around the world emits about 3,000 tons of mercury into the atmosphere every year. The main influence that mercury has on foodstuffs arises from waste water and exhaust fumes from combustion engines. The accumulation of mercury in environmental water is much higher than in agricultural food chains. Ingestion of mercuric salts can cause acute poisoning which affects the intestines and kidneys. Chronic poisoning leads to accumulation in the body – for instance, in the hair – and in permanent damage to the central nervous system.

Toxic seed coating

Some mercury compounds are used to treat cereal seeds to delay spoilage during storage. In sporadic incidents, starving people in famine-affected areas of Iraq, Pakistan and Guatemala ate such seeds rather than planting them and were poisoned.

As mad as a hatter

In the past, hatters treated the felt, from which many hats were made, with a mould inhibitor made from mercury salt solutions. During their professional lives hatters working with felt were constantly exposed to mercury vapours. Inhalation and skin contact often led to chronic poisoning which manifested itself as, among other symptoms, depression, hallucinations and mental deterioration. This may be the origin of the saying 'as mad as a hatter'. Some people suggest that the character of Lewis Carroll's hatter in 'A Mad Tea-Party' in *Alice's Adventures in Wonderland* may be explained in this way.

'Minamata disease'

Between 1953 and 1960 more than 100 people in Minamata Bay, Japan, were first suffering from unidentified, serious nervous complaints, and 45 people died. (Some environmentalists say that several hundred people died.) Eventually, the symptoms were traced to methyl mercury compounds which had drained into the sea from a chemical factory. Mercury had been accumulating in local marine fish on which the local fishing community were more or less living. The Minamata victims had about 70mg to 100 mg of mercury to every kilogram of their body-weight.

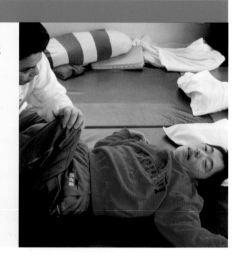

Other toxic metals

Acute poisoning can arise from ingesting aluminium, copper, tin and zinc. Symptoms include burning pain in the mouth and throat, vomiting and retching, watery or bloody diarrhoea, tenesmus (a disorder of the rectum), haemolysis (destruction of red blood cells), anuria (kidney failure), liver damage with jaundice, hypotension, collapse and convulsions.

Copper

All copper salts are highly toxic. Copper poisoning typically occurs when antique copper and novelty souvenirs, such as copper kettles, are used for the preparation or decorative display of *acidic* foods. In these circumstances copper ions will migrate from the container into the product and cause poisoning.

Arsenic

Used in ant poisons, insecticides, weed killers, paint, ceramics and glass, arsenic is not only a strong poison but is also carcinogenic.

The initial symptoms of acute poisoning from ingestion include those of gastro-enteritis, burning sensation in the throat, vomiting and bloody or watery diarrhoea. Later the skin becomes cold and clammy, the blood pressure falls and death may follow from circulatory failure. If the victim survives, there may be jaundice. Chronic poisoning from ingestion or inhalation includes symptoms of polyneuritis (disorder of the peripheral nervous system), burning pain in the hands and feet, changes in skin colour and texture, weight loss, liver damage, cancer and cardiac failure.

Thallium

Once used as a rodenticide and an ant killer, thallium is now prohibited as a pesticide. Poisoning resulted most frequently from accidental ingestion of bait.

Aluminium

Aluminium can leach from old, worn kitchen utensils and containers. Some herbs, such as leaf tea, are known to accumulate aluminium in high doses as they grow.

Zinc

This is a natural component of many enzymes, so many foodstuffs contain zinc in small concentrations. In industry, base zinc is used in welding, metal cutting and smelting galvanised iron. Zinc salts are water soluble and can be formed by reaction with acidic foods on galvanised utensils. As zinc can become corroded by aggressive sanitizers, zinc surfaces should not come into contact with food at all. Fatalities have been reported following the ingestion of 10g of zinc sulphate.

Tin

Contamination can occur when tin-plated cans are used for the long-term storage of acidic foods, such as stewed fruit, causing the tin to leach. This is why it is good practice to store canned food in a non-metallic container once the can has been opened. The Food and Agriculture Organization and the World Health Organization have recommended a critical limit of 250mg of tin to every kg of food.

Cleaning chemicals

Chemical poisoning from substances such as lubricants, glue and cleaning chemicals used in a food room usually results from careless handling or a lack of know-how.

The cleaning process

Some products have to be diluted with water to the chemical concentration specified, then used from a dosing container such as a spray. Some products are then rinsed or wiped from surfaces, after the specified contact time, to remove any chemical residues. While most traces of residue from cleaning chemicals will only taint food products so that they may smell or taste unpleasant, or both, there are some cleaning chemicals which should never be used in food premises as they contain toxic components. Examples are phenolic substances and aldehyde compounds.

The disinfection process

Chemical disinfectants are designed and formulated to kill micro-organisms by interrupting essential metabolic actions or by denaturing vital cell components (changing the protein or nucleic acid structure). It is, of course, important to ensure that these effects are not transmitted to the food or to humans because the chemicals cannot distinguish between micro-organisms and other types of cell. As many disinfectants contain substances such as chlordioxide, iodine, sulphuric acid, formaldehyde, fluoride and nitric acid, which can poison humans in certain doses, their application needs to be controlled with considerable care.

Legal requirements and advice

Manufacturers and employers have legal obligations for chemicals under the Control of Substances Hazardous to Health Regulations 2005 (COSHH). Manufacturers, for example, must provide information about their chemical products on Material Safety Data Sheets (MSDS). Employers must carry out safety risk assessments into the use of chemical products at work and must ensure that staff are properly informed, trained and supervised in the use of chemicals. For more information, see *Supervising Health and Safety at Work* available from the Chartered Institute of Environmental Health. Reputable manufacturers of chemical cleaning and disinfection substances can also offer advice and training information for the use of their products in every branch of the food industry. You will find more information on the control of chemical hazards in Part 4.

Making it easier for others

- Ban the use of equipment that is unfit for food contact, such as zinc or lead containers.

- Ensure that staff use work surfaces, containers and equipment only for their approved and designated purposes.

- Ban the use of utensils and equipment that have not been bought from approved suppliers.

- Encourage staff to report damage, such as flaking protective coatings, to their manager or supervisor.

- Make certain that cleaning chemicals will not cause corrosion.

- Train staff how to use and store cleaning chemicals safely.

- Supervise the use of cleaning chemicals with care.

- Remind staff regularly that cleaning chemicals are carefully formulated to do particular jobs and that using more of the chemical than recommended by the manufacturer is unlikely to improve their effectiveness but may cause food poisoning or injury.

Management matters

Chemical contamination of food is much less common than bacterial contamination and occurs in various forms – naturally occurring, mycotoxins and introduced – which may require slightly different preventive measures. From a management perspective perhaps the most important questions to ask yourself are:

- which chemical hazards can appear in particular products used in my workplace?

- why could the contamination happen – for example, because of pollution, contamination of raw materials or improper handling of introduced chemicals during production?

- what is the likely effect on the consumer?

- how can I influence and/or control the risk from this hazard?

More information about answering these questions and on dealing with chemical hazards is given in Part 4, but it is always important to remember that chemical contamination can occur at any stage of the production chain – from the growing of the raw materials through to the finished product. When chemical contamination happens in food premises it is usually due to carelessness in handling introduced chemicals. Nonetheless, managers must also be aware of the possibility that foods already contaminated by chemicals could be brought their food premises. The following general points are suggestions for your consideration.

- Develop appropriate buying policies for foods and ingredients –for example, cereals that might be especially vulnerable to chemical contamination.

- Nominate approved suppliers and ban from the premises any ingredients or products from other sources. (This is a requirement under certification standards such as ISO 9001/22000 – see page 199.)

- If your company purchases cereals directly from the primary producer, check the training of the staff at supplier companies – the ability to recognise ergot contamination, for instance – and carry out annual reviews.

- Ensure that checks for signs of mould are made before purchase, but ensure that your staff are also trained to make thorough checks on deliveries to your premises.

- Provide adequate suitable storage for cereals, such as dry goods stores with dry conditions.

- Make regular checks on all food in storage.

- Provide separate lockable storage areas for cleaning chemicals and cleaning equipment and emphasise the importance of segregating such materials and equipment to prevent contamination.

- Make sure that containers, cupboards, stores, refrigerators, freezers and utensils are kept clean to prevent the growth of moulds.

- Ensure that staff are trained to carry out cleaning procedures in ways that could not cause chemical contamination of food, and ensure that cleaning activities are supervised adequately.

Physical hazards

Have you ever found a hair or a fingernail in your food or even the proverbial fly in your soup? How did it make you feel? Probably reluctant to continue eating. Perhaps you complained. If so, you were not alone. Physical contaminants in food cause many customer complaints simply because – unlike microbes and most forms of chemical contamination – they are so obvious. They do not always cause injury, but they are still completely unacceptable to consumers – and to the law. What's more, they are clear evidence that something has gone wrong in the management of food safety.

This chapter outlines the kinds of physical hazard that affect food. Additional advice about detecting and controlling physical hazards is given in Part 4.

What is a physical hazard?

You will recall that a food hazard is anything that might cause harm to a consumer. Physical hazards are simply physical contaminants, which are sometimes called 'foreign bodies' and fall into two main categories:

- objects that could cause physical injury – such as splinters, buttons, or glass fragments

- objects that are offensive but not necessarily dangerous – such as hair, caterpillars, plasters or dirt.

Medically, the first kind is more serious. The objects may cut the skin, obstruct the respiratory or digestive system, or lodge inside the body causing tearing. They can also create a hazard to general health and well-being. However, the second category of object is just as damaging for a food business – perhaps even more so, because of the strong emotional reaction that objects in food can provoke in customers.

Disgust – the power of the mind

People vary enormously in what they find disgusting in food. Some like to think of themselves as tough and claim not to be put off by anything. Others, perhaps the majority, feel there should be nothing even faintly offensive in their food. Disgust also depends on culture and society: in some parts of the world insects and larvae, such as termites and maggots, are gourmet food, while in other regions cheese is regarded as rotten milk.

If everyone has a different idea of what is disgusting, why should we bother about the concept at all? Consider a situation in which you bite into a cockroach in your bread roll. You are unlikely to be physically injured and, strictly speaking, you have not been exposed to a health hazard because the poor insect has been thoroughly baked and is microbiologically sterile. Still, you will probably not regard a cockroach as welcome extra nutrition but as a cause for disgust and a reason to complain. If you are really horrified you may vomit. Perhaps you will never be able to eat a roll again or may suffer nightmares about cockroaches.

Remember that a hazard is anything with the potential to harm a consumer. Clearly for some people the reaction to a cockroach will be so strong that it falls into this category.

Unseen hazards

An interesting question arises here that is worth a brief diversion: is the cockroach a hazard only because people notice it and are revolted by it? After all, many other things could theoretically happen behind the scenes that would disgust consumers if only they knew about them.

Objectionable
Food that consumers find disgusting can be classed as hazardous.

takeaway cooked cockroaches

The owners of a _____ takeaway have been ordered to pay more than £6,000 in fines and costs after a customer found two cockroaches cooked into apple fritters.

The pest infestation at the _____ that cockroaches were found all over the grease and dirt-caked work surfaces, floor and even in a box used to store prawn crackers on top of a refrigerator.

Ian Moore, principal EHO, said it was the worst cockroach infestation he had witnessed, cockroaches were crushed underfoot as the evidence was being gathered.

Business operators, _____, admitted 11 counts of breaching the Food Safety Act 1990 and various Articles of Regulation (EC) No. 852/2004, to Derby magistrates.

Eight of the 11 offences relate to failing to comply with Article 5 concerning critical control points. The operators also failed to register the premises with South Derbyshire District environmental health department and failed to address the pest problem.

Chairman of the bench Chris Pritchett said: 'We found the photographs offered in evidence appalling. It's obvious the defendants showed total disregard for food hygiene legislation.' _____ was fined £2,250 and ordered to pay £1,000 costs, while _____ was fined £1,450 and told to pay £1,767 in costs.

Manchester seizes counterfeit clothes

Manchester City Council's trading standards service has seized 5,000 items of counterfeit clothing and £9,500 in cash from an address in _____ counterfeit goods in the Manchester area. The seizure included footwear, handbags, watches and sunglasses bearing the trade marks of many a maximum penalty of 10 years imprisonment and/or a fine.

Neil Swannick, executive member for planning and environment, said

Imagine for a moment that, even though your roll was free from cockroach, it had been mixed, kneaded and baked by staff with unwashed hands in a filthy bakery, full of mould, dirt and pest excretions. The baking process would have killed the pathogens in the bread and, even if the filth and mould recontaminated the bread, there would be nothing visible to upset you. However, if you came to know about the conditions under which the food had been produced, you would quite probably feel nauseous. So there is still a theoretical potential for harm, just as when the evidence is there for all to see.

Food safety law, as you will see in the next chapter, is as much concerned with the potential for harm as it is with actual, visible contaminants. By law food premises must be kept clean and maintained in good repair and condition, employees must work in hygienic ways and businesses must identify the hazards in their own workplaces then adopt measures to prevent the *potential for harm* from becoming *actual harm*.

The source of the problem

As far as preventive management is concerned, it is helpful to consider the sources of physical hazards in two main categories – those:

- associated with the food itself (intrinsic contamination)

- introduced from external sources (extrinsic contamination).

Intrinsic contamination

Intrinsic contaminants were part of the original plant or animal and are inedible or undesirable, or both. Plants used as food or ingredients may include twigs, pits, stones or kernels, while meat and fish may have bones, gristle or skin that consumers expect to have been removed before service or sale. In either case, the problem lies at the start of the food processing chain.

Not in the recipe

Some of the items that have found their way into food can be difficult to credit. A researcher reported coming across objects including a rubber boot, an umbrella handle, a hat, half a Bible, pieces of farm machinery and a typewriter.

Extrinsic contamination

Wood, glass, cardboard, insects, hairs and dozens of other objects can be introduced into food during storage, processing, transport, display or almost any other stage between harvesting or slaughter and the consumer's point of purchase. Such incidents are serious because they can cause severe injuries and give rise to extremely damaging publicity. Prevention is therefore vital and if lapses do occur, they must always be investigated thoroughly and a fresh hazard analysis must be conducted (see Part 4).

The following paragraphs suggest some of the most typical extrinsic contaminants in food.

Metal
Nuts, bolts, swarf and other metal hazards usually come from machinery and equipment.

Glass and other brittle materials
Fragments of glass, plastic, porcelain or other brittle materials can cause serious injuries and must be prevented from entering food products at all costs. There are many potential sources of sharp fragments, such as lamps and light tubes, bottles and jars, crockery and windows.

Packaging materials
Staples, strings, cardboard, soft plastic and polythene can enter food when deliveries are unpacked or during the packaging and dispatching of finished products.

Rubber and plastic
Small rubber and plastic items such as utensils, disposable gloves, vending machine cups and rubber bands can all find their way into food.

Home-made patches and repairs
Staff are often very creative in finding ways to patch up utensils and equipment with tape, wire and other inappropriate means. This must be prohibited, as all such materials could easily contaminate food.

Wood
Containers, pallets and surfaces made of wood can all produce splinters that may contaminate food.

Animal pests

Insects, birds, rodents and other animals can all introduce physical contamination. The problem is not just the animals themselves, which sometimes end up in food products, but also their hair, droppings, feathers, eggs, pupae, larvae and skins.

Personal items

Cigarette butts, sweet wrappers, chewing gum, jewellery and other small personal objects show that somebody has not understood the relevant company rules and legislation about eating, smoking and personal hygiene.

Building materials

Sometimes the building structure itself can cause contamination. Broken tiles, flaking paint and rust from old pipes can all find their way into food.

Tools and clothing

Pens, pencils, pen caps, screwdrivers and other small tools – even pagers – can easily slip out of a breast pocket. Insufficient or unsuitable protective clothing can also be a source of contaminants, adding hairs, buttons, fibres and other odds and ends to the list of potential problems.

Malicious tampering

The deliberate contamination of food is known as malicious tampering. It is sometimes done by blackmailers outside the company but it may also happen on the premises if employees are disaffected. The type of physical contaminant involved depends to some extent on the opportunities for tampering without raising suspicion.

Making it easier for others

Teaching people about physical hazards is easier than explaining microbiological or chemical contamination. Offending items such as hairs, insects and glass can be seen and there is no complex theory to explain.

- Encourage staff to identify and categorise likely physical hazards in their own workplace.

- Consider teaching prevention in terms of five key factors:

  - good housekeeping

  - buildings and equipment

  - personal hygiene

  - awareness and hazard spotting

  - pest control.

Management matters

Compared to microbiological hazards, physical hazards are in many ways much easier to deal with – they do not, for example, breed and multiply, so problems are more readily identifiable and containable. On the other hand, processes such as heat, chemical treatment and irradiation that kill bacteria are absolutely useless when it comes to physical objects. While standardised measures can deal with microbiological hazards, preventing 'foreign bodies' from entering food depends on a host of factors to do with the individual nature of the premises and processes involved.

Preventing physical hazards calls for a two-pronged approach aimed firstly at the physical environment (building materials, equipment, packaging, fittings) and secondly at people and their attitudes. Often the second aspect is overlooked even though the personal aspect is usually far more significant to food safety than the objects that members of staff work with. The issues involved are discussed in greater detail in Part 4.

Allergen hazards

The old saying, 'One man's meat is another man's poison' aptly describes the range and peculiarities of people's personal preferences, but for food allergy sufferers the saying may literally be true. Adverse reactions to allergens in food cause misery to millions of people around the world, and for some people the reaction is so severe that it is life threatening. About ten people a year die in the UK from allergic reactions to food.

About 18 million people in the UK– one in three of the British population – are thought to have an allergy of some kind. True food allergies are believed to affect about 1.5 million people. Most of these are children, some of whom grow out of their allergies, but adverse reactions can develop at any time in life and can affect anyone, whatever their age, health or physical fitness.

Record-breaking Scottish hurdler Ross Baillie (centre) died in 1999 from a severe allergic reaction to peanuts he did not realise were one of the ingredients in a coronation chicken sandwich.

Where you live and your ethnic background can, however, have a bearing on your sensitivity to particular foods and ingredients. The foods that cause problems can vary from country to country and between ethnic groups. For example, an allergy to celery is common in mainland Europe, but not in Britain. Many more people in France are allergic to mustard than in Britain. Lactose in milk causes problems to many people with Asian ancestry.

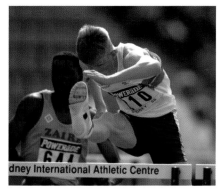

dney International Athletic Centre

Whatever the statistics, there are groups of your customers who are at risk of illness or even death from particular foods that are harmless to others.

A different type of hazard

Food containing biological, chemical or physical contaminants can affect anyone who eats it, and these are well-established types of hazard that you must identify and control in your workplace. There are also foods and ingredients, such as peanuts and milk, that are perfectly safe for most people to eat but are a hazard to others.

Peanuts are one of the main causes of food allergies.

This type of hazard also needs to be identified in your line of work and measures must be taken to eliminate the hazard altogether or to minimise the risk from it.

The steps you need to consider are discussed in Part 4. For now, it is important to understand what allergies and other food sensitivities are, and the common foods involved.

Allergy (to food)
An adverse response to food or ingredients that involves the immune system and causes a variety of symptoms, some of which can be life threatening.

What an allergy is

The people who become ill after eating products that are harmless to others have a food allergy. They have a sensitivity to allergens – natural substances, usually proteins, in foods that make certain people ill, even though the foods are perfectly safe for most people to eat. Their immune system reacts to the allergens by creating specific antibodies – natural protective chemicals. When the food is next eaten, the immune system reacts as if the body were under attack and releases massive amounts of antibodies which prompt a variety of allergic reactions.

A body rash and extreme swelling of the lips – symptoms of anaphylactic shock – preceded the death of this young child. His parents agree to the use of his photograph to help to warn of the dangers of allergic reactions to foods.

Allergy symptoms

Allergic reactions can be triggered by eating a very small amount, or even the slightest trace, of a food or ingredient. The reaction can occur within minutes or can take several hours to develop.

Some reactions are mild, but others may lead to death without prompt medical treatment – usually adrenaline (epinephrine) injections.

There is a wide range of possible symptoms and not everyone suffers all of them. Some symptoms, such as sickness, diarrhoea and abdominal cramp, are similar to those of food poisoning. Other allergic reactions may give no visible external clue, or they may include rashes or tingling of the lips, tongue and throat.

Anaphylactic shock

An especially severe allergic reaction, known as anaphylactic shock, may start with a mild reaction but can lead to symptoms such as a swelling in the throat, difficulty in talking and breathing, a dramatic drop in blood pressure, collapse and unconsciousness. If medical help is not swift, death can follow.

Anaphylactic shock
A severe and possibly life-threatening response to certain foods.

Food intolerance

There is another form of sensitivity to particular foods that is correctly termed an intolerance, rather than an allergy. Food intolerance does not involve the immune system and is rarely a threat to life. Even so, the symptoms can be unpleasant or painful and may significantly affect people's overall health and life in general.

Intolerance to food
A sensitivity to certain foods that does not involve the immune system

Food intolerance arises from a failure in the body's digestive system to produce enough of the enzymes needed to break down and digest proteins in a particular food. This leads to a bloated feeling, gas and abdominal pain. Lactose, the sugar in milk, causes a common food intolerance, particularly among some ethnic groups.

Coeliac disease

Coeliac disease is not an allergy, but is conveniently considered alongside allergies and food intolerances. It is an auto-immune condition in which the body's own antibodies (protective chemicals) attack body tissues, leading to a wide range of digestive symptoms, possible nutritional deficiencies and other problems. The disease is triggered by gluten – types of protein present in wheat, rye, barley and oats. Some people who do *not* have coeliac disease can also be allergic to cereals, such as wheat, but this this is uncommon in the UK.

The foods implicated in allergen reactions

Many different types of food could contain an allergen for someone, but eight foods are responsible for most of the sensitivities to food in the UK. They are:

- milk

- eggs

- ground nuts – such as peanuts (or monkey nuts)

- tree nuts (such as Brazil nuts, hazelnuts, almonds and walnuts)

- fish

- crustaceans – shellfish including prawns, shrimps, crab, langoustine and lobster

- soya

- wheat.

The most common allergic reactions to food among children in the UK are milk, peanuts, nuts, eggs, soya and wheat. For those who do not grow out of the allergy, the most common allergic reactions in adulthood involve peanuts, nuts, fish, shellfish and wheat.

Other problem foods in Europe and America include:

- sesame seeds– growing numbers of people in the UK are allergic to sesame

- other seeds including pine nuts (which are actually the seeds from the cones of a particular species of conifer)

- fruit – including kiwi, strawberry, banana, mango, avocado and apricots

- cereals other than wheat

- celery

- gluten

- mustard

- sulphur dioxide and sulphite – preservatives used in some foods, soft drinks and fermented drinks such as beer and wine

- lupin – a member of the pea (legume) family used to make flour in some brands of products such as brioche, hot dog buns and batter coatings

- molluscs – such as cockles, winkles, squid, abalone and land snails.

Legal requirements

It is illegal to to sell or offer for sale any unsafe food. This includes food that could harm people with particular health sensitivities, such as allergy suffers. There are legal requirements for labelling packaged food and for not misleading consumers, and it is illegal to sell or offer for sale any food containing *unexpected* ingredients.

Minimising the risk

As with biological, chemical or physical hazards to food, food companies need to identify the allergen hazards in their products, consider the risk to consumers and take appropriate action. This could involve getting rid of the hazard altogether or putting in place controls that minimise the risk to consumers. Some of the steps involved are discussed in Part 4.

Making it easier for others

- Train everyone involved in producing, serving or selling food in basic allergy awareness.

- Emphasise that food allergies affect particular individuals who could die if they eat even the slightest trace of foods or ingredients to which they are allergic.

- Explain that allergic responses are specific to individuals and the symptoms range from mild, through severe, to life threatening.

- Make it clear that an allergy is *not* food poisoning, even though some symptoms, such as vomiting, gastro-enteritis and skin rashes, may resemble those of some types of bacterial food-borne illness.

- Make clear which foods and ingredients in your workplace could cause problems.

- Make clear what staff should do to avoid contaminating food with allergens.

Legal requirements

Key points

Food safety legislation in the UK

The relationship between British and European Union food safety legislation.

The application of European legislation to member states.

The main requirements of legislation in the UK dealing with food safety, including the requirements for procedures based on HACCP principles and the requirements for product traceability.

Terms defined by legislation.

How legislation is enforced and the actions that can be taken by enforcement officers.

The consequences of legal non-compliance.

The role of industry guides, codes of practice and guidance on food safety.

Legislation as a guide to effective management practice.

Key words

Ambient shelf stable
Products that do not readily support the multiplication of pathogens and spoilage organisms, so can be stored unrefrigerated or unfrozen during storage or transport.

Authorised officer
A qualified person authorised by a food enforcement authority to take action on food safety matters in the UK.

Batch
Legal definition: 'a group or set of identifiable products obtained from a given process under practically identical circumstances and produced in a given place within one defined production period'.

Due diligence
A legal defence that every possible precaution was taken to avoid breaching food safety legislation.

Enforcement authority
The authority responsible for executing and enforcing food hygiene legislation. This is usually the local council.

Final consumer
Legal definition: 'the ultimate consumer of a foodstuff who will not use the food as part of any food business operation or activity'.

Food
Legal definition: 'any substance or product, whether processed, partially processed or unprocessed, intended to be, or reasonably expected to be ingested by humans' including 'drink, chewing gum and any substance, including water, intentionally incorporated into the food during its manufacture, preparation or treatment'.

Food business
Legal definition: 'any undertaking, whether for profit or not and whether public or private, carrying out any of the activities related to any stage of production, processing and distribution of food'.

Food business operator
The person in charge of food premises at any given time. Legal definition: 'the natural or legal persons responsible for ensuring that the requirements of food law are met within the food business under their control'.

Hazard
Legal definition: 'a biological, chemical or physical agent in, or condition of, food...with the potential to cause an adverse health effect'.

Hygiene Emergency Prohibition Order/Notice
Legal documents authorising the closure of a food business that is considered to be an imminent risk to health.

Hygiene Improvement Notice
A legal document requiring improvements to be made in food premises.

Microbiological criterion
Legal definition: a way to 'define acceptability of a product, a batch of foodstuffs or a process, based on the absence, presence or number of micro-organisms, and/or on the quantity of their toxins/metabolites, per unit(s) of mass, volume, area or batch'.

'Nature or substance or quality'
A legal description requiring food to be constituted as the consumer is led to expect.

Packaging
Legal definition: 'the placing of one or more wrapped foodstuffs in a second container' and 'the latter container itself'.

Placing on the market
Legal definition: 'the holding of food ... for the purpose of sale, including offering for sale or any other form of transfer, whether free of charge or not, and the sale, distribution, and other forms of transfer themselves'.

Premises

Any place, including a vehicle, stall, movable structure, ship or aircraft, that is used for the purposes of a food business.

Primary production

Legal definition: 'the production, rearing or growing of primary products including harvesting, milking and farmed animal production prior to slaughter. It also includes hunting and fishing and the harvesting of wild products'.

Ready-to-eat

Food produced for immediate consumption, without further treatment (except perhaps for heating). Legal definition: 'food intended by the producer or the manufacturer for direct human consumption without the need for cooking or other processing effective to eliminate or reduce to an acceptable level micro-organisms of concern'.

Retail

Legal definition: 'the handling and/or processing of food and its storage at the point of sale or delivery to the final consumer, and includes distribution terminals, catering operations, factory canteens, institutional catering, restaurants and other similar food service operations, shops, supermarket distribution centres and wholesale outlets'.

Risk

Legal definition: 'a function of the probability of an adverse health effect and the severity of that effect, consequential to a hazard'.

Risk analysis

'a process consisting of three interconnected components: risk assessment, risk management and risk communication'.

Risk assessment

Legal definition: 'a scientifically based process consisting of four steps: hazard identification, hazard characterisation, exposure assessment and risk characterisation'.

Risk communication

Legal definition: 'the interactive exchange of information and opinions throughout the risk analysis process as regards hazards and risks, risk-related factors and risk perceptions, among risk assessors, risk managers, consumers, feed and food businesses, the academic community and other interested parties, including the explanation of risk assessment findings and the basis of risk management decisions'.

Risk management

Legal definition: 'the process, distinct from risk assessment, of weighing policy alternatives in consultation with interested parties, considering risk assessment and other legitimate factors, and, if need be, selecting appropriate prevention and control options'.

Shelf life

Legal definition: 'either the period corresponding to the period preceding the *use by* [date] or the minimum [legally defined] durability date'.

Stages of production, processing and distribution

Legal definition: 'any stage, including import, from and including the primary production of a food, up to and including its storage, transport, sale or supply to the final consumer'.

Traceability

Legal definition: 'the ability to trace and follow a food, feed, food-producing animal or substance intended to be, or expected to be incorporated into a food or feed, through all stages of production, processing and distribution'.

Unfit food

Food that is not suitable for human consumption.

Wrapping

Legal definition: 'the placing of a foodstuff in a wrapper or container in direct contact with the foodstuff concerned' and 'the wrapper or container itself'.

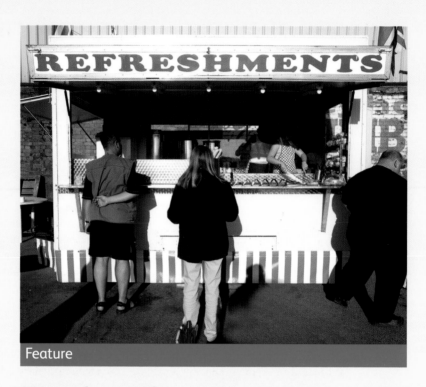

Feature

Food on the move

Whether you are catering for a society wedding in a grand marquee, selling burgers and hot dogs from a van or market stall, serving afternoon teas in a church hall or providing food from a vending machine, the highest standards of food safety are still a legal requirement.

The specific requirements for movable and temporary premises, as well as for domestic premises used to prepare food for sale, and vending machines, are covered by Annex II, Chapter III of Regulation (EC) No. 52/2004 on the hygiene of foodstuffs. Many mobile and temporary premises also need a street trading licence from the local council.

The easiest way to consider all such operations is as if they were producing or selling food from permanent food premises.

So, the business must be positioned, designed, constructed, kept clean and maintained in ways that avoid the risk of

contamination, especially from animals. Foods, too, must be stored, prepared and displayed so as to avoid contamination.

Food-contact surfaces must be easy to clean and, where appropriate, to disinfect. There must be suitable provision for personal hygiene, controlling food temperatures and storing and disposing of rubbish and food waste.

The ways in which movable businesses fulfil legal requirements can be different from those of permanent businesses. They might, for example, need to arrange for the use of water tanks and hoses. They would need to ensure that they were filled from a potable supply – ideally the mains – and to arrange for the tanks to be cleaned and disinfected regularly.

Whatever static or on the move, every food business needs effective food safety measures to avoid causing illness.

Food safety legislation in the UK

Managers like you are rarely expected to become legal experts, but you do need to know of the existence of the main legislation and understand how it affects what you do in your workplace. You should also know when and how to seek specialist advice on legal matters affecting the safety of food.

Scope

There is a very long list of legislation connected with food, covering broad issues of food safety and hygiene, composition, quality, labelling, standards and wrapping. In this chapter we concentrate on the legislation covering the *general* issues of food safety and hygiene in Britain. Great care has been taken in compiling the information, but you should be aware that the chapter does not claim to be a comprehensive or authoritative interpretation of food safety legislation. The contributors and publishers cannot be held responsible for actions or omissions taken on the basis of this general guidance which is provided in good faith. Managers are advised to:

- always have to hand a copy of the current relevant legislation (including sector-specific or product-specific legislation, where relevant)

- keep themselves up to date

- continue their professional development (CPD) in food-related topics including legislation

- take qualified specialist and/or legal advice on legal matters.

UK law in context

British laws are aligned with and formed by European Community (EC) legislation created by the member countries of the European Union (EU). There are currently 27 member states. They provide elected Members of the European Parliament (MEPs), of whom 78 come from the United Kingdom – England, Wales, Scotland and Northern Ireland. The European Commission proposes the draft European laws and the MEPs vote on the legislation in the European Parliament and the Council of Ministers. The member states must then enact their own national legislation in order to enforce the European legislation.

In the UK laws are made by elected Members of Parliament (MPs) and, under devolved powers, by the elected representatives of the Welsh Assembly, Scottish Parliament and Northern Ireland Assembly. Acts of Parliament – such as the Food Safety Act 1990 – usually deal with broad principles. British Regulations and Orders are made to deal with detailed requirements. The legislation gives enforcing officers their powers.

The legislation outlined in this chapter is *criminal* law which is dealt with by the criminal court system – for example, magistrates' and crown courts in England and Wales, and sheriff courts in Scotland. Offences under this legislation are criminal matters and create a criminal record on conviction. Under *civil* proceedings – for example, in county courts in England and Wales – a court may order a food business to pay compensation to someone who suffered a severe food-borne infection. For historical reasons the legal systems of Scotland and Northern Ireland vary slightly from that of England and Wales.

European legislation

There are three types of European legislation of relevance to food safety – Regulations, Directives and Decisions.

Regulations are legally binding in member states as soon as they have been agreed by the Council of Ministers. Member states must enforce them word for word.

The wording of a *Directive* is to some extent open to interpretation in each member country and, unlike an European Regulation, must be re-enacted in the country's own legislation. Almost all current national food safety legislation in member states has its origin in an EU Directive.

Decisions are applied either to a particular product, or to a particular country, whether an EU member or not. For example, Decisions have been used to ban the importation of products into the European Union from a country which has a particular food safety problem, or to ban the export of a product from an EU country where there has been a problem. There was, for example, a ban on exporting British beef, for example, in the wake of BSE. Decisions are legally binding on relevant member states.

Introduction to the main food safety legislation

A few major pieces of food safety legislation now cover all sectors of the food chain 'from farm to fork', consolidating a lot of previous sector-specific and product-specific requirements. The main legislation we discuss is:

- Regulation (EC) No. 178/2002 – this contains many of the definitions and basic principles for most matters relating to hygiene

- Food Safety Act 1990 – this deals mainly with food standards

- The Food Hygiene (England) Regulations 2006 and the equivalent legislation for Wales, Scotland and Northern Ireland – these deal with general food hygiene requirements in the UK, offences and the provision of enforcement powers.

- Regulation (EC) No. 852/2004 on the hygiene of foodstuffs – this contains the main hygiene requirements with which all businesses must comply, including a requirement to incorporate HACCP principles into company procedures

- Regulation (EC) No. 853/2004 on laying down specific hygiene rules for food of animal origin – this deals mainly with the approval of premises and is important mainly in the manufacturing sector

- Regulation (EC) No. 2073/2005 on the microbiological criteria for foodstuffs – a prescriptive piece of legislation dealing with microbiological standards in certain foods

- General Food Regulations 2004 – deals mainly with legal issues, including offences under Regulation (EC) No. 178/2002.

Regulation (EC) No. 178/2002

This piece of legislation is sometimes unofficially referred to as 'the European food safety Act' because it establishes the principles of food law and identifies the legal obligations of businesses and governments.

Regulation (EC) 178/2002
The foundation for other European legislation.
Includes many crucial definitions.
Food safety based on risk management and the precautionary principle.
Products to be traceable and retrievable.

It covers all stages of the food chain from primary production to the sale ('placing on the market') of products and establishes the rights of consumers to safe food and to accurate and honest information about it.

It includes:

- many of the definitions used in EU food law

- the general principles of food law based on risk management and the precautionary principle

- safety requirements for food placed on the market

- procedures for dealing with food safety problems

- the principle of traceability

- arrangements for the removal of unsafe food from the market.

Article 1 & 4
All stages of production, processing and distribution.

Scope of the legislation
The Regulation covers all the stages of the production, processing and distribution of food but does not apply to primary production for private domestic use or to the domestic preparation, handling or storage of food for private domestic consumption.

Jail term for meat fraud farmer

Articles 2 & 3
Definitions of food etc.

Definitions
The legal meaning of many words that are central to food safety are defined in this Regulation. They include final consumer, food, food business, food business operator, hazard, placing on the market, primary production, risk, risk assessment, risk communication, risk management, stages of production, processing and distribution and traceability. The legal definitions are shown in the Key words on pages 150 and 151.

London pub closed while mice removed

Article 5
Protect consumer health and interests.

Objectives
Food law must achieve a high level of protection of human life and health and the protection of consumers' interests, including fair practices in food trade, taking account of, where appropriate, the protection of animal health and welfare, plant health and the environment.

Cadbury fined £1m over salmonella

Article 6
Risk based approach required.

Risk
Food law must be based upon risk analysis, consisting of risk assessment, risk

Grisly haul: condemned 'on the spot'

management and risk communication. Risk assessment must be based on available scientific evidence.

Article 7
Precautionary principle to govern decisions.

Precautionary principle

If, after assessing the circumstances, an initial risk assessment suggests a possibility of harmful effects on human health, then the EU may act to protect public health even if there is no scientific proof that there is a real problem rather than a perceived problem. Any action taken must be proportionate to the risk, no more restrictive than is necessary and should be reviewed within a reasonable period depending on the nature of the risk and the type of scientific evidence required to do a full risk assessment.

(One of the issues raised at the time of the enquiry into BSE – bovine spongiform encephalopathy – in the UK was that initially, at least, there was no scientific evidence to confirm that the condition in cattle was also a human health problem. As a result no action was taken early on to minimise the risk to human health. Subsequent events showed, although still the subject of some controversy, that there was a link between BSE in cattle and nvCJD in humans. The precautionary principle in Article 7 allows the EU to take action in such circumstances.)

Articles 8, 9 & 10
Consumer interests.

Consumer interests

The legislation aims to protect the interests of consumers; help them to make informed choices in relation to the foods they consume; prevent fraudulent or deceptive practices, the adulteration of food and any other practices that could mislead the consumer; and ensure that consumers are consulted and informed.

Article 14
Unsafe food defined as being injurious to human health or unfit for human consumption because of contamination or spoilage.

Food safety requirements

Food must not be placed on the market if it is unsafe. It is deemed to be unsafe if it is considered to be:

(a) injurious to health

(b) unfit for human consumption because of contamination or spoilage.

In deciding whether or not food is 'injurious to health' account must be taken of the probable short-term and long-term consequences, both for a person consuming it, and for subsequent generations. Consideration must also be taken of the probable cumulative toxic effects of a food and the particular health sensitivities of a specific category of consumer where the food is intended for that group. Emphasis is placed on informing the consumer, including on the label, about any possible adverse affects.

If part of a batch of food is considered unsafe, then the whole batch is considered unsafe, unless it can be demonstrated otherwise.

Article 16
Packaging etc must not mislead consumers.

Misrepresentation

The promotion, packaging, labelling, display setting and so on must not mislead consumers.

Article 17
Official controls.

Responsibilities

This Article provides for official enforcement, monitoring and verification of legal obligations.

Article 18
Product tracing systems required throughout the food chain.

Traceability

At all stages of production, processing and distribution there must be systems in place, which may include such things as identification documentation, to ensure that food placed on the market can be traced, and the information can be made available to the competent authorities when requested to do so. Business operators must be able to identify their suppliers and their customers, except where the customer is the final consumer. The identification requirement is often known as 'one up, one down' traceability.

Article 19
Systems for withdrawing and recalling unsafe food.

Withdrawal and recall

If a food business believes that a food is unsafe, it must immediately initiate procedures to withdraw that food from the market and, if necessary, must recall food that has already reached the consumer. It must also inform the competent authority.

EFSA
Europe-wide system of food safety alerts.

Europe-wide food body

The European Food Safety Authority (EFSA) was established by this Regulation. Its mission statement says that it is 'the keystone of European Union (EU) risk assessment regarding food and feed safety. In close collaboration with national authorities and in open consultation with its stakeholders, EFSA provides independent scientific advice and clear communication on existing and emerging risks.'

The Authority also co-ordinates a Europe-wide rapid alert system for food safety problems and common measures to be taken in the event of a serious risk to human health.

Food Safety Act 1990

Parts of this Act, which applies in England, Wales and Scotland, are now covered by more recent legislation, but the enforcement of food *standards*, among other things, remains. The following paragraphs summarise some key aspects of the legislation. Similar provision is made under the Food Safety (Northern Ireland) Order 1991.

Section 7
Offence to sell food for human consumption if it is injurious to health.

Food injurious to health

It is an offence for a food business to sell food for human consumption if it has been made injurious to health by:

- adding any article or substance to a food that renders it injurious to health

- using any article or substance as an ingredient that renders it injurious to health

- abstracting any constituent from the food that renders it injurious to health

- subjecting the food to any other process or treatment that renders it injurious to health.

If food intended for sale is treated in a way that it becomes injurious to health, the law also takes into account the short-term, long-term and cumulative effect of eating such food. The ill effect of eating such food could be temporary or permanent.

Section 9
Inspection, removal and seizure of food.

Seizure of food

An authorised officer of a food authority may inspect at any reasonable time any food intended for sale for human consumption. If the officer believes that the food fails to meet food safety requirements or is likely to cause food poisoning or any communicable disease, the officer may either:

- give notice and detain the food on the premises, or at a specified place, for up to 21 days so that the food is not used for human consumption

- seize the food and remove it to have it dealt with by a Justice of the Peace (magistrate or sheriff) who may issue an order to have it condemned.

A food business may ask the court to refuse such an order. If a notice to detain food is withdrawn, or the court does not condemn the food, the owner is entitled to claim compensation for any depreciation in its value caused by the action of the officer.

Duties and powers of ministers

The Act allows ministers to make regulations and imposes certain duties or powers. Under Section 13 ministers can, for example, issue an Emergency Control Order covering commercial operations where something is considered to pose an imminent risk of injury to health.

Section 13
Emergency control orders.

Consumer protection

All food sold must be 'of the nature or substance or quality demanded by the purchaser'. While the meaning of these three terms is straightforward, people are often confused by them in the context of food safety.

Section 14
Nature – food different to what was requested. Substance – not of the correct composition or containing physical contaminants. Quality – the standard expected.

Nature deals with type or variety and is concerned with authenticity. So, you should not sell Golden Delicious apples as if they were Granny Smith apples, or whiting fillets as haddock, and you should not say that something was produced in Scotland when in fact it originated in Argentina.

Substance refers to the composition of food, which should have the proper ingredients. If it is stated that a food contains x, y and z but it actually contains only x and y, then the food is clearly not what the customer reasonably expected. Although this could be considered to be just a labelling infringement, it is a significant matter about food composition.

Quality, although a hard concept to define generally, is relatively easy to understand in this context. The customer expects a certain quality, such as firm but ripe fruit, and should not therefore receive something inferior, such as bruised mouldy fruit.

Food hygiene regulations 2006

These Regulations, which came into force in January 2006, are:

- The Food Hygiene (England) Regulations 2006
- The Food Hygiene (Wales) Regulations 2006
- The Food Hygiene (Scotland) Regulations 2006
- The Food Hygiene (Northern Ireland) Regulations 2006

and subsequent amendments.

The legislation deals largely with the regulation and enforcement of food safety, plus temperature control, and is the main British route to *enforcing* the main European Regulations. The following summary is of the English regulations, but the regulations and schedules are generally numbered the same in the other three sets of Regulations. There are four parts and several schedules, one of which, Schedule 4, deals with temperature control provisions. The first part largely deals with definitions, while Part 2 contains the main provisions of the Regulations.

Regulation 2
Definitions.

Definitions

Some key words are defined, such as authorised officer enforcement authority and premises. The legal definitions are included in the Key words list on pages 150 and 151.

Regulation 3
Food in food premises shall be for human consumption.

Food in food premises

Food normally used for human consumption that is found on food premises is assumed to be intended for placing on the market for human consumption.

Regulation 6
Improvements required.

Hygiene Improvement Notices

An authorised officer may serve a Hygiene Improvement Notice on a food business operator requiring work to be done to comply with the Regulations. The Notice must specify which Regulation has been contravened, the work to be done and the time in which the work must be carried out – a minimum of 14 days. It is an offence not to carry out the specified work within the specified time. These Notices can be used for many things including processes, structure, equipment and methods, but cannot be used for something ongoing, such as measures to keep something clean.

Regulation 7
Ban on activities. Possible ban on business operator or manager.

Hygiene Prohibition Orders

This is arguably the toughest section in the Regulations. If a food business operator is convicted of any offence under relevant Regulations and if there is a risk to health from the use of any process or treatment, the construction of food premises or the use or condition of any equipment in food premises, a court can be asked to impose a Hygiene Prohibition Order. The Order can apply to processes, the premises or parts of the premises and the use of equipment. A copy of the Order must be displayed conspicuously on the premises as soon as possible. It is an offence to contravene it.

When the business operator believes that the problems have been rectified, it can apply to the enforcement authority for a certificate of satisfaction that there is no longer a health risk. The certificate would allow the premises to re-open. The local authority must decide within 14 days whether it is satisfied and issue a certificate, or give the reasons why not.

There is a sting in the tail, because the court can also ban the business operator or manager from working in a food business. Only the court can lift the ban.

Regulation 8
Imminent risk to health.

Hygiene Emergency Prohibition Notices and Orders

If an authorised officer believes there to be an *imminent* risk to health, then he or she can issue a Hygiene Emergency Prohibition Notice to close the premises *immediately*. Examples of an imminent risk to health include severe pest infestation, sewage disposal problems and outbreaks of food poisoning or food-borne infection. The Notice, which can apply to the whole business or to any part of it, must be ratified by a magistrates' or sheriff court within three working days. Provided that the court is satisfied that the Notice was served justly, it will issue a Hygiene Emergency Prohibition Order. This remains in force until a certificate of satisfaction is issued by the local enforcement authority. The Notice and Order must be displayed conspicuously on the premises.

If the court fails to ratify the Notice, or the application for the Order was served later than three days after the Notice, then the food business operator may seek compensation for any loss suffered as a result of the serving of the Notice.

Regulation 9
Remedial action and detention of food in 'approved premises'.

Remedial Action and Detention Notices for 'approved premises'

This applies only to premises that are subject to approval under Regulation (EC) No. 853/2004 laying down specific hygiene rules for food of animal origin. These include slaughterhouses and cutting plants. Where an authorised officer believes that the Hygiene Regulations are being breached or the inspection is being hampered, he or she can issue a Remedial Action Notice. The Notice may prohibit the use of equipment or any part of the premises specified; prohibit, or impose conditions upon, the carrying out of any process; or stop, or reduce the rate of, the operation. The Notice is withdrawn once the officer is satisfied that the specified remedial action has been taken. A Detention Notice may also be served to enable the detention of any animal or food for examination, including the taking of samples. It is withdrawn once the officer is satisfied that detention is no longer necessary. Failure to comply with either type of Notice is an offence.

Defences and offences

Regulations 10 & 11
Defence of due diligence.
Offence committed by someone else.

As mentioned in Part 2, there are only two main defences under these Regulations, either:

- that the offence was the fault of another person
- **due diligence**.

To prove due diligence a business must be able to demonstrate that it took every possible reasonable step to achieve safe food. It is likely that the court would demand written records to support the defence. These might include documents based on HACCP principles and records of staff training, temperature measurements, cleaning schedules, supplier specifications, traceability systems, remedial action where food safety problems have arisen and pest control measures.

Samples

Regulations 12 & 13
Taking and analysing samples.

An **authorised officer** can buy or remove samples of any food or any other article or substance that may be required as evidence. If the officer considers it necessary, the samples can be analysed or examined by a public analyst or food examiner.

Powers of entry

Regulations 14 & 15
Powers of entry.
Offence of obstruction.

An authorised officer of the **enforcement authority** has the power of entry into food businesses at all reasonable hours and, after giving 24 hours' notice, may also enter a private dwelling house. Authorised officers may inspect any records, including computer records, and seize them if they are required as evidence.

If there is resistance to the right of entry, a warrant may be issued by a Justice of the Peace (JP) at short notice to authorise entry, by force if necessary.

Obstruction

Regulation 15
Offence of obstruction, lack of co-operation or giving misleading information.

It is an offence to deliberately obstruct an officer, to be unco-operative or to give misleading information.

Offences and penalties

Regulations 17, 18 & 19
Fines.
Imprisonment.
Offences by individual directors, managers and senior staff.

If a court finds someone guilty of an offence under the Regulations, it can impose:

- a fine of up to £5,000 on summary conviction (magistrates' or sheriff court)
- an unlimited fine or imprisonment for up to two years for conviction on indictment (by a higher court, such as a crown court).

In addition, the offence of obstructing an authorised officer or knowingly giving misleading information is punishable by a fine of up to £5,000, or imprisonment for up to three months, or both.

Where a food business has committed an offence, its company directors, partners, managers and anyone acting in a directorial or managerial capacity may also be guilty of an offence if they knowingly consent to the food business committing the offence, connive in the offence or neglect to take steps to avoid the offence.

Regulations 20, 21 & 22
Provision for appeals,

Rights of appeal
Provision is made for aggrieved people to appeal against lower court decisions, Hygiene Improvement Notices and Remedial Action Notices.

Regulation 27

Food not produced, processed or distributed in accordance with the Hygiene Regulations
If an authorised officer certifies that food has not been produced, processed or distributed in accordance with the Regulations, it is treated as if it fails to meet food safety requirements under Section 9 of the Food Safety Act 1990 (see pages 157 to 158).

Temperature control England, Wales and Northern Ireland

Schedule 4
Detailed temperature control requirements. High-risk foods must be kept at or below 8°C or at 63°C or above.

The main thrust of these Regulations is to ensure that food likely to support the growth of pathogenic micro-organisms or the formation of toxins is kept at a temperature either of 8°C or below, or at 63°C or above . There are detailed temperature control requirements for England, Wales and Northern Ireland and more general, separate controls for Scotland.

The Regulations apply to most food business operations. *Exceptions* include slaughterhouses, meat-cutting premises and food business operations carried out on a ship or aircraft. There are some *additional* requirements for some fish retailers.

Chill holding below 8°C
High-risk foods must by law be kept at below 8°C.
Some important exemptions apply.

Chill holding requirements
It is an offence to keep food that is likely to support the growth of pathogenic micro-organisms or the formation of toxins at a temperature above 8°C.

Food sent by mail order to the final consumer is exempt, but the food must still be kept at a temperature that does not give rise to, or is likely to give rise to, a risk to health.

General exemptions from the chill holding requirements
The chill temperature of 8°C does not have to be applied to a food that:

- has been cooked or reheated and is for service or on display for sale, and needs to be kept at or above 63°C in order to control the growth of pathogenic micro-organisms or the formation of toxins

- can for the duration of its shelf life be kept at ambient temperatures without any risk to health

- is being or has been processed, such as by dehydration or canning, to make it safe to eat, except when the food has been in an hermetically sealed container and that container has subsequently been opened

- must be ripened or matured at ambient temperatures (such as cheese), but not when the process of ripening or maturation is completed

- is raw and intended for further processing (including cooking) before human consumption, but only if that processing, if undertaken correctly, will make the food fit for human consumption

- is covered by certain other Regulations, such as the selling of eggs.

Upward variation of the 8°C temperature by manufacturers etc.

8°C chill variation
Documented scientific assessment required.

There is a defence against holding a processed food at a temperature above 8°C if the manufacturer recommends in writing that it can safely be kept at a temperature above 8°C for the period until the end of its shelf life. The manufacturer's recommendation must be supported by a well-founded scientific assessment of the safety of the food at the specified temperature. Any defence based on the recommendation would need to show that the specified shelf life had not been exceeded.

8°C chill tolerance
Exemptions include allowing for food preparation and displaying it for sale.

Chill holding tolerance periods

There is a defence for an alleged contravention of the chill holding requirements if food:

- was for service or on display for sale, and

- had not previously been kept for service or on display for sale at a temperature above 8°C, and

- had been kept for service or on display for sale for a period of less than four hours, or

- was being transferred to a vehicle from storage at or below 8°C, or

- was unavoidably kept at above 8°C for a limited period that did not compromise food safety, for example, during handling; during and after processing or preparation; during the defrosting of equipment; or during the temporary breakdown of equipment.

Hot holding
Hot high-risk food must be held at or above 63°C. Variation based on scientific assessment or time control may be defendable.

Hot holding requirements

It is an offence to hold food at a temperature below 63°C if the food:

- has been cooked or reheated

- is for service or on display for sale, and

- needs to be kept at or above 63°C to control the growth of pathogenic micro-organisms or the formation of toxins.

Hot holding defences

There is a defence that hot food was kept at below 63°C if:

- there is a well-founded scientific assessment that it is safe to keep that food at a specified temperature below 63°C for a specified period and those specifications have been followed

- had been kept for service or on display for sale for a period of less than two hours and had not previously been kept for service or on display for sale by that person.

Other temperature requirements

Some other temperature requirements for food that could be a risk to health can be found in Regulation (EC) No. 852/2004 and for food in 'approved premises' in Regulation (EC) No. 853/2004.

Temperature control Scotland

There are differences in some temperature requirements in Scotland which are covered by Regulation 30 of The Food Hygiene (Scotland) Regulations 2006 .

Chill and hot holding requirements

It is an offence to hold food other than either:

- in a refrigerator or refrigerating chamber or in a cool ventilated place

or

- at a temperature above 63°C.

Permitted exceptions are when food:

- is undergoing preparation for sale

- is exposed for sale or has been sold

- is being cooled, immediately after cooking, under hygienic conditions as quickly as possible to a safe temperature

- can safely and reasonably be stored at different temperature so that it can be offered for sale

- can safely be kept at ambient temperatures for the duration of its shelf life.

Reheating (Scotland)
Reheated food must
reach at least 82°C.

Reheating of food

Cooked food which is then reheated for immediate consumption or sale must be reheated to a temperature of not less than 82°C. It is a defence to prove that the food could not have been raised to a temperature of not less than 82°C without a deterioration of its qualities.

Regulation (EC) No. 852/2004 on the hygiene of foodstuffs

The fundamental aim of any hygiene regulation is to create conditions in a food business that will lead to the safe production of food. Generally speaking, this Regulation takes a two-pronged approach:

- the management and control of the structure of food premises and the equipment used

- the management and control over what happens in food premises.

These requirements aim to create the correct hygienic environment from which food can be produced, processed, cooked, served, stored or transported. As may be expected, there are provisions for the structure of the building itself and the design of equipment.

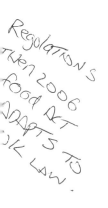

While the basic structure of food premises and equipment are very important, it is recognised that it is far more important to manage and control people and processes in order to eliminate food hazards and reduce the risk of food-borne illness. These requirements therefore deal with such matters as hazard analysis, hygiene training, supervision, personal hygiene, cleaning methods and pest control.

This European Regulation came into force in January 2006, largely replacing (the British) The Food Safety (General Food Hygiene) Regulations 1995. Most of the requirements are the same, but there is a new requirement to put in place procedures based on the principles of Hazard Analysis and Critical Control Point (HACCP).

The Regulation covers most food businesses. Exceptions include primary production for private domestic use or for the supply of small quantities of primary produce direct to the final consumer.

There are many detailed requirements and the following information deals generally with the topics covered. The practical application of many of the requirements are discussed in various chapters of Part 4 of this book.

Article 5
Procedures must exist
based upon HACCP
principles.

Hazard analysis and critical control points

Food business operators must put in place, implement and maintain permanent procedures based on the principles of Hazard Analysis and Critical Control Point (HACCP). These involve food businesses in:

- identifying any hazards that must be prevented, eliminated or reduced to acceptable levels

- identifying the critical control points (CCPs) at the step or steps in the food processes at which control is essential to prevent or eliminate a hazard or to reduce it to acceptable levels

- establishing at critical control points the critical limits that distinguish what is acceptable from what is unacceptable for the prevention, elimination or reduction of identified hazards

- establishing and implementing effective monitoring procedures at critical control points

- establishing corrective actions when monitoring indicates that a critical control point is not under control

- establishing procedures that are carried out regularly to verify that what should be happening is indeed happening

- establishing documents and records that are appropriate to the type and size of the food business to demonstrate the effective application of CCPs and the other required measures

- reviewing and making any necessary changes to the procedure whenever any modification is made to the product, process or steps.

Details of the implementation of this requirement are discussed on pages 182 to 195.

Article 6
Food businesses must register.

Registration

Food businesses must register all premises with the competent authority, usually the local council, and notify any significant changes in activities or closure of the business.

Annex II
Chapters I and II
Requirement for food premises and food rooms

Premises

Detailed requirements are listed in Annex II of the Regulation for food premises in general and in particular for rooms where foodstuffs are prepared, treated or processed. The implementation of these requirements are discussed on pages 240 to 254. In general, whatever the purpose or construction of the food premises, they should be:

- constructed in such a way that prevents contamination of the food

- easy to clean

- designed in such a way that prevents pests getting in

- large enough and suitably designed and equipped for the purpose to which the premises are being put.

Also covered are certain social welfare issues such as the provision of toilet facilities, changing rooms and so on. There are slightly different requirements for different types of premises because of differing hazards and risks.

Chapter III

Temporary and movable premises

Specific requirements are listed for temporary and movable food premises, domestic premises used to prepare food for sale, and vending machines. See page 152.

Chapter IV

Transport

Vehicles and containers used for transporting food must be kept clean and maintained in good repair. Their condition must protect the food from contamination and they must be designed and constructed to enable adequate cleaning and disinfection, where appropriate, to be carried out.

Receptacles and containers in vehicles must not to be used for transporting anything other than food if this could result in food contamination. Vehicles or containers also used for non-food products or for transporting different foods at the same time must, where necessary, separate the products effectively.

Where necessary, vehicles and containers used for transporting food must be able to keep the products at an appropriate temperature and allow those temperatures to be monitored.

Chapter V	**Equipment**
	Equipment should also be designed so that it can be cleaned easily and positioned so that it is easy to clean under and around it. Aspects of these requirements are discussed on pages 242 to 256.
Chapter VI	**Food waste**
	Food waste must be taken out of food rooms regularly and as quickly as possible.
Chapter VII	**Water supply**
	There must be an adequate supply of potable water, which must be used whenever necessary to ensure that food is not contaminated.

Ice that comes into contact with food, or which may contaminate food, must be made from potable water. It must be made, handled and stored under conditions that protect it from contamination. Steam used directly in contact with food must not contain any substance that presents a hazard to health or is likely to contaminate the food.

The water used to cool foods in hermetically sealed containers, such as cans, must not be a source of contamination for the food.

Chapter VIII **Personal hygiene**

Anyone who works in a food-handling area must maintain a high degree of personal cleanliness and wear suitable, clean and, where necessary, protective clothing.

Anyone employed in a food business who is likely to come into contact with food must tell the food business operator immediately if they have, or are a carrier of, a food-borne illness or certain other illnesses or symptoms. They must not work with food until they are cleared as safe to do so and they must not enter any food-handling area in any capacity if there is any likelihood of direct or indirect contamination. The Regulation applies to any disease likely to be transmitted through food, infected wounds, skin infections, sores or diarrhoea.

Chapter IX **Provisions applicable to foodstuffs**

These requirements are central to food safety.

- A food business operator must not accept raw food or ingredients if they are known to be, or are suspected of being, contaminated with parasites; pathogenic micro-organisms; or toxic, decomposed or foreign substances to such an extent that, even after the normal sorting and/or preparatory or processing procedures, the final product would be unfit for human consumption.

- Stored raw materials and ingredients must be kept in appropriate conditions designed to prevent harmful deterioration and to protect them from contamination.

- At all stages of production, processing and distribution, food must be protected against any contamination likely to render the food unfit for human consumption, injurious to health or contaminated in such a way that it would be unreasonable to expect it to be consumed in that state.

- There must be adequate pest control measures, including procedures to prevent domestic animals, such as household pets, getting in to places where food is prepared, handled or stored.

- Raw materials, ingredients, intermediate products and finished products likely to support the reproduction of pathogenic micro-organisms or the formation of toxins must not be kept at temperatures that might result in a risk to health – in other words, within the danger zone.

- The cold chain must not be interrupted. However, limited periods are permitted outside temperature control to allow for handling during preparation, transport, storage, display and service of food, provided that this does not result in a risk to health.

- Food businesses that manufacture, handle and wrap processed foods must have enough suitable space to store raw materials separately from processed material and sufficient separate refrigerated storage.

- Where foods are to be held or served at chilled temperatures, they must be cooled, to a temperature that does not result in a risk to health, as quickly as possible following the heat-processing stage or the final preparation stage if no heat process is applied.

- Thawing must be carried out in a way that minimises the risk of the growth of pathogenic micro-organisms or the formation of toxins in the foods.

- The liquid from the thawing process must be drained so that it does not present a risk to health.

- Following thawing, food must be handled in a manner that minimises the risk of growth of pathogenic micro-organisms or the formation of toxins.

- Hazardous substances, such as cleaning chemicals, and inedible substances, including animal feed, must be adequately labelled and stored in separate, secure containers.

| Chapter X | **Wrapping and packaging**
Definitions are given for wrapping and packaging. |

Materials used for wrapping and packaging must not be a source of contamination. Wrapping materials must be stored in such a manner that they are not exposed to a risk of contamination.

Wrapping and packaging operations must be carried out in ways that avoid contamination of the products. Where appropriate, and in particular in the case of cans and glass jars, the integrity of the container's construction and its cleanliness must be assured.

Any wrapping and packaging material re-used for food must be easy to clean and, where necessary, to disinfect.

| Chapter XI | **Heat treatment of food placed on the market in hermetically sealed containers**
Any heat treatment processes used must conform to an internationally recognised standard, such as pasteurization, ultra high temperature or sterilization. |

The process must raise every part of the product to a given temperature for a given time and prevent the product from becoming contaminated during the process.

Food business operators must check regularly the main relevant parameters (particularly temperature, pressure, sealing and microbiology). This may be done by the use of automatic devices.

Chapter XII

Training

Food business operators must ensure that food handlers are supervised and instructed and/or trained in food hygiene matters commensurate with their work activity, and that the employees responsible for the development and maintenance of the procedures based on HACCP principles have received adequate training in the application of the principles.

Regulation (EC) No. 853/2004 – dealing with food of animal origin

Registration as 'approved premises' Deals with foods of animal origin. Complicated criteria. Advice should be sought.

This Regulation sets out rules for official controls on products of animal origin. It requires that products such as meat, milk, fish, honey and eggs be processed only in 'approved premises'.

Generally speaking, the Regulation covers manufacturers, but in certain situations approval is also required for premises that would not normally be thought of as manufacturing. This may include some retail businesses, such as butchers, that supply only other businesses. Other criteria that may be relevant to a particular business deal with the percentages of food sold from retail outlets direct to final consumers or other businesses, and the geographical area of sale. As the criteria can seem complicated, it would be wise to seek the advice of your local environmental health department or home authority if you handle foods of animal origin.

Businesses that are granted 'approved premises' status must, among other things, use a health mark or identification mark on products of animal origin that are placed on the market. They may, depending on the animal of origin, need to provide certificates and other documentation with consignments of animal-derived foods, in addition to having systems of traceability.

Regulation (EC) No. 2073/2005 – on microbiological criteria for foodstuffs

Criteria for microbes Sampling and testing for levels of microbes that are or are not permitted in food.

This legislation sets out the acceptable microbiological content of food. It provides tables of microbiological criteria for different types of food. There is a list that covers food from processing to the end of its shelf life and another list covering manufacture only.

A microbiological criterion is described as a way to 'define acceptability of a product, a batch of foodstuffs or a process, based on the absence, presence or number of micro-organisms, and/or on the quantity of their toxins/metabolites, per unit(s) of mass, volume, area or batch.' Definitions are also given for batch, ready-to-eat foods and shelf life.

The Regulation requires all food business operators to take measures to ensure that the relevant process hygiene criteria and food safety criteria are met throughout the foreseeable life of the product. This must be done as part of their procedures based on HACCP principles, together with their implementation of good hygiene practice. It is up to the food business itself to decide any necessary sampling and the testing frequencies. The decision must be as part of the procedures based on HACCP principles and other hygiene control procedures, and must take into account the instructions for the use of the product. The Regulation expects the decision to be in proportion to the type and size of the business, provided that the safety of the food is not compromised.

Manufacturers also have specific obligations to conduct studies throughout their products' shelf life to ensure that their foods comply with the criteria. This is particularly important for ready-to-eat foods that can support the growth of *Listeria monocytogenes*. Food businesses may collaborate in conducting those studies. Specific rules are laid down for sampling and testing and for action to be taken, including withdrawing or recalling products from the market, if the tests provide unsatisfactory results.

Other regulations

You might come across mention of The General Food Regulations 2004, which provides for such things as offences in Britain under certain EU legislation and the powers of competent authorities. Bear in mind that there are likely to be many other pieces of legislation that apply to your business, such as those concerned with processes including freezing and canning, the handling of products of animal origin, animal health, wrapping and packaging, labelling (including allergens and genetically modified foods), public health, the reporting of illness, hazardous chemicals and the ban on smoking in enclosed or party enclosed public places and work spaces.

Industry guides

Guidance has been developed for several food sectors on how to comply with the regulations – for instance, *The Catering Guide to Good Hygiene Practice*. At the time of writing, many of these are being updated. The guides tend to go beyond simple legal compliance and deal with what is good practice, even if it is not a legal requirement. The guides have no *defined* legal standing, but in practice environmental health practitioners and the courts pay attention to them when making decisions about compliance.

Codes of practice

British ministers have the power to issue codes of practice. They cover a wide range of topics including the qualifications required to be an enforcement officer, the issuing of notices such as Hygiene Improvement Notices, and standards for carrying out a food safety inspection. Enforcement officers are expected to be fully conversant with the codes and to carry out their work in accordance with them.

Enforcement

Food safety legislation is enforced by officers authorised by:

■ local authorities (usually your local council) or port health authorities, and

■ central government, through the Meat Hygiene Service (MHS), which is an executive branch of the Food Standards Agency.

Enforcing officers have job titles including environmental health officer (EHO), environmental health practitioner (EHP), trading standards officer, food safety officer, technical officer (food safety), food safety technician, official veterinarian (OV) and official auxiliary (OA).

The Food Standards Agency (FSA) oversees local authority enforcement activities for food legislation by setting and monitoring their standards. It also audits local authorities' performance to ensure that enforcement is 'proportionate, consistent and transparent'. The codes of practice are among the criteria for measuring performance.

The FSA also issues two types of food alert. A Food Alert for Information warns local authorities and consumers about food-related problems, and a Food Alert for Action gives information about specific action to be taken. The information also goes to consultants in communicable disease control, trading standards officers and food trade organisations. Alerts are often issued in conjunction with a product withdrawal or recall by a food business.

Finding out more

A great deal of information about legislation and enforcement is available on the Internet. General guidance can be found on the Food Standards Agency website, together with copies of legislation for downloading free of charge and links to other government websites from which legislation can be downloaded (see pages 415 to 419).

Your local environmental health department or home authority will be happy to guide you, and a wide range of services is on offer from independent environmental health practitioners and solicitors specialising in food matters.

Making it easier for others

It is not necessary for every food handler to have a detailed knowledge of food safety legislation or to memorise the title of Acts and Regulations. Even so, it is important to ensure that every member of staff has a good general awareness of how food safety legislation affects their daily activities and the general operation of the company. Detailed guidance on this is given in Part 4 and incorporates the following points.

■ Emphasise that everyone who works with food has a legal responsibility to work in a way that safeguards the health of consumers.

■ Make sure that all food handlers understand that they *must*:

– keep themselves clean

– keep their workplace clean

– wear clean and suitable protective clothing

– do everything possible to protect food from contamination

– store, prepare and display food at safe temperatures

– tell you, or another senior staff member, if they have any symptom of food-borne illness or certain other conditions or illnesses (see page 275).

■ Emphasise that food handlers *must not*:

– do anything that would expose food to contamination

– serve or sell food that is unfit for human consumption

– sell food with an expired date mark

– work with food if they have symptoms of a food-borne illness or until they have been cleared as safe to do so.

Feature

On the trail of food

It's Monday morning and Joe Bloggs doesn't feel too good. As an attack of diarrhoea hits him, Joe has to ask himself what he had eaten in the past 36 hours. Which food was the culprit? Was it the steak and kidney pie from a local pub-restaurant? Had it been refrigerated, then reheated? Where had the fish and chip stand bought its fish? How many hours had the frying oil been in use? What about the beer he had drunk in the evening?

Every food has a story. If the consumer does not enjoy a 'happy end', or if any problem with food is suspected, it must be possible for professionals to track back to the point where things started to go wrong. Where necessary, food must then be withdrawn from sale or recalled from consumers who have already bought it.

To make this easier all food businesses are legally obliged to implement systems of product identification and tracing – known as 'traceability'. This is the ability to identify and follow raw food ingredients, food products, animal feed and other substances through all the stages from farm to fork – in this case, Joe Bloggs' fork.

The systems depend upon unique codes that are applied to foods. They can identify details as specific as the field in which a cow grazed, the glasshouse in which a tomato was grown and, in combination with food safety records such as HACCP documents, the cooking and storage temperatures of food products and dishes.

Although traceability can provide an astonishing level of detail, individual food companies must be able to identify only the businesses from which they have obtained their supplies, plus the businesses they have provided with products – a requirement popularly called 'one up, one down' or 'one step back, one step forward'. There is no need to record 'the final consumer', such as customers of most shops and restaurants. Companies must be able to provide traceability information to the competent authority within a short period of being asked to do so.

There are no rules for how the records should be kept or for exactly how long they should be retained. The Food Standards Authority suggests that, as a minimum, traceability records should include the address of the customer or supplier, the nature and quantity of products, and the date of the transaction and delivery. Recording the batch number or durability indication, where applicable, is also helpful.

In small food businesses traceability requirements are based mainly on delivery and production notes and basic accounting records.

In larger businesses a more detailed system of codes identifies individual ingredients and individual processes. An alpha-numeric code is usually used, consisting of a series of letters and numbers that can be read and processed by computers. The code starts for the raw materials and is passed on to intermediate products, semi-finished and end products. Details about processing and packaging are added.

Traceability can involve the whole food chain or just a small part of it. The underlying principle is the gathering and passing of information from one link of the food chain to the next. Of course this chain is not merely linear: it also branches to form a network, or system of chains, that includes manufacturers of auxiliary products, such as packaging, and service providers such as road hauliers and warehouse companies.

There are two aspects (or directions) involved in the gathering and passing of information. They are *downstream* tracing, from the source of the food to final consumer, and *upstream* tracing, from the consumer back to the primary producer.

Downstream tracing starts with a particular *lot* or *batch*. A lot (also called an *order quantity*) is the products manufactured under identical conditions and bought and shipped together as a joint order. A lot could be a number of bakery products produced from the same dough, delicatessen salad portions taken from the same container, or a shift's entire production output.

A batch is a group of similar items that are processed or gathered together and treated as a single unit.

Upstream tracing starts with the food on the consumer's fork and follows the food back to the primary production. This is the direction of tracing followed when Joe Bloggs became ill.

After laboratory analysis of a stool sample, Joe's illness was put down to a cream dessert he had enjoyed as a late-night snack and had initially forgotten about. The investigation was carried out because he was not the only person who became ill at that time.

The culprit food was established as a packaged tiramisu bought from a particular supermarket. The bar code led back to the manufacturer of the product. HACCP records then established details such as raw materials, individual production lines, process methods (such as pasteurization), the staff involved and action taken at critical control points (see page 188).

So, effective systems of product tracing can help companies to take remedial action if they discover failures at critical control points. It can can also help them to demonstrate due diligence. Traceability is of particular importance for product withdrawals and recalls where a food business needs to identify potential sources of contamination as soon as possible so that it can remove affected lots or batches from the market and break the chain leading to illness or injury.

Management matters

Food safety legislation has a simple aim – to prevent consumers from becoming ill and perhaps dying. The manager's role is to ensure that both the letter and the spirit of the law are observed. To achieve this, managers need to ensure a mixture of legal compliance and good practice so that:

- the premises are registered with the local enforcement authority

- the business is properly designed and equipped for the kind of food operation being carried out to prevent contamination and food-borne illness or injury – bear in mind that staff cannot be expected to work within the law if they are not, for instance, provided with adequate and appropriate protective clothing

- there are adequate washing facilities and arrangements for personal hygiene

- staff are trained on appropriate hygiene subjects and to a level that is in line with the kind of work they do and the responsibilities they have

- staff who are not food handlers but whose work could affect food safety are also given appropriate training in basic food safety

- everyone knows exactly what is expected of them

- the manager and senior staff set an excellent example

- there is adequate supervision

- food hazards are analysed and appropriate systems put in place to eliminate them or to minimise the risks from them.

You may decide that legislation states only the minimum standards that you wish your staff to achieve and you may establish higher standards or stricter performance criteria than are required by law. For example, many companies have house rules for cooking and reheating times and temperatures.

There is plenty of practicable advice on food safety available to you, whether in the form of free publications, advice from your local environmental health department or independent food safety adviser, or from one of the professional food safety bodies or trade associations listed in the Reference section.

4. How should we manage food safety?

How should we manage food safety?

Managers involved in food safety need to take account of microscopic details *and* to see the bigger picture of business management.

Parts 1 and 2 gave you an overview of the food industry and the impact of food-borne illness upon food businesses and their customers. Part 3 identified the main food hazards and legal requirements – all of which need to be managed. Part 4 outlines the management issues involved in making food safe to eat – how you might set things up and run them.

The approach in Part 4 is through the general context of business management, so that you can lock your particular areas of responsibility into the overall running of the operation. This should help you to see the bigger management picture that is sometimes lacking from some narrowly focussed food safety training programmes.

You might not be directly responsible for every aspect of food safety mentioned. You might not, for example, be directly responsible for cleaning, maintenance, pest control or training. Even so, you need to consider them and to be able to communicate effectively with the manager who does have the direct responsibility for such matters.

A book of this size can deal only with the principles involved. So, when you have finished reading each chapter, it is worth considering how to follow up the issues raised. One way is to seek additional information by using the sources listed on pages 415 to 424. The other way is to set aside time to ask yourself questions about the operation where you work.

For example, ask yourself: is this procedure already in place in my company and how does it contribute to the safety of the food we produce; if it is not in place and implemented, would it help to improve food safety standards? What do I, as the manager, need to do about each of the issues raised in the chapter? Which one thing could I do or change in my company that could improve food safety standards? How can I make it easier for staff to produce safe food? What do I need to discuss with senior colleagues to improve standards of food safety? How can I stay up to date and continue my own professional development?

By the end of the book, we hope that you will have a short list of points to put into action in your workplace.

Food and risk

Key points

Managing risk

The central importance of risk-based forms of food safety management.

The distinction between hazard and risk.

Criteria for risk management.

Prerequisites for HACCP and other systems of hazard analysis.

Hazard Analysis and Critical Control Point

Legal requirements for procedures based on the HACCP principles.

The seven principles of HACCP.

Preliminary activities to setting up a HACCP system.

Who should be involved in setting up a HACCP system.

Why the flow diagram and its verification are so important.

How to conduct a hazard analysis.

How to determine a critical control point.

The significance of critical limits and tolerances.

Why control criteria must be monitored.

Establishing procedures for appropriate corrective action, where it is required.

The importance of verifying the whole HACCP system.

Why record-keeping is essential.

Differences between full, or product-specific, HACCP and other similar systems.

Possible benefits and disadvantages.

Key words

Critical control point (CCP)
In HACCP, a stage in the process of handling food at which a food business can eliminate a hazard or minimise the risk from it.

Critical limit
In HACCP, the border between safe and unsafe.

Due diligence
A defence that every practicable measure was taken to avoid breaching food safety legislation.

HACCP principles
The seven steps to creating and maintaining a HACCP system.

Hazard (food)
A source of danger: anything microbiological, chemical or physical, or any condition or circumstance that could cause harm to the consumer.

Hazard analysis
A systematic process for identifying, assessing and controlling hazards and risks associated with food and drink; a simplified system of HACCP.

Hazard Analysis and Critical Control Point (HACCP)
A system for identifying, assessing and controlling hazards associated with food and drink.

Prerequisites
Essentials of good hygiene practice that must be established and carried out before any system of risk management, such as HACCP, can be carried out effectively.

Product recall
A procedure to locate contaminated products, or products that create any kind of risk to health, and to remove them from sale or use before they can harm consumers.

Risk
A measure, or scale, of the likelihood (or probability) that a hazard will occur, and the severity of the effect (or consequences) of the hazard.

Target level
In HACCP, a specified value for a control measure that eliminates a hazard or minimises the risk from it at a critical control point.

Tolerance
In HACCP, a specified variation from the target level which is acceptable for the safety of food.

Traceability
The ability to identify and track food through all the stages of production, processing and distribution.

Verification
In HACCP, the checking or reviewing of the entire HACCP system to ensure that it is operating as planned.

Managing risk

Until the mid 1970s the subject of risk was probably most closely associated with actuarial and insurance businesses. If the premiums for a life insurance policy were being assessed, it was easy for the lay person to see why a rock-climbing instructor who went parachuting every weekend might be considered to be at a higher risk of injury or death than an office worker who went swimming in a municipal pool once a week.

Since then carrying out risk assessments has gradually become central to most aspects of business life. As you may know from some of your other work responsibilities, there are legal requirements to carry out risk assessments for such activities as manual handling and the use of work equipment and for occupational health hazards and environmental impact. Even where there is no legal requirement to carry out a risk assessment for some aspect of work, it is often considered good practice to do so.

Risk and the food industry

In 1996, following a serious outbreak of *E. coli* O157 linked to meat in Lanarkshire, Scotland, Professor Hugh Pennington was asked to chair an expert group to look at ways of improving food safety. Among other things, the group recommended that food businesses that handled both cooked and raw meat should have procedures in place that followed the principles of Hazard Analysis and Critical Control Point (HACCP). This later became a legal requirement. Since 2006 most sectors of the food industry must base food safety procedures on the principles of HACCP.

Hazard and risk

How, then, does the subject of risk fit in with what we have already discussed about hazards in the food industry? In fact it is the other way around and hazards fit in to the much bigger topic of risk. But before we start to trip over terms, let's review and expand upon what we have outlined so far.

From listening to general conversation or consulting a dictionary, you'll know that the three words *hazard*, *risk* and *danger* are pretty much interchangeable in everyday speech to describe the possibility that something unpleasant, unwelcome or harmful may happen. When it comes to managing public health, we do, however, need to be more specific in our use of words.

Early in the book we described a hazard as being any thing, condition or circumstance that could cause harm to the consumer. Later on we talked about *food hazards* as being anything microbiological, chemical or physical that might cause harm to the consumer (and legal definitions are given on pages 150 and 151).

In comparison, we described risk as being a measure, or scale, of the likelihood (or probability) that a hazard will occur. (You may also come across the word *severity* in the context of risk analysis, where it is used to indicate the seriousness, gravity or magnitude of a hazard or its possible consequences.)

Part 3 looked in some detail at the typical hazards to be found in food businesses, so you may still wonder why we also need to consider the management of *risk*? The answer is that hazard management is just one small part of risk management because:

- hazards to human health exist at every stage of the food chain

- the risks from these hazards vary from food to food and from situation to situation

- some hazards cannot be eliminated, but we can influence the level of risk that they will occur and the damage they could cause – risk can be managed.

We spot hazards and estimate risks every day of our lives without too much difficulty. For instance, we know that moving motor vehicles are a hazard. We quickly evaluate the risk from crossing a road at a designated crossing point with traffic lights, or from dashing across a stretch of road when the traffic flow is light or when vehicles are travelling fast. Even so, the business use of the words *hazard* and *risk* can sometimes cause confusion, so we hope that our lighthearted illustrations (below) will help you to make the distinction more easily. As you can see, the hazard always remains a hazard. What changes is the *risk* from the hazard.

Making the distinction between hazard and risk

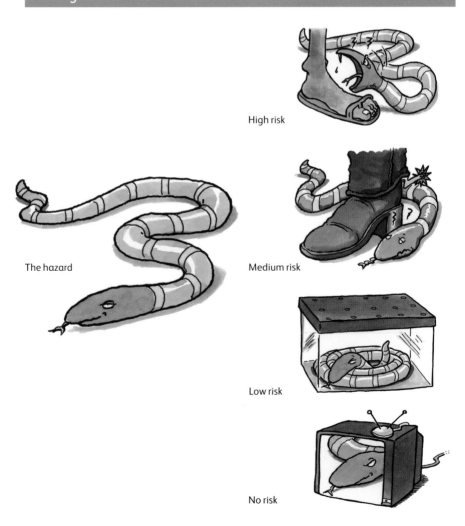

High risk

The hazard

Medium risk

Low risk

No risk

What do you need to manage?

Managing risk
The management of risk enables managers to concentrate efforts at the points that make the greatest difference to the safety of food.

It is worth emphasising and expanding what we have just said. There are hazards all around food at every stage from farm to fork. You can get rid of some of these hazards, but not all of them. What you can do, however, is to control the level of risk from hazards. In other words, you *can* manage risk.

Of course, you *should* manage risk because customers expect you to produce safe food, whether they think of this as being risk management or not. You *must* manage risk because the law expects you to create and maintain procedures that are based on HACCP principles (see page 182).

For all the reasons mentioned in Part 1, it makes sound economic sense to do so. What's more, the HACCP principles help you to set priorities that concentrate the company's food safety efforts (and budgets) at the points in your activities where they make the most significant difference.

How do you manage risk?

HACCP is not the only system of risk management available to help you to manage food safety, and some of the alternatives are mentioned on pages 197 to 200, but as HACCP principles are a legal requirement we concentrate on them for the rest of the book.

Prerequisites

There are certain prerequisites – things that must be in place first – for HACCP and other risk management system to work properly and bring real benefits. After all, there is no point in trying to produce safe food if the premises and equipment are not clean. Adequate prerequisites also help to reduce the number of critical control points (see page 188).

Prerequisites include such matters as:

- the proper design and construction of the food premises

- thorough cleaning and disinfection procedures

- effective staff training and supervision (for instance, of personal hygiene)

- effective pest control

- waste management

- and, possibly, proper policies and procedures, which we discuss on pages 372 to 376.

These topics are covered in some detail later in Part 4.

Criteria for risk management

The general features to be expected from a risk management system are outlined in the following eight paragraphs. If you are new to the management of food safety, you may prefer to read the rest of Part 4 before returning to these criteria later.

Proactive

Your system should be able to make you aware of a potential problem before it becomes a crisis of food safety or financial loss. There is little point in having such a warning system if it alerts you to a problem when it is too late to do something about it or to salvage anything from the situation.

Timely

When the advance warning system works properly, it lets you know in good time that something has indeed gone wrong, whether by a system of warning bells, flashing lights or a message from staff, so that in the worst scenario your crisis management plan (see pages 360 to 364) can swing into action.

Measurable

Intrinsic factors, such as pH, and extrinsic factors, such as time and temperature (see pages 60 to 66), can be measured accurately and relatively cheaply, but your management of risk also needs to take into account factors such as appropriate timing, frequency and standards – for instance, when, how often and how well a food handler washes his or her hands.

Controllable

Your system needs to be based on factors that are genuinely controllable. It is relatively easy to train staff to check time and temperature and to satisfy those who are interested in auditing your records, but it would be unwise to base any decisions about food safety on trying to control how often a food handler rubs his or her nose with the back of a hand.

Understandable

It is essential for all the staff involved to know why a system is in place; what benefits are expected to accrue from it; how much work, responsibility, inconvenience or time may be involved; what exactly staff have to do; why they have to do it; when they have to do it; and what standards are expected of them.

Visible

Your risk management system should be clear to all. If *Salmonella* species are a hazard, for example, your system should openly acknowledge this and explain what staff should do to eliminate the hazard or minimise the risks from it. There is no point in denying that there is a potential problem or in trying to deal with it secretly. Only if all risks are looked at openly and honestly and with accountability can there be any hope of managing them effectively. Your staff, your customers and clients, and the enforcement authorities all need to be confident that every possible step is being taken to ensure that the food your company produces is safe to eat.

Cost-effective

For your peace of mind it might be reassuring to take a microbiological and chemical sample of products every five minutes, but the company would soon go bankrupt (or suffocate under the pile of data). The whole point about risk management is to prioritise and to concentrate the efforts at the critical points in the food production process – where it makes the most significant difference. You'll read more about such critical points on pages 188 to 189.

Rectifiable

To be cost-effective, safe, and legal you need to build in the opportunity to put things right before the product has been eaten (and caused illness), or has to be discarded or completely reprocessed.

Retrievable

If all else fails, your traceability system should enable you to find and retrieve suspect products or ingredients.

Hazard Analysis and Critical Control Point

Hazard Analysis and Critical Control Point (HACCP) is a well-established system for managing risks in the food industry. It was initiated in the 1960s to give the burgeoning American space industry a system guaranteeing safe food for astronauts on space flights. By the 1990s the system was being adopted in many countries around the world, many of which have now incorporated it into legislation.

Since 2006 European Union legislation has required food businesses in member states to put in place and maintain permanent documented procedures based on the seven HACCP principles. It was, however, recognised that small food businesses in the catering and retail sectors might be able to fulfil their legal obligations simply with good hygiene practice and food safety prerequisites (see page 180). Various national approaches, or cut-down versions of the full HACCP system, have been developed for smaller businesses, including (in England) *Safer Food, Better Business*; (in Scotland) *CookSafe* and *RetailSafe*; and (in Northern Ireland) *Safe Catering*.

A manager at your level should have a thorough working knowledge of the HACCP principles and how they are applied, even if you currently work in a very small business that does not operate a full HACCP system. The knowledge will help you to identify hazards, evaluate risk, create critical control points and implement suitable controls.

What HACCP is

Hazard Analysis and Critical Control Point is a formal, systematic and scientifically based approach to making decisions about the procedures affecting the safety of food. In broad terms, it involves identifying the *particular* hazards that could affect the safety of a food ingredient or product at any stage in a *particular* food business, then determining the most significant points (the 'critical control points') at which effective controls can be made. The system has been described as being the use of the simplest possible controls at the points where the controls matter most.

The HACCP principles

The HACCP system consists of seven activities which are known as principles.

Principle 1	Carry out a hazard analysis.
Principle 2	Decide which points in the food production process are critical control points (CCPs).
Principle 3	Establish critical limits (tolerances or target levels).
Principle 4	Set up a system for monitoring the control of the CCPs.
Principle 5	Establish corrective action to be taken when the monitoring system shows that a CCP is out of control.
Principle 6	Create procedures to verify that the HACCP system is working as planned.
Principle 7	Set up a documentation system to record all of the above.

Implementing a HACCP system

Putting the seven principles of a HACCP system into place is fairly straightforward, although it may be time-consuming at the outset.

Preliminary tasks

As with many other tasks, there are some essential preparatory steps. These are to:

- create a HACCP team
- describe the products or ingredients in turn
- identify the intended use and the consumers of the product in question
- construct a flow diagram which accurately shows all the process steps involved
- verify the flow diagram in the workplace.

You may also come across mention of 'the terms of reference' of a HACCP plan. This simply means that you need to decide the 'boundaries' of your plan. These could be the sorts of hazard your HACCP plan will cover – normally these are microbiological, chemical and physical hazards, but may also include allergens – and whether the cut-off point is the sale of the product or its consumption.

Creating the team

The first part of the process is to assemble a team with sufficient expertise to formulate the HACCP plan. Where possible, the team should include representatives of all the company's job specialisms and levels of the staff hierarchy.

Other than in the smallest companies, it is typical to include food processing, engineering, maintenance, quality assurance, pest control and marketing staff as well as external consultants, where appointed, and, most importantly, a representative of the management team who is sufficiently senior to make decisions and drive the project forward. Some members of the team may be involved only for discussion of aspects of processes that are involved in their job description and others, such as cleaning and maintenance managers, might be co-opted from time to time, but there should always be a core membership.

It is, of course, impossible to have a large team in many small businesses. Even so, the principle of having more than one person applies, and consulting an external specialist is often advisable.

Training

While HACCP is not a difficult system to set up or operate, it is not something that can be undertaken at the drop of a hat.

Every member of the HACCP team should be aware of the principles of HACCP. At least one member must have undertaken a specific training course on the subject. Ideally this person should have at least a level 4 qualification (advanced or manager level) in food safety.

Describing the product

Before the HACCP team can carry out a hazard analysis (Principle 1), the team members need to describe each product used by the business. (If your company manufactures one product only, this activity will not be time-consuming. If your company produces or sells many product lines, you may be able to carry out a *generic* hazard analysis.) The description of the product needs to cover factors such as the ingredients, all the processing methods, the packaging and storage requirements, the shelf life and instructions for consumers about the intended use of the product.

Identifying the intended use and the consumers of the product

It is important to establish both the intended use of each product and its most likely consumers, as the same type of product could be used, or abused, in various ways before consumption, or could be eaten by people in the 'at risk group'.

Let us take a seafood pizza as an example. Its intended uses could involve being made in a restaurant for immediate service and consumption on the premises, or made in a factory and frozen for retail sale (at which point the consumer could ignore the storage or preparation instructions), or made in a take-away and delivered hot to the consumer's home. The consumer could be of almost any age and could also include a hospital patient who is in the 'at risk group'.

Constructing a flow diagram

Before the HACCP team can carry out a hazard analysis on any product, the team members need to draw up a flow diagram. Although this activity could seem superfluous at first glance, it is an essential preliminary activity that enables you to carry out later parts of the HACCP process.

The flow diagram needs to show *all* the steps in the process (process steps) for each product from the purchase of raw materials through all the stages of storage and preparation to the sale to the consumer. It is very important to include all the process steps involved, even if they seem to be very minor activities.

As an example, on the page opposite we show one company's flow diagram of how they make tea for themselves in the staff room. You may not agree with how they make the tea, but the point is to record all the process steps on the flow diagram.

Verifying the flow diagram in the workplace

The HACCP team needs to confirm the flow diagram on site, ideally by walking the route of the process steps and talking with the staff involved. No matter how well they have drawn up the flow diagram, they are almost bound to discover that something has been overlooked or that a process is actually carried out in a slightly different way to what was believed. It could simply be that the night shift legitimately does things in a slightly different way – they may need to store a product ready for cooking the next day, for example – and this needs to be taken into account.

Whatever the reason, it is essential for the flow diagram to represent what *actually* happens. After all, the discrepancy between what should and what does happen may point you in the direction of a food safety hazard!

Once all these preliminary activities have been carried out, you are ready to start putting the HACCP principles into practice – see page 188.

Simplified flow diagram of making a cup of tea

Purchase ingredients

Receive delivery

Store ingredients in refrigerator and dry goods store

Prepare tea

Pour water into kettle

Ensure that teapot and cups are clean

Boil the water 100°C/1sec

Rinse teapot with very hot water from the kettle

Collect teabags and milk from storage

Place teabags in teapot

Pour boiling water into teapot

Leave to infuse for three minutes

Pour milk into cup

Pour tea into cup

Drink the tea

Simplified flow diagram of making Black Forest gateau

Purchase and receive ingredients

Store in dry goods store and cold store

Cake base

Biscuit

Prepare biscuit mix eggs, water, cocoa

Mix for 6min

Place in baking tray

Bake 200°C/25min

Cool to <10°C/60min

Store temporarily

Cut to size and shape

Pastry

Prepare butter, sugar

Sieve flour into butter and sugar

Knead dough

Roll pastry to shape

Place pastry on baking tray and prick with fork

Bake 200°C/7min

Cool to <10°C/30min

Store temporarily

Cherry filling

Mix sugar, cinnamon, wheat starch and salt with cherry juice

Cook 100°C/>1 sec, then add cherries

Cool to <10°C/60min

Open can of cherries

Drain cherries

Add cherries

Cream

Whip, then sweeten

Add a cherry liqueur

Assemble gateau

Spread apricot jam on pastry

Put in cake ring

Put biscuit layer on top of jam

Spread cherry filling on biscuit layer

Add cream on top of cherry filling

Decorate with cream, cherries and icing sugar

Keep cool <6°C/1 day

Display for sale

Simplified flow diagram of a small retail outlet

Purchase and
receive goods

Store in appropriate
storage areas

Preparation
Bakery
Butcher

Display for sale

Sale

The principles in practice

HACCP involves identifying the food hazards, assessing the risks and establishing controls that stop the hazards, or reduce the risk from them to a minimum.

Principle 1 – Conduct a hazard analysis

In simple terms, a hazard analysis involves:

- describing all the hazards (microbiological, chemical, physical and allergenic) that could occur at *each* process step for each product in turn

- describing all the measures that could control the hazards identified – these preventive measures may already be in operation.

Needless to say, there are many food hazards and the HACCP team will probably identify a large number, so it is essential to distinguish between those hazards which have a risk of occurring in the particular food business and those for which the risk is negligible. Assessing the risk from a hazard (how likely it is to occur) is one of the most difficult parts of designing a HACCP system. You may sometimes see this activity described as being the process of deciding which hazards are the 'significant' ones. Factors that could be included in the assessment are the:

- history of hazards in the company that have led to food-borne illness

- history of the hazard in connection with particular foods

- possibility that the hazard will occur even if there is no history of its occurrence.

Factors such as the severity of the consequences of a hazard and the number of people involved could also be considered, but not in cases where the risk is judged to be negligible.

Principle 2 – Identify critical control points

This principle involves determining the critical control points (CCPs) – the points at which the controls matter most. Such 'points' could be a location, practice, procedure or process – those at which a *loss of control* would lead to an unacceptable risk to health, but at which the *exercise of control* over one or more factors could prevent a hazard altogether, or minimise the risk that it will occur.

It is important to recognise this dual nature of critical control points. Some CCPs can *prevent* a hazard occurring altogether – for example, a botulinum cook will kill spores as well as pathogenic micro-organisms. (These are often referred to as CCP 1s.) Other CCPs, such as the refrigerated storage of high-risk foods, can only minimise the risk that a hazard will occur. (These are known as CCP 2s.)

The correct identification of CCPs is at the heart of the HACCP system, but can be tricky at first. Codex Alimentarius, the international food safety organisation, has produced a decision tree to assist with this process. It is shown on page 395. If you are unaccustomed to using decision trees, you may find the simplified decision ladder (opposite) a little easier to use. By asking yourself the questions in turn, you should be able to decide reasonably quickly what is or is not a critical control point. Question 3 is often the one that will make you certain whether or not a process step is a critical control point.

It is important to note that CCPs are concerned only with food safety and do not cover quality or matters of good practice. There is no limit to the number of CCPs you identify, but the fewer there are, the easier it is to keep them under control in practice.

A simplified decision ladder to identify Critical Control Points (Principle 2)

Q1 **Is there a hazard present at this process step?**

No → Then this is not a CCP → STOP! Proceed to the next step for this product

Yes

Q2 **Is the risk from this hazard significant enough that I need to control the hazard?**

No → Then this is not a CCP → STOP! Proceed to the next step for this product

Yes

Q3 **Will a subsequent process step deal with the hazard (by eliminating it altogether or by reducing it to an acceptable level)?**

Yes → Then this is not a CCP → STOP! Proceed to the next step for this product

No

Q4 **Do existing procedures allow me to deal with the hazard at this step?**

Yes → This is a CCP

No → Not acceptable!

Proceed to Principle 3

Modify or change the process step or product

Principle 3 – Establish critical limits

Snapshot definitions
The target level is the ideal.
The critical limit shows what is safe or unsafe, while tolerances indicate the safe operating zone.

Critical limits are the 'borders' you establish between the safe and unsafe practices and processes affecting food, and they help to ensure that each CCP is genuinely under control. Control criteria must be established at each critical control point to ensure the safety of the product. For example, the pasteurization of milk requires a time and temperature combination of 72.2°C for 15 seconds. This control is a target level – a specified value for the control measure which has been shown to eliminate or minimise a hazard at a CCP.

As it is often impracticable for the target level to be achieved with one hundred per cent accuracy, there should also be a tolerance for each CCP – a specified variation from the target level which is acceptable in terms of food safety. For example, the time and temperature combination of 72.2°C for 15 seconds is the minimum target level for pasteurization required by law, so there would be no point in permitting a downward tolerance. As a consequence, most pasteurizing plants set themselves a slightly higher requirement than the legal target level – say, 73.2°C for 16 seconds, with a temperature tolerance of +/-1°C (in other words, +1°C or -1°C), coupled with a time tolerance of +/-1 second.

The HACCP plan should explain what staff should do if they discover that something is not meeting its target level or operating within its tolerance.

Apart from time and temperature, other common factors specified for target levels and tolerances are the pH, water activity, colour and texture. These target levels and tolerances should be written into the HACCP plan and form the basis on which the product's safety is founded.

Principle 4 – Establish a monitoring system for CCPs

This principle requires you to monitor (measure or observe) your control criteria – the critical limits you established under Principle 3. Effective monitoring of what happens each day enables you to take corrective action (Principle 5) where it is necessary.

As we say many times in this book, there is no point in having a system set up if you do not keep a close eye on how it is working. Once all the CCPs have been established and targets and tolerances have been defined, the HACCP team must establish a system of monitoring. Among other things, the monitoring system should:

■ provide a written record of criteria such as time, temperature and pH, to help you to manage food safety and to provide evidence of due diligence if required

■ detect any deviation from the target level or its tolerances

■ reveal in good time any deviation, so that corrective action can be taken to regain control

■ give you, as manager, a picture of how well your controls are really working and whether there are any trends that indicate that remedial action is required.

In many cases recording and monitoring can be carried out continuously and automatically in-line, but a member of staff with a watch and a calibrated thermometer can be just as effective.

Members of staff must be designated to be specifically responsible for the monitoring and should be trained effectively so that they are in no doubt as to what is required of them and when.

Principle 5 – Establish corrective action

If the monitoring indicates that there has been a deviation from the target level at a particular critical control point, then corrective action must be taken, ideally without wasting the product. Your HACCP plan should specify:

- what the action is that should be taken

- who is responsible for taking the action.

Principle 6 – Establish verification procedures

Verification is the process of confirming periodically that your whole HACCP system is functioning effectively and just as planned. The word verify comes from the Latin for *true*, and your verification should ensure that the whole system is indeed running true to form. This is not the same as monitoring, which confirms whether particular, individual controls are working every day as they should.

Verification should be carried out at regular intervals as a matter of course to confirm that the whole system is still operating as it should. It should also take place whenever there is a change in the process – for example, when new ingredients or equipment are introduced – or when there is a system failure or new hazards are identified. Any such changes should be taken account of and the HACCP plan amended if necessary.

Some of the verification activities that companies undertake include:

- contracting an independent scientific study to confirm that the critical limits, tolerances and so on are justified

- taking measurements to confirm the accuracy of the monitoring

- collecting samples and sending them for microbiological analysis

- interviewing staff about the way they monitor critical control points.

Principle 7 – Establish a system of documentation

Keeping proper HACCP records is an essential part of the system, although the type of records is not specified. In practice, you need to ensure that two sets of records are kept – those associated with the setting up of the system and those associated with monitoring the system.

The former are an intrinsic part of the HACCP system and are best described as permanent records which are updated as necessary following verification. The latter are records of the system as it operates every day. These should be kept for a period of time which at least exceeds the shelf life of the product, plus a safety margin to allow for customer misuse of the product. (In some cases, there are legal minimum periods specified for retaining documents.)

Examples of how HACCP works

Let us take two examples to see how HACCP can help in the production of safe food.

Making tea – the CCPs

For the first example, consider the flow diagram for making tea, which is shown on page 185. Work your way through the decision ladder: identify a hazard, then ask yourself whether it is a significant one. Then consider what kind of control measure could be in place. If there is no later point in the operation where you can use a control measure, then you are at a critical control point.

You will probably decide that there are three critical control points in this example – the receipt of goods, the boiling of the water and the storage of the milk in temperature-controlled conditions. At the second process step – 'Receive delivery' – the hazards could include microbiological ones affecting the milk. The milk could have been transported at the wrong temperature, or it could have exceeded its *use by* date. The relevant control measures would be to check the temperature of the milk on delivery and the *use by* date of the consignment.

In a later process step, when the water is 'boiled', any microbes present in the water could survive the heating unless the control measure is applied of heating the water to 100°C for at least one second. The temperature of the refrigerator where the milk is stored is also a CCP, because the milk will not have any temperature-controlled treatment that would eliminate microbiological hazards before it is consumed.

Cooked chicken – the HACCP system

For this example we shall assume that we are preparing a cooked chicken product and consider just one CCP. The numbers in brackets refer to the relevant HACCP principle.

One *hazard* (1) is the survival of micro-organisms such as *Salmonella* or *Campylobacter* species. The cooking stage is a critical control point (2). A control measure at this CCP is for the core temperature of the chicken to be raised to at least 75°C for at least two minutes.

The *critical limits* (3) need to show how far below 75°C is safe and how much less than two minutes is safe. The time and temperature need to be *monitored* (4) using, for instance, a probe thermometer and a clock. The reading should be recorded (7). If a reading is unsatisfactory, a *corrective measure* (5) is to increase the time or the heat input.

Vital information

The important thing is that any member of staff involved in monitoring the chicken should know:

- why a CCP is critical in ensuring the safety of the food

- what the time and temperature combination should be

- what the critical limit or tolerance is

- what needs to be done when something goes wrong

- what needs to be written down

- who needs to be told that there is a problem.

Other systems

HACCP in its original, full form is applied to one product, such as baked beans, through all its production stages. (This is why you may hear HACCP described as product-specific HACCP.) Of course, this type of approach is impracticable in some businesses, such as bakeries or restaurants, which have a multitude of food or menu items to assess. So modified systems, known as process-specific HACCP or generic HACCP, have been developed. Products based to a greater or lesser extent on the HACCP principles which are more suitable for these caterers and small retailers have also been developed. Some such approaches are listed on page 182.

Benefits and problems of HACCP

HACCP and allied systems have had a mixed reception from the British food industry and food safety enforcers over the years, so it is worth taking a moment to review some of the issues that generally arise.

Benefits

The traditional (pre-HACCP) method of checking the safety of food is end-product testing. This involves sending samples of a finished food item to a laboratory for microbiological tests, for instance. This is a slow and expensive process which deals only with selected hazards, is sometimes inaccurate and means 'wasting' the food samples.

Sometimes the process is perceived as being the responsibility of quality assurance specialists rather than as being an everyday matter of food safety practice involving all.

In contrast, HACCP and allied systems are generally viewed as being:

- proactive and rapid, because problems are dealt with as they occur rather than later when it may be too late

- inexpensive, because laboratory controls are minimised

- cost-effective, because there is less wastage due to inadequate processing

- all-embracing, because all significant hazards are considered, not just selected ones

- relevant to all personnel, not just quality assurance staff.

A difficult reputation for setting up the system

HACCP has sometimes been criticised for being 'difficult' so we mention some of these objections here.

It has to be acknowledged that some of the material produced on the subject is complicated and some people may have gained the false impression that they were obliged to buy bulky and costly ready-made packages in order to carry out the principles. Like any specialist subject and system, there are some special terms associated with HACCP and these may have been off-putting to some people when they first tried to get to grips with the subject. It is also true that two particular procedures may seem tricky at first. These are Principle 1 – the risk assessment ('significant' hazards) aspect of hazard analysis – and Principle 3 – the setting of critical limits.

Your business might benefit from some specialist advice about the application of these two principles in your workplace, but the rest can be carried out fairly easily. We assure you that HACCP systems are simple to operate by anyone with a knowledge of their particular food business. Indeed, if food managers have insufficient knowledge of their own food businesses to implement a simple hazard analysis, it is hard to understand how they could possibly run any aspect of that business!

Problems with implementation

HACCP is a good, well-proven system for ensuring safe food. However, the system is not a cure-all and there have been some difficulties in its implementation. Of course, it could be argued that the only thing in a food business which is worse than no HACCP-based procedures in place is a system that exists but does not work, so lulling everyone into a false sense of security. Some of the issues that regularly crop up are outlined below.

Prerequisites

There is no point in even trying to create and implement HACCP-based procedures (as required by law) unless the prerequisites mentioned on page 180 are in place. These systems will not function in a food business where the staff have no idea about hygiene, nothing is cleaned or disinfected and which is overrun with mice or cockroaches.

Communication

Good communication lies at the heart of the success of any system. It needs to involve everyone concerned with food production and sale or service in the individual food business, everyone in the food chain from producer to retailer, the consumer, the media, the legislator and the enforcer.

Some of the links in the necessary chain of communication may have broken in the past and everyone's priorities may not always have been the same. There may have been misunderstandings about individual expectations of each other or of where responsibilities lay, with the result that some of the people best placed to benefit from procedures based on the HACCP principles were themselves responsible for many of the problems encountered.

SMEs and non-manufacturing businesses

The majority of food businesses in Europe (some estimates put it as high as 95 per cent) are small-size or medium-size enterprises (SMEs) or non-manufacturing food businesses.

This can create a few challenges, especially in a one-person business, now that all food businesses are legally obliged to have permanent procedure in place that is based on the HACCP principles. How could such a business create a HACCP team, find all the necessary expertise in-house for setting the critical limits or maintaining food safety standards during busy periods?

Flexibility, pragmatism and some sound advice from outside specialists, such as environmental health practitioners, can go a long way, as they usually do in SMEs, and EHPs in England are reporting a good uptake of approaches such as *Safer Food, Better Business*.

Verification

There is a tendency to assume that once a system of HACCP-based procedure has been created, it can look after itself. This ignores the fact that the HACCP system requires verification. In neglecting to undertake these processes, a legal requirement is overlooked.

Training

It is worth emphasising that all the time, effort and money spent on establishing and implementing systems will be wasted if the employees in a food business are not properly trained. In most cases the job training need be only at a basic level, with the simplest of introductions to the fact that the company has to follow the principles of HACCP. Refresher training should happen on a regular basis.

Even the best of HACCP systems, or allied approaches, will not work if the food handlers ignore, or are ignorant about, the need to wash their hands, let alone the more complicated aspects of food hygiene.

The way forward?

The continuing high level of statistics for food-borne illnesses worldwide, even when there are occasional improvements in a part of the picture, provide ample evidence that traditional methods of food control were not always totally effective. Can HACCP or hazard analysis change this? Only time will tell, but for the food manager these systems should at the very least ensure fewer sleepless nights about food safety.

Making it easier for others

- Ensure that all food staff have a basic awareness of the importance of the hazard analysis or HACCP system operating in your workplace.

- Make sure that at least one member of your HACCP or hazard analysis team has been trained to at least an advanced level (level 4) in food safety.

- Bring in experts if necessary to complement the skills of the in-house members of your HACCP or hazard analysis team.

- Establish clear procedures for dealing with critical limits and tolerances.

- Train all the relevant staff in monitoring, recording and remedial action procedures.

- Encourage staff to report hazards to their manager or supervisor.

Management matters

HACCP-based procedures can help you to make essential activities clear to all and to improve your control, but, like any system, HACCP is only as good as the daily monitoring of control points and regular reviewing of the effectiveness of the system.

Ever since the principles of HACCP became compulsory for all food businesses, the system has experienced an evolution of its own. Some companies use it wisely as an umbrella concept, while others have adopted an over-cautious and usually unworkable approach, making every tiny process step a critical control point. A lot of the frustration of recent years comes from the misunderstanding that HACCP should cover *all* controls – including personal hygiene, cleaning and disinfection, maintenance schedules, pest control, waste disposal and so on. However, HACCP works much better if a company also concentrates on prerequisites.

Systems should work for you, not make you and your colleagues into slaves of the system. Whatever else you do, make sure you do not merely create an unbreakable paper chain, rather than providing a safe food chain. Used wisely, your food safety systems should enhance your company's operational efficiency and the safety and, possibly, the quality of the food you produce.

Measuring up to standards

As customers (or 'final consumers') of a shop or restaurant we are protected by standards of food safety that are laid down by law. Those standards are the *minimum* level of food safety that a food business must meet and it is common for large food companies to try to achieve standards that *exceed* the basic legal requirements.

One way to do this is through a food safety audit. This is a systematic way of measuring a company's performance against agreed, clearly defined criteria (or standards).

In simple terms, an audit checks that a company is indeed doing what it says it is doing. In some cases, it also checks that what it is doing is the most appropriate thing to be doing.

The criteria may be specific to a company – a supermarket may, for example, produce its own product specification for manufacturers that supply its own-brand foods. (The product specification provides details of the content, design, composition and intended use of the product to be supplied.) Often, however, the standards are agreed nationally or internationally and adopted by individual companies as their own standards.

Certifiable industry standards are created and overseen by retail industry associations, such as The British Retail Consortium (BRC), or by international standards bodies, such as the International Organization for Standardization (ISO) based in Switzerland.

In general these standards attempt to pull together all the aspects of HACCP and its prerequisite programmes so that they can be measured against common standards. The approaches involved differ slightly but the objective is always the same – to provide a guarantee of the quality, safety and consistency of a product.

Obviously this all eventually benefits the final consumer. It is also a valuable safeguard in business-to-business transactions, helping to protect the whole food chain, and it is a business benefit, providing a competitive advantage for companies that can demonstrate that they conform to a particular standard.

There is a difference between the methods used to check whether a company is complying with the law or with a standard. An inspection is usually carried out to ensure compliance with the *law*, while an audit is done to assess conformity with a particular *standard*.

Confusion often arises over the difference between inspecting and auditing and the terms are sometimes used interchangeably. It is, however, a mistake to do so. Although there are some similarities there are some essential differences between the two.

An inspection usually includes sampling, measurement, testing, analysis and interpretation. In many circumstances it involves an inspection of the *product* rather than the *process*.

It is common for an inspector to suggest ways of complying with a criterion that has not entirely been met. By contrast, it is usually inappropriate for an auditor to do so. Instead, it is for the company itself to suggest corrective actions and for the auditor to agree them.

If you are interested in such things, the derivations of the words may help you to remember the differences. The words *inspection* and *inspector* come from the Latin *inspicere* – meaning to look into or examine. The origin of the words *audit* and *auditor* is the Latin *audere* – meaning to hear. So, an inspection is 'looking' at what a food business is doing and an audit is 'listening' to how they are conforming to the standard they are trying to achieve.

Food safety inspections are usually carried out by environmental health practitioners, trading standards officers or veterinary surgeons. They may be employed by the company or may be independent.

Food companies may undertake food safety audits themselves on their own systems. This is called a *first party audit or* an *internal audit*.

A *second party audit*, also known as a *supplier audit* or a *customer audit*, is one carried out by an outside company or individual specialising in such work. A *third party audit* is carried out by an independent auditor on behalf of a third party – to comply, for example, with ISO or BRC criteria. This is also known as a *certification audit* (or, in the USA, a *registration audit*).

An audit consists of various stages which might include planning, pre-audit checks, an opening meeting, document checks, an on-site visit, a closing meeting and production of the audit report.

It is then up to the company to make any major changes or minor adjustments necessary to improve or maintain the level of performance identified during the audit.

It is common for large companies, such as supermarkets, to make rigorous checks on their suppliers. Safeguards offered by an audit include information about whether a supplier is adhering to a product specification, whether its systems conform to the agreed standard and whether the supplier is operating good manufacturing practice (GMP).

If the audit reveals non-conformity to the desired standards, the supplier then has an opportunity to take appropriate remedial action.

Despite the many benefits from food safety audits, there are some shortcomings to bear in mind. For example, you may need to establish whose standard a supplier conforms to where there is more than one client company, each with its own special requirements.

Many auditing or consultancy companies work to a national standard and are accredited as such, but it is also worth checking what their experience is and asking for a reference from one of their existing customers.

In the event of a court case, every defence of due diligence is taken on its merits. Even so, it is hard to imagine that a court would give much credence to a company's claim of diligence if it had not taken account of both the standard of the product delivered and the people who are supposed to safeguard that standard.

As with many issues of food safety, there is always the consideration of cost. Is the cost of an audit justified in its contribution to food safety, especially for a small company? This is for you to decide, but you do need to make some kind of checks on what your suppliers send you.

Mainly because of the cost, small businesses often rely on suppliers' product specifications and documentary evidence. This is satisfactory provided that the supplier can show evidence that it does indeed meet your standard. Take care to keep the product specification under review and occasionally have the product checked by a laboratory against the specification.

Small businesses often buy from wholesalers rather than direct from the manufacturer so they have to rely on the wholesalers' specifications. Ask each wholesaler to give you copies of its controls over its own suppliers, and incorporate the standard into your company's food safety policy and documentation.

If your company does not already work to certifiable standards and is considering doing so, it needs to take full account of the cost of implementing a chosen standard in comparison to both the benefit to food safety and to business opportunity and retention. Are certifiable standards the 'norm' in your sector of the food industry? Do you need to comply with those standards to secure profitable business-to-business contracts? Would the 'seal of

approval' to be gained from certification give your final consumers greater confidence in your products and help to create customer loyalty?

Could you cope with all the additional documentation these systems involve? Do you really need to exceed the minimum standards laid down by law? After all, it is the safety of food that is the main aim, not a paper chase of good intentions.

The following paragraphs give you a flavour of some of the certifiable standards you may encounter. Website addresses for the organisations involved are included on pages 415 to 419.

ISO 9001:2000 is a generic standard dealing with quality issues. Its main thrust deals with topics such as customer satisfaction, continuous improvement, management commitment, corrective actions, preventive actions and documented procedures. Although it does not directly deal with food safety it does provide a sound platform on which to build food safety management systems. This standard is achieved by successfully undergoing a third party, or certification, audit.

ISO 22000:2005 incorporates many of the ISO 9001:2000 requirements plus food safety requirements including HACCP and all the prerequisite programmes. It is a relatively straightforward system which can be implemented by even small businesses. As with most ISO standards it requires a certification audit to show conformity. Many people in the international food manufacturing sector believe that this will eventually become the universally accepted and adopted system.

There are five BRC global standards written for British supermarkets' own label products. One deals with food, one with food packaging and one with non-food consumer products. The other two standards deal with storage and distribution, and with foods that are not genetically modified. These are third-party audits that are carried out by companies accredited by the United Kingdom Accreditation Service (UKAS) (see page 419) or the equivalent body in other countries. The standards have gained reasonably wide international acceptance, even from companies who are not supplying to BRC members.

The International Food Standard (IFS) was originally drafted by an association of German supermarkets which, allegedly, did not like the word *British* in the BRC Global Standard and agreement on a joint standard with the BRC could not be reached.

The standard is a mixture of clauses like those from the BRC standard and from ISO 9001:2000, plus a rather complicated scoring system. It has become widely accepted in both Germany and France.

The National Sanitation Foundation (NSF) is an American organisation with a large number of standards covering, for example, food and water equipment, drinking water, food retailers and food manufacturers. Some of the standards are certification (registration) standards and some are supplier or second-party standards. In addition to acceptance throughout North and Central America, these standards have a wide international acceptance, especially for companies exporting to America.

As its name suggests, the American Institute of Baking (AIB) has its origins, and still has its core business, in the baking industry. It has, however, expanded into the wider food industry and food packaging industry with a number of standards that are both supplier and certification (registration) orientated. Outside America it appeals mainly to companies wishing to export to the USA.

Protecting food from contamination

Key points

Contamination and its consequences

The relationship between hazards and contamination.

Different types of contamination – direct, indirect and cross-contamination.

Sources of contamination.

The differences between vehicles of contamination and vectors.

Microbiological contamination

Problems in dealing with ubiquitous contaminants.

Common sources of microbiological contamination.

The role of high-risk foods.

Vehicles of microbiological contamination.

Typical sequences leading to contamination.

Breaking the chain of microbiological contamination.

Protecting food, preventing multiplication and destroying bacteria.

Chemical contamination

Common sources of chemical contamination.

Controls before and after food reaches food premises.

Physical contamination

Common sources of physical contamination.

Physical and spatial barriers.

Intrinsic and extrinsic contamination.

Controls within food premises.

Methods of detection.

Allergen contamination

Including allergens in the hazard analysis.

Ingredients and products with allergens that may not be obvious.

Labelling requirements.

Tailoring information for the people at risk.

Key words

Allergen
A substance, usually a protein, in food that make certain people ill, even though the food is harmless to others. The allergen prompts the immune system to create antibodies, as if the body were under attack.

Allergic reaction
Symptoms of illness caused by an allergy.

Allergy (to food)
An identifiable immunological response to food allergens that results in a variety of symptoms, some of which are life threatening.

Ambient temperature
The environmental temperature, often used to describe 'normal' room temperature.

Anaphylactic shock
An especially severe type of allergic reaction with possible life-threatening consequences.

Antibody
A blood protein which counteracts the harmful action of antigens ('foreign bodies' or substances) such as bacteria, pollen grains or allergens.

Carrier
A person who is infected by a pathogen and can pass it on to others, but who does not experience symptoms.

Contaminant
Any unwanted material, object or substance in food.

Contamination
The presence in food, or the process of transferring to food, any unwanted material, object or substance.

Critical control point
In HACCP, a stage in the process of handling food at which food businesses can exercise controls which could prevent a hazard or minimise the risk from it.

Critical limit
In HACCP, a border between what is safe and unsafe.

Cross-contamination
The transfer of a contaminant from one contaminated product, such as raw meat, to another previously uncontaminated product, such as a ready-to-eat food.

Direct contamination
The route directly from the source of contamination to a food.

Due diligence
A legal defence where it can be shown that all reasonable steps were taken to avoid committing a food safety offence.

Extrinsic contamination
Contamination from sources other than the raw food itself.

Faecal coliform
An organism, such as *E. coli*, the presence of which indicates faecal contamination.

Food intolerance
The body's failure to produce enough of the particular enzymes needed to break down and digest some types of proteins in a particular food. Unlike an allergy, a food intolerance does not involve the immune system.

Hazard
Anything, whether microbiological, chemical or physical, that might cause harm to the consumer.

Hazard analysis
The systematic identification of hazards and the estimation of the degree of risk from them.

High-risk food
A food that easily supports the multiplication of pathogenic micro-organisms.

Indirect contamination
Contamination due to the action of a vehicle of contamination or a vector.

Infective dose
The number of micro-organisms required to cause symptoms of a disease.

Inherent
Inbuilt.

Intrinsic contamination
Contamination associated with the food itself.

Microbiological flora
The microbial species normally found in a particular habitat, such as the intestine.

Multiplication
Microbial reproduction, such as by binary fission (bacteria) or budding (yeast).

Mycotoxin
A toxin produced by some fungi.

Potable
Safe to drink.

Product specification
A customer's detailed description of the content, design, composition and intended use of the product to be supplied.

Ready-to-eat
Food that is either eaten raw, or is not prepared or treated by the consumer (such as by cooking) in a way that would kill any pathogens present immediately before it is eaten.

Source of contamination
Where a contaminant has its origin.

Sterile
A condition in which all living organisms have been destroyed.

Supplier's certificate
A supplier's guarantee of the wholesomeness of a product based on criteria set by the purchasing company.

Vector
Animals, insects or birds serving as vehicles of contamination.

Vehicle of contamination
Any substance, object or living being that carries contamination from A to B. Vehicles are factors in indirect contamination.

Contamination and its consequences

What is the common feature in the way that microbiological, chemical and physical hazards move from being *potential* threats to food safety to become *actual* threats of harm? Contamination is the simple answer, as you can see in the diagram on page 45.

Tracing the origins and routes of that contamination might, however, seem far from simple at first and could appear rather like a whodunnit where the detective has justifiable suspicions about the identity of a culprit but forms only a confused picture of the way the culprit reached the victim. The good news is that careful detection over the years has revealed regular patterns of clues to contamination – clues that can place you in a good position to prevent harm to your customers.

Understanding contamination

The word contamination derives from the Latin verb *contaminare*, meaning to soil, spoil or make impure. In current usage contamination indicates the presence in food of, or the process of transferring to food, a contaminant – any unwanted material, object or substance. In short, contamination is anything in food that should not be there.

(The word contamination is sometimes muddled with the word contagion, which means the transmission of a disease from one person to another by direct contact, but the words are *not* interchangeable.)

Contamination can involve an unwanted ingredient that is fairly easy to see, such as a slug in a salad, or something invisible to the unaided human eye, such as a bacterial toxin. All types of contamination – whether easily visible or not and whether they cause illness, injury or just disgust – make food unfit for human consumption and it is illegal to sell contaminated products.

Allergens also need to be considered. They are a form of contamination if they are present in foods that are supposed to be allergen-free.

Starting out

It may help you to think of the process of contamination as a journey. The starting point is the source of contamination – where the contaminant has its origin. The destination is food, often high-risk food.

Routes

If the route of contamination is straight from the source to a food, we call the process direct contamination. Examples include raw food touching a high-risk product in a display cabinet, blood dripping onto a cooked ready-to-eat food in a refrigerator or a screw from overhead ducting falling into unpackaged food on a conveyor belt below.

More often – and this is especially so for microbiological contamination – contaminants are carried or transmitted by a vehicle of contamination. This is a substance, object or living thing which moves the contaminant away from its source and on to food. An example is when a knife used for cutting raw poultry is then used for slicing a quiche without cleaning and disinfecting the knife between tasks. The route taken is not straight from the source, so the process is called indirect contamination.

If the vehicle of contamination is an animal, insect or bird, then it is properly termed a vector. The difference between a vehicle of contamination and a vector is that a vector moves under its own power.

Another form of contamination is cross-contamination, which usually refers only to microbiological contamination. It occurs when a contaminant is moved from one contaminated product, such as raw meat, on to another as yet uncontaminated product, such as a ready-to-eat product like cold ham. Cross-contamination creates a high level of risk of illness when it involves products which do not receive any additional treatment, such as heating, immediately before they are consumed.

Managing contamination

To start to manage contamination you should be able to answer the following questions, which are similar to those suggested by HACCP.

- Which *contaminants* am I likely to encounter in my workplace?

- Where are the potential *sources* of contamination of foods in my workplace?

- What are the potential *routes* of contamination in food in my workplace?

It may help you at the outset to consider the hazards which are associated with:

- specific ingredients and products

- specific processes or forms of preparation

- specific types of food business.

Contaminants	Potential sources	Potential routes
Usually depend on specific:	**Usually depend on specific:**	**Usually depend on specific:**
– ingredients and products	– ingredients and products	– processes or forms of preparation
– processes or forms of preparation	– processes or forms of preparation.	– types of food business.
– types of food business.		

Examples of contaminants are given on the following two pages. Potential sources and routes are discussed later in this chapter.

You may find it helpful at this stage to refresh your memory about hazards and contamination by reviewing the flow chart on page 45 which shows the typical routes from contamination to illness. Bear in mind that microbiological hazards include multiplication and survival, as well as contamination.

Examples of contamination

Food	Contaminant
Plants	
Cereals	unwanted plant material insects and larvae insecticide residues fertiliser residues rodenticides rodent droppings moulds and other micro-organisms mycotoxins
Fruit (including concentrates and preserves) and **nuts**	insects and larvae twigs unwanted plant material insecticide residues wax coating on fruit skin fertiliser residues moulds and other micro-organisms mycotoxins
Herbs	soil unwanted plant material insects and larvae small stones insecticide residues fertiliser residues micro-organisms
Spices	soil insects and larvae insecticide residues rodenticides rodent droppings micro-organisms
Vegetables – cooked	insecticide residues fertiliser residues micro-organisms
Vegetables – prepared	insecticide residues fertiliser residues micro-organisms small stones unwanted plant material
Vegetables – raw	unwanted plant material insects and larvae small stones insecticide residues fertiliser residues micro-organisms

Food	Contaminant
Dairy	
Eggs	veterinary medicine residues micro-organisms chemicals
Pasteurized	veterinary medicine residues cleaning chemicals micro-organisms heavy metals
Raw milk and **dairy products made from raw or heat-treated milk**	veterinary medicine residues cleaning chemicals micro-organisms heavy metals
UHT or sterilized milk	veterinary medicine residues cleaning chemicals heavy metals
Meat	
Meat – cooked	veterinary medicine residues micro-organisms and toxins
Meat – raw	veterinary medicine residues parasites other micro-organisms faeces
Fish	
Fish – farmed	parasites other micro-organisms veterinary medicine residues
Fish – freshwater and marine	heavy metals toxins parasites bacteria mycotoxins
Shellfish and **crustaceans**	pieces of shell heavy metals toxins parasites viruses bacteria
Liquids	
Liquids other than water	chemicals toxins micro-organisms
Water	plant material soil pieces of metal, wood and rubbish small crustaceans naturally occurring chemicals chemicals added during purification micro-organisms, including bacteria, viruses and parasites faeces

Microbiological contamination

In a laboratory that breeds pure monocultures (colonies of identical individual micro-organisms) everyone has to take special precautions to prevent microbiological contamination and cross-contamination. Laboratory staff often have to work in sterile conditions where even the air flow is controlled. Sterile conditions are certainly not possible, or even necessary, in most food businesses. But we must never forget that micro-organisms are ubiquitous – they are here, there and everywhere – and that many of their sources, such as the air, humans, animals, food, water and the environment, are unavoidable.

Typical sources – the start of the problem

Microbial hazards
Microbes are a constant hazard to food.
Many foods are contaminated even before reaching your premises.

Food managers need a thorough understanding of potential microbial sources so that they can establish procedures to prevent contamination in line with HACCP principles. The following paragraphs consider the main sources in detail.

Raw food

There is no such thing as sterile food. You have to live with the fact that you manage potentially contaminated ingredients. Examples of typical pathogens that may be present in raw food are:

- *Campylobacter jejuni*
- *Clostridium perfringens*
- *Listeria monocytogenes*
- *Salmonella* species
- *Staphylococcus aureus*
- *Vibrio parahaemolyticus*
- *Yersinia enterocolitica.*

Critical controls?
Temperature control or chemical treatment, or temperature control and preservation methods may be a critical control point (CCP) for one of your products.

Raw food can contain between 100,000 and 200,000 bacteria per gram of food. These may not all be pathogens, but you still need procedures to keep bacteria at levels that will not accelerate spoilage or cause illness. To keep the bacterial population in its lag phase (see page 55) for as long as possible, you need to eliminate bacteria by:

- either heat or chemical treatment
- or by temperature control and preservation methods.

With the continual spread and evolution of micro-organisms (see pages 24 to 27) the work of food managers has not become any easier. Food preparation techniques that seemed to have produced safe food in the past may continually need to be reviewed and adjusted to combat emergent pathogens such as *E. coli* O157 and deal with concerns about residual veterinary drugs, such as antibiotics, in foods of animal origin.

Dust and soil

The soil is probably one of the most important sources of initial microbial contamination. Depending on the amount of vegetable mould and other organic substances that make up the earth, soil can contain billions of microbes in every gram. Anaerobic spore-formers, psychrotrophs and fungi are the main micro-organisms in soil, but there may also be faecal organisms from manure used to increase plant yields and from sewage that has contaminated groundwater and soil. Soil organisms can also get into food premises in dust particles.

Leafy vegetables, cereals, fruit and especially root vegetables are contaminated by soil particles. Washing is the first step to get rid of this microbiological and physical contamination.

Washing raw food
Washing can be a critical control point for many foods, especially for ones that are eaten raw.

Vegetables and fruit

Most soil and water organisms can contaminate plants, so the surfaces of fruit and vegetables can be loaded with micro-organisms.

The types of microbiological organism on land-grown fruit and vegetables are usually those of the soils in which these foods are grown. Faecal coliforms may survive in some manure that is spread on the soil and may contaminate plants. Lactic acid bacteria and some yeasts and moulds are spoilage organisms that persist on plant products because of their special adherence to surfaces.

Microbiological surface contamination is best controlled by washing raw fruit and vegetables thoroughly, whether they are to be heat-treated or eaten raw.

High-risk foods

Certain foods support microbiological multiplication more easily than others, so they create a greater risk of causing food-borne illness than other types of product. These high-risk foods are characterised by all, or most, of the following:

- high levels of protein

- intrinsic factors (such as pH and a_w) that easily support multiplication

- strict temperature control required to keep the food wholesome and safe to eat

- usually intended for immediate consumption without further heat treatment or any preservation method that would destroy or control the growth of micro-organisms.

If we consider two different foods, such as an apple and minced meat, we know that both products have a reasonable amount of moisture. However, the minced meat has a higher level of protein, and this makes the crucial difference to whether a food is a high-risk one or not. All foods with high levels of protein (especially protein of animal origin) need to be handled, stored and processed with special care because they easily support microbiological multiplication.

Ready-to-eat high-risk foods pose special problems for food safety because they are consumed without treatment immediately before eating that would destroy micro-organisms acquired by re-contamination or cross-contamination. Products that come under this category include processed foods, such as cooked meat that is eaten cold, and raw and ready-to-eat products, such as minced meat served as beef tartare.

Rice and cereals

The microbiological flora of wheat, rye, corn, rice and related products are also heavily influenced by the soil in which they were grown. As these foods are often stored for quite long periods, the condition of their storage environments can make them vulnerable to further contamination as well as to microbial multiplication. Usually the level of micro-organisms is fairly low as the relatively low water activity (a_w) of these foods inhibits the growth of micro-organisms. Aerobic spore-formers such as *Bacillus cereus* and moulds such as *Claviceps purpurea* and *Aspergillus* species are the main organisms.

Herbs and spices

Although spices do not suffer from microbiological spoilage as much as some other products, all spices and herbs may be contaminated by soil organisms such as those of the *Clostridium* genus. These products are not always cleaned thoroughly after harvesting, so spores can easily survive in *dried* herbs and can germinate under favourable conditions when they are added to protein-rich foods.

Water

This is one of the most overlooked sources of food-borne pathogens and is often neglected in a hazard analysis. Many pathogenic organisms can be transmitted by water. Typical ones include:

- *Campylobacter jejuni*
- *Cryptosporidium parvum*
- *Entamoeba histolytica*
- *Escherichia coli*
- *Giardia lamblia*
- Hepatitis A
- Norovirus
- Rotaviruses
- *Salmonella* species
- *Shigella* species
- *Vibrio cholerae*
- *Vibrio parahaemolyticus*.

Most of these water-borne pathogens are strong survivors in the environment and are highly infectious even in small numbers.

Use of water

Bear in mind how many different tasks water is used for in a food business. For example, it may be used as an ingredient, for personal hygiene (for instance, washing hands), cleaning food and for cleaning food-handling equipment and food-contact surfaces. There are many methods for controlling pathogenic micro-organisms in potable water, including filtering, ultraviolet irradiation, addition of biocides and temperature control.

Hazard analysis
Water supplies must
not be overlooked
during hazard
analyses.

Many food handlers in Britain are convinced that water must be safe if it comes out of a tap. This is largely true, but even controlled supplies of potable water are occasionally contaminated at source or may become contaminated by leaking sewage pipes or seepage from slurry. Potable water can also become contaminated by using unsuitable construction materials and water fittings which may not only affect the taste, odour or chemical composition of the water, but may also support the growth of micro-organisms such as fungi.

In drought years water companies have sometimes drawn water from a source such as a bore hole that has been contaminated by *Cryptosporidium parvum*. Additional problems may be caused by water drawn from storage tanks which have not been maintained properly or covered adequately, so that bird faeces and air-borne contaminants have got into the water.

Outdoor activities, such as walking, camping and watersports, may bring food handlers into contact with contaminated water in their leisure time and they need to be made aware of water-borne organisms, such as the parasites *Giardia lamblia* (see page 100 to 101) and *Leptospira interrogans* (which causes leptospirosis – Weil's disease), that could affect food safety.

Humans

Everyone is a universe of living micro-organisms. Most relationships between humans and our microbiological guests are simply a quiet co-existence, and some micro-organisms, such as our intestinal microbiological flora, are essential for our well-being. As we know, however, other micro-organisms are pathogenic and can cause diseases when present in critical numbers – the infective dose. Typical micro-organisms associated with, and distributed by, humans are:

■ *Escherichia coli*

■ Hepatitis A

■ Norovirus

■ *Salmonella* species

■ *Shigella* species

■ *Staphylococcus aureus*.

Some pathogens are carried by humans who do not themselves experience symptoms of illness but who nonetheless pass on the pathogen to others. Even healthy people carry bacteria like *Staphylococcus aureus* and *E. coli* and may spread them if special precautions are not in place.

When people who work with food are infected with certain bacteria, or are carriers of certain pathogens, such as *Salmonella* species, the law prohibits them from working with uncovered food and there are strict rules governing when they may return to working with food (see pages 275 to 277).

There needs to be a 'hygiene barrier' between food and food handlers, so you must establish and supervise rules covering such issues as personal hygiene, protective clothing, the washing of hands and general good hygiene practice – see pages 271 to 278. There also need to be physical barriers, such as sneeze guards in shops, to protect food from customers – see page 235.

Animals

Animals, insects and birds may carry and spread a wide range of pathogenic micro-organisms, which tend to be specific to the type of animal, and include:

- *Brucella* species
- *Campylobacter jejuni*
- *Clostridium perfringens*
- *Cryptosporidium parvum*
- *Escherichia coli* O157
- *Giardia lamblia*
- *Mycobacterium tuberculosis*
- parasites such as tapeworms
- *Salmonella* species
- *Toxoplasma gondii*.

Beloved family pets can also create food safety problems if they are allowed into food areas. This is illegal. Managers of small family businesses often need to take a firm line on pets and to make sure that all family members and staff wash their hands after handling pets.

Food can be contaminated in the abattoir by direct contact between an uncontaminated and contaminated animal or carcass. Raw milk may contain some of the udder flora, while the intestinal flora of slaughtered animals may contaminate the meat in the abattoir, the hands of the staff, the storage containers and the general abattoir environment.

Pests and domestic pets can also carry pathogens and cause contamination, and it is illegal to allow either pests or pets into food areas. This may not be possible at the point of primary production of foodstuffs of animal origin, so there is a high risk of contamination from animals if proper hygiene procedures are not in place.

Refuse

Prerequisite
Effective waste management is a prerequisite for safe food.

Rubbish and waste, especially when it contains food waste, is also a source of contamination and at an ambient temperature is obviously an ideal growth medium for bacteria. The contamination caused can be either *direct*, by spilling or contact, or *indirect* via the hands of food handlers. In addition, food waste can attract pests which in turn can cause contamination. Bins need to be emptied frequently and you should consider how much encouragement and supervision staff will need to do so – a small bin in a food preparation area, for example, needs to be emptied more frequently than a large one.

Vehicles of contamination – a detective's task

Cross-contamination occurs when microbes (or other contaminants) from one food, usually a raw one, are transferred to another food, usually a cooked or ready-to-eat one. This may happen directly. One example is when pathogens are transferred from the viscera (such as the gut) and the hides of one animal carcass in a slaughterhouse directly to another if the carcasses touch each other. Another example is when frozen raw meat left to thaw in a multi-purpose refrigerator drips onto cooked meat stored below it.

Most cross-contamination is, however, caused by vehicles or vectors, of which the most common are:

- hands

- hand-contact surfaces, including utensils and handles (of cupboards, refrigerators and so on)

- food-contact surfaces, including work surfaces and cutting boards; storage containers; crockery; mixers, cooking pans and other cooking equipment; knives and other utensils

- wiping cloths, dishcloths and other cleaning equipment

- clothing

- pests.

The routes, vehicles and vectors involved may be as difficult to track down as a criminal in a detective novel, because many of the vehicles and vectors are long gone, thrown away, or cleaned and disinfected once the 'crime' (contamination) is discovered. But an understanding of the principles involved will help you to investigate so that you can prevent a recurrence. Although we cannot *see* the routes that micro-organisms take, it needs only a little imagination to sketch a map of the way they travelled.

Hands

Personal hygiene
Hand washing is a prerequisite to safe food production.

We use our hands to manipulate various food utensils, operate food equipment and to shape, divide and arrange food. Without deliberation, we also scratch our heads, either to relieve an itch or to help us to think. Every hand movement we make can imitate a pick-up truck – our hands load up with micro-organisms, dump off some at the next stop and collect others, then drop off more as we continue our rounds. Small wonder, then, that managers need to emphasise the importance of washing hands properly (see pages 272 to 274) and supervise it as far as they can.

Hand-contact surfaces

These are the surfaces that are often forgotten when it comes to cleaning and disinfecting. As a result, an inconspicuous refrigerator or tap handle can develop into a contamination storage area, just waiting for the next pick-up truck (our hands) to load up and move the microbes on to the next food or surface.

Food-contact surfaces

All foods, especially raw ones, can leave micro-organisms on any surface they touch. They can also easily pick up micro-organisms when a surface has not been cleaned and disinfected between processes. This is why food managers must emphasise both the importance of cleaning and disinfecting food-contact surfaces regularly (see pages 298 to 305), *and* the importance of cleaning and disinfecting surfaces between use for different products, for different batches of a product or for raw then cooked food.

Food equipment
The construction and ability to clean food-contact surfaces should be included in your hazard analyses.

Colour-coded equipment and utensils may help staff to separate types of use, but effective cleaning procedures are still essential. Cleaning and maintenance should be carried out in a way that avoids contaminating ingredients, products or packaging materials and also ensures that equipment is microbiologically safe before it is used again.

The equipment you choose for food preparation and storage should be designed to minimise cross-contamination (see pages 242 to 249). If food processing equipment were to have 'dead ends' that were difficult to clean, microbiological flora could build up on the food residue and cross-contaminate the product.

Key questions to ask yourself when evaluating the risk posed by equipment include:

- can effective cleaning be carried out?
- can the equipment and its construction provide additional hazards?

Wiping cloths, other cleaning equipment and utensils

Cloths and other items of cleaning equipment are unobtrusive and can be easy to forget when it comes to food safety.

A dishcloth or wiping cloth, or even a tea towel, could be used for almost any task: to wipe down a work table, to absorb liquid from a food preparation surface, to remove dirt and grease from a piece of equipment and to dry a food handler's hands.

You might object that *your* staff would never use a cloth in a sequence such as this one. But can you be certain that they *always* use a fresh cloth when they need to use one – and if not, how do they know about its true recent past? The same question can be posed for other utensils and equipment that come into contact with different products during the course of the day. Colour coding is one way to help to restrict the use of these items to a certain area, process or product.

Clothing

You need to ensure that the people who work with food understand that protective clothing is not there to protect their own clothes from becoming soiled but to protect the food from contamination from human sources.

Even the most suitable protective clothing can become a contamination vehicle if it is not properly cleaned or is worn outside food areas. Protective clothing should be restricted to the food production or preparation and storage areas only, and should *not* be worn outside the workplace or during breaks.

If personal clothing, such as T-shirts or sweatshirts, are worn – by serving staff, for example – their use should also be restricted to the workplace. Of course, it may be necessary to put on a different protective garment, such as an apron, when starting a different task or when a garment becomes soiled.

Pests

Rodents, insects and birds carry a wide range of pathogenic micro-organisms as well as creating a physical hazard and should be kept out of food premises at every stage. An effective pest management system is essential (see pages 310 to 322). Pests can load and unload pathogens everywhere, just as human hands can.

Supervision
Unobtrusive supervision and management are essential to maintain the safety of food. Hand washing, the use of cloths and appropriate use of protective clothing all need to be reinforced regularly so that sloppy habits do not develop.

The microbiological chain

There is usually a *sequence* of events, not just one activity, that leads to food-borne illness and it is common to describe that sequence as a *chain of contamination* or a *microbiological chain*. A typical chain of events is shown in the top diagram on page 216. To make better sense of it, consider this example of actions that are likely to lead to *Salmonella* food poisoning. The numbers correspond with those in the diagram.

Example

1 Raw meat contaminated with *Salmonella* is cut up on a chopping board with a cook's knife.

2 Immediately after, a hot roast joint of meat is placed on the same chopping board and cut in half (to speed up the cooling time) with the same cook's knife.

3 The roast meat is left on the board to cool before it is stored in a refrigerator.

4 Later, the cold roast meat is sliced then very briefly reheated just before it is served.

5 Someone eats the food and becomes ill with *Salmonella* food poisoning.

Breaking the links in the chain

The bottom diagram on page 216 indicates how the chain can be broken.

Contamination

As microbiological contamination is an ordinary part of the natural world, the only way to break this part of the chain is to *protect* food from contamination.

Multiplication

Microbiological multiplication can occur rapidly. For example, bacteria can multiply when:

■ high-risk food is left at an ambient temperature

■ hot food is cooled over a prolonged period

■ hot food is kept hot (or warm) at a temperature below 63°C

■ food is not preserved adequately (for instance, if the pH level or the salt concentration is inappropriate)

■ there is no, or little, microbial competition.

The way to break this part of the chain is to *prevent* multiplication.

Survival

Microbiological *survival* occurs whenever a process that is designed to kill pathogens is not carried out in the right way. This could occur, for example, as a result of:

■ the wrong time and temperature combination during cooking or reheating

■ the wrong combination of factors (such as a_w and pH) during preservation.

The way to break this part of the chain is to *destroy* microbes in the food.

The chain of microbiological contamination

| 1 | 2 | 3 | 4 | 5 |

contamination **multiplication** survival **ILLNESS**

The first link in the chain forms between actions 1 and 2: contamination occurs. The second link in the chain is between actions 2 and 3: a suitable combination of time and temperature allows microbes to multiply. The third link in the chain occurs between actions 3 and 4: the temperature does not become hot enough for long enough to destroy the microbes, so they survive in sufficient numbers to cause a food-borne illness. The three links in the chain – contamination, multiplication and survival – lead to illness.

Where to break the chain

contamination **multiplication** survival

protect prevent destroy **NO ILLNESS**

There are three points at which you can break the microbiological chain – by protecting food from contamination, preventing microbiological multiplication or destroying microbes.

Protect, prevent, destroy

To control microbiological hazards you must ensure that all your food safety systems work in line with the principle of *protect, prevent, destroy*. Staff who work with food need to understand why the principle works and what they must do to follow it.

The chances of preventing a food-borne illness become more and more limited the longer the microbiological chain becomes. Once food has been contaminated, depending on the type of pathogen present, the level of contamination may still be below the critical level that causes illness. This may be the case with organisms like *Salmonella*, *Staphylococcus aureus* and *Clostridium perfringens* which cause problems only when they are present in high numbers. However, many organisms that cause food-borne infection, such as *Campylobacter* or *Shigella*, can cause harm even in very small numbers.

As there are only limited opportunities for destroying such organisms and the techniques, such as cooking, may not be suitable for every product, the most important word to remember is *protect*. If you limit the opportunities for contamination, you improve the chances of preventing multiplication and destroying those bacteria that survive.

Protection

Protection generally involves:

- removing the sources of contamination

- putting barriers between sources and vehicles of contamination

- putting barriers between sources and products.

Removing sources

Actions include:

- effective pest control

- thorough cleaning and disinfection

- effective personal hygiene and habits

- proper waste management.

Creating barriers

These can be:

- physical, such as covering food before storing it

- spatial, such as separating raw food from cooked food and ready-to-eat food.

Separation

Separation is one of the simplest but most effective ways of protecting food against microbial and other forms of contamination. It includes:

- separating raw food from cooked food and ready-to-eat food

- separating preparation areas for dirty products and processes from preparation areas for clean products and processes (see page 244)

- providing different sets of utensils and equipment for the preparation of different products

- providing separate cleaning facilities, such as basins for hand washing only and sinks for cleaning foods and washing up.

Protection checklist
Premises and equipment

- Make sure that work areas are properly designed and constructed.

- Choose equipment made from appropriate materials.

- Choose equipment that can be cleaned and, if appropriate, disinfected properly.

- Ban the use of dirty or damaged equipment.

- Consider providing colour-coded utensils or colour coding for food preparation and storage areas.

- Schedule regular maintenance and servicing of equipment to prevent the build-up of microbial colonies.

- Consider buying disposable wiping cloths.

- Try implementing the principle of separation by *time* if space constraints prevent physical separation. As an example, if food rooms are too small to have separate areas for the preparation of raw and cooked foods, try organising timetables and workflows so that raw food is dealt with before, say, 9.30 in the morning and cooked food is prepared after this time when all equipment, utensils and surfaces have been thoroughly cleaned and disinfected. The principles of time separation can be effective in managing the use of production lines for different products.

Cleaning and disinfection

- Instigate effective cleaning and disinfection procedures, including cleaning schedules and a clean-as-you-go policy (see pages 305 to 306).

Poorly constructed and inadequately cleaned premises can easily contaminate and recontaminate food. The mould in this bakery makes the premises unsafe for food production.

- Monitor the results of cleaning and implement remedial steps if necessary.

- Ensure that there is an efficient system for waste disposal.

Pests

- Deny pests access to the premises and shelter within or around them.

- Store food in pest-proof containers.

- Implement a pest management programme (see pages 319 to 323).

Food

- Keep food covered.

- Separate raw and cooked products during transport, storage and display.

- Separate raw and ready-to-eat products.

- Use separate, clean and disinfected utensils, such as boards and knives, when preparing raw and cooked products.

Food handlers

- Ensure the highest possible standards of personal hygiene.

- Ensure that staff wear appropriate protective clothing.

- Follow recommended good practice for your industry sector.

- Work with other managers, such as production managers, chefs, food and beverage managers and sales managers, to develop ways to minimise hand contact with food.

Prevention and destruction

Although protection against contamination is the crucial first part of the food safety armoury, the prevention of multiplication and the destruction of micro-organisms are also important alternative ways to break the microbiological chain.

Aspects of prevention and destruction are discussed throughout the rest of Part 4 and in particular in 'Controlling time and temperature' (see pages 326 to 332) and 'Clean enough for food' (see pages 295 to 309).

Making it easier for others

A good and enjoyable way to help food handlers to understand the typical routes and consequences of microbiological contamination is to give them an informal case study. They could, for example, trace how *Salmonella* contaminated a salad in a salad bar offering salads made from raw and cooked vegetables, fruits, rice and mixed foods, as well as cold sauces such as mayonnaise.

- Establish clear and simple rules that staff can follow to protect food from microbiological contamination, prevent multiplication and destroy micro-organisms.

- Ensure that senior staff set an excellent example.

- Provide suitable training.

- Reinforce the rules covering personal hygiene and habits.

- Supervise food handlers.

- Monitor hygiene practices and adjust rules and procedures if necessary.

Chemical contamination

Chemical hazards are wide-ranging. They include naturally occurring chemicals, which are inherent in the product; mycotoxins produced by some fungi; and introduced chemicals such as residues of veterinary drugs, pesticides, food additives used in unsafe quantities, contact reactions from inappropriate food containers and the careless use of cleaning products. Chemical contamination can be *direct* or *indirect* and the route of contamination can start inside or outside food premises.

Routes of contamination

The careless use or storage of pesticides on a farm could directly contaminate cereals, vegetables or fruit, or could cause indirect contamination by contaminating containers or packaging used for food. In food preparation areas the use of the wrong concentration of a cleaning product or the careless application of a machine lubricant could cause it to splash or drip directly onto food.

Contamination risks increase if chemicals are stored in containers that are not purpose-made because they may leak. If they are kept in unmarked containers, such as soft drinks bottles, the contents may be mistaken for food, with potentially fatal consequences. Purpose-made containers that have been recycled for food storage without full decontamination have also caused food poisoning outbreaks.

Poisoning can occur from contact reactions when food touches inappropriate materials – for example, zinc poisoning from galvanised containers – or as a result of the leaching or migration of toxic substances into food – for example, acid foods carried through pipes or containers made from metals such as antimony, copper, cadmium or lead.

Detection

Specialist checks Arranging regular audits and random tests could help to detect chemical contamination and residues.

Although all food deliveries should be checked for contamination, detecting chemical contaminants is complicated or even impossible because many residues, such as heavy metals, can be detected only by laboratory methods.

This is a point at which your controls may be obliged to depend upon those of your supplier, whose supplier's certificate should guarantee that your product specification has been fulfilled to the letter. Even so, you should consider arranging regular audits (see pages 197 to 200) and random tests. Whenever you undertake a hazard analysis, include possible chemical *residues*, as well as potential contamination on your premises.

Transport

Vulnerable movement Supplies could travel on several vehicles, so you need documented assurances about food safety during transport.

Delivery vehicles used for transporting food should ideally be used only for food. Other products transported with food or carried on the vehicle during a previous delivery can contaminate food by spilling or as a result of evaporation. The legal requirements (see page 165) for the separation and protection of foodstuffs must be followed. As consignments of goods may pass through the hands of several transport companies and be loaded on and off several vehicles before the products reach your premises, you need written assurances from your immediate supplier about the steps taken to protect food from contamination during transport.

Controls

As you can see, although some measures can be controlled on your premises, many others that you need to put in place are indirect or at arm's length. You must ensure that you do establish appropriate systems of control.

Before receipt

- Create a product specification.

- Obtain a supplier's certificate.

- Arrange product sampling.

Before use

- Ensure that a supervisor or manager has checked that the chemical is of the right kind and strength and that it is correctly labelled.

- Ensure that staff check the purpose and function of chemicals.

- Establish and supervise the rules for the dosing and dilution of chemicals.

Storage and transport

- Label all chemical containers if substances must be decanted from the manufacturer's containers.

- Use only purpose-designed containers.

- Store chemicals in lockable, labelled storage areas away from food and food equipment.

- Inspect and control stocks regularly.

In general

- Use only non-toxic food-grade substances (such as food-safe machinery oil) where there is a risk of direct contact with a product.

- Keep an inventory of all chemicals used and stored on the premises.

- Consider documenting the *application* of chemicals.

- Train and supervise staff in the safe use of chemicals.

Making it easier for others

- Outline the measures that your company puts in place to protect food from contamination that could occur outside the premises.

- Explain the importance of using cleaning and other chemicals on the premises in a way that does not cause contamination.

- Ensure that cleaning, maintenance and relevant food-handling staff have appropriate training and refresher training in dealing with chemicals.

- Remind staff of personal safety when using chemicals.

Physical contamination

Is it better to concentrate on *preventing* physical contamination in the first place or to accept that it will happen and put your main effort into *detecting* it when it does? The only correct answer is that you must do both.

Physical contaminants, such as pieces of glass or splinters of wood, must be prevented at all costs. Not only can they cause serious injury, but they are also extremely difficult to detect. Other forms of physical contamination – such as stones, pits and soil in raw foods including fruit and grain,– may not be completely preventable and must be detected instead. The problem is that detection is never one hundred per cent effective, so it should be seen as the last line of defence, never a main strategy.

Sources

As we have seen in Part 3, intrinsic physical contaminants are part of the original raw food and include leaves, twigs, scales and bones. They may be present in deliveries of raw ingredients and may remain during production or preparation.

Extrinsic contaminants can enter the food flow at any stage. Some may be a severe hazard, causing major injury or even death. Others may be unpleasant but physically harmless. Even so, a food business can be prosecuted for the presence of any contaminant in food simply because the product is not of the nature, quality or substance expected by the consumer (see page 159).

Typical contaminants and their sources

Contaminants	Likely source
Wood	Wooden pallets, packing cases, wooden surfaces, wooden utensils
Bolts, nuts, wire, staples, swarf	Equipment, machinery, utensils, blades, maintenance staff, packaging materials
Cardboard, string, plastic, rubber bands, tape	Packaging materials, staff
Insects, larvae, eggs, pupae	Raw products and ingredients or through infestation of food premises
Animals, fur/hair, feathers, droppings	Raw products and ingredients or through infestation of food premises
Glass	Lights, windows, auxiliary items (such as stop watches and manometers), bottles, jewellery (especially watches)
Fragments of paint, rust, enamel	Equipment and premises
Personal items: hair, fingernails, pieces of jewellery, hair clips, plasters, cigarette ends	Staff, visitors

Prevention

Every food business can use various forms of barrier to prevent physical contamination and cross-contamination. These barriers may be:

- physical – for example, the use of lids on containers of food in storage or the use of filters and sieves during food preparation

- spatial – for example, the separation of 'clean' and 'unclean' materials and processes.

Some barriers are obvious, but others may be identified only through a hazard analysis of products, processes and management controls such as waste disposal and pest control.

Contamination that comes from food

It is important to sort out intrinsic contaminants at an early stage because processing and preparation can reduce the size of a contaminant and disguise it, making it more difficult to detect and remove the contaminant at a later stage.

It may not be a pleasant thought, but it is a sad fact that primary producers often have to deal with a high level of organic material that counts as physical contaminants, such as insects and little vertebrates that are picked up by harvesting machines. Washing and floating loose items such as fruit and vegetables can be a first step to sorting out these 'foreign bodies'.

Agreeing responsibility and standards

The key to ensuring that intrinsic contaminants are removed lies in establishing and implementing effective controls, either with your supplier, or within your own premises, or both.

Sometimes the main responsibility is with the supplier. However, your company still needs to check the condition of food on delivery and to keep an eye open for problems during processing or preparation.

Wherever the responsibility lies, it needs to be clearly spelled out. Bear in mind that while external measures may save you time and effort, in-house checks, where they are practicable, may give you greater confidence and control over standards.

Specifying

Management control
Product specifications can provide a clear standard for suppliers to aim for and a clear statement of agreed tolerances.

When you contract with a supplier to provide a product or ingredient you need to state as precisely as possible in the product specification the nature, type and quality of the product you require. This should protect you from having to accept inferior or unsafe goods.

If you expect suppliers to provide you with food from which some parts (such as bone or leaves) have been removed, this must be clearly set out in your product specification. You also need to agree with the supplier on the exact controls and standards to be applied. Should salad vegetables be washed before delivery? Will you accept a small amount of soil on carrots, but not cakes of mud, or must they be entirely free from visible contaminants?

Contamination introduced during processing

Non-food items (extrinsic contaminants) can be accidentally introduced into food at almost any stage of the food flow, with the possible consequence of serious injuries or damaging publicity, or both. So prevention is your company's first line of defence. If lapses

Barriers to safety

Physical barriers work only when they are used correctly and replaced if they become worn or damaged. Spatial barriers require everyone's full co-operation and vigilance.

do occur, despite your best intentions, you must carry out corrective action and a thorough investigation, then review and verify your HACCP system.

There is not a single, universal method of prevention. Instead, you need to tackle potential contaminants one by one, as revealed by your hazard analysis. The following paragraphs suggest some *general* controls that may be appropriate to consider for your workplace. In each case it is important to:

- establish proper procedures for checking food

- train staff to understand the importance of following the workplace procedures

- ensure that all incoming deliveries are checked carefully – this involves special training for the staff who are given the responsibility for checking deliveries

- establish procedures for reporting contamination and encourage staff to do so

- establish procedures for dealing with contaminated products, including quarantine and lines of responsibility

- keep the premises clean, tidy and in good repair

- set a good example.

Buildings

- Maintain the premises in good condition.

- Encourage staff to report defects.

Pests

- Keep the premises pest-free and implement a rigorous pest control programme (see pages 318 to 323).

- Get professional advice on the positioning of insect traps and electrical fly-killers. Ensure that staff understand why rodent bait boxes are positioned as they are and that only trained and authorised personnel should touch them.

- Deal immediately with any signs of pests in a food processing or storage area.

- Quarantine, then destroy pest-damaged or part-consumed products and call in expert assistance.

- Reject any infested incoming material before it enters the storage area.

- Set up a quarantine zone for contaminated goods.

- Establish a safe disposal method for contaminated food.

- Train and encourage staff to spot and report signs of infestation.

Food packaging materials

- Keep packing and unpacking processes away from areas where food is handled.

- Ensure that the unpacking area is kept clean and tidy.

- Provide suitable containers for packaging refuse.

- Train staff to look out for pieces of plastic wrapping adhering to frozen food.

- Avoid using metal staples to secure cardboard cartons containing food.

Responsibility
Lines of responsibility
need to be established
as well as procedures.

Glass and other brittle materials

- Use unbreakable, shatter-proof or splinter-proof materials whenever possible.

- Protect breakable light fittings with shatter-proof sleeves or diffusers.

- Prohibit the use of glass bottles, jars and other glass objects in food areas, other than the jars or bottles intended to contain the finished product.

- Establish breakage control and disposal procedures where breakable materials have to be used and ensure that staff are fully trained in the procedures.

Home-made patches and repairs

- Establish procedures for reporting defects and problems with machinery and equipment, including lines of responsibility.

- Encourage staff to report problems or suspected problems and ban attempts at do-it-yourself repairs, however well-intentioned they may be.

- Make sure that proper maintenance help is available and that staff know who to call on.

- Provide good supplies of new utensils and insist that broken items be thrown away.

- Service equipment regularly, rather than having to deal with emergency repairs, and keep spare parts in stock.

Metal

- Position equipment and machinery in such a way that loose pieces cannot fall into food on a work surface or conveyor belt, or in a mixer, cutter or filling hopper.

- Train maintenance personnel not to leave screws, nuts and machine parts lying around after a job or between tasks.

- Insist that maintenance staff check machinery and conduct a trial run after adjustment, repairs or moving. (If there is friction between moving parts metal swarf may shear off and contaminate food.)

- Ensure that every engineering task is rounded off by a check to eliminate loose parts an ensure that everything is thoroughly clean.

- Establish clear rules for employees and for contract, or off-site, personnel who maintain, service or repair any kind of machinery. Do not forget to include vending machines and refrigerators under this heading.

- Ban the use of the company's packaging, such as jars, buckets, cartons and bottles, to contain anything other than the final product. A container holding screws or drawing pins, for example, could accidentally be filled with food later.

Personal items and non-food items

- Ensure that supervisors and managers set a good example.

- Provide staff facilities for relaxation and eating. Ensure that they are pleasant and well maintained. If people are not using them, find out why.

- Make certain that staff are aware of the rules for personal hygiene and personal habits, such as not wearing jewellery (see page 277).

- Put up notices to remind everyone about contamination and arrange regular refresher training as a matter of course, and whenever physical contamination occurs.

- Ensure that plastic cups, sweet wrappers, chewing gum, rubber bands, paper clips, pens, personal stereos, mobile phones, pagers, screwdrivers and other such non-food items are not brought into food areas.

- Consider motivational factors if things go wrong. Deal with any issues such as stress or examples of poor supervision that might prevent rules being taken seriously.

- Provide suitable protective clothing and check that it is always in good repair so that fibres do not get into food.

- Consider embroidered or iron-on name labels on protective clothing, rather than pin-on badges.

- Consider providing sealed boxes, or similar containers, for carrying small tools and equipment through food areas.

Wood

- Whenever possible, replace wooden items with stainless steel or hard plastic.

- Consider banning wooden pallets from food areas. Alternatively, consider transferring goods to clean plastic pallets before they enter these zones.

- Handle wooden and plastic crates and pallets with care and introduce a pallet policy to identify and dispose of defective ones.

- Take special care when wood is part of the finished product, such as cocktail sticks in rollmop herrings or sticks in lollipops or iced lollies. Ensure that the wood is close-grained and splinter-free and is kept in suitable containers.

Detection

Even when you have taken every possible care to prevent contamination, there may still be scope for contaminants to get into food and remain there. Every food business therefore has a responsibility to detect contaminants that could remain. Exactly what you do and how you do it depends on the type of food business and its size.

Small businesses, for example, may need to contract to place the main responsibility for removing physical contaminants on suppliers. This may be the only realistic way that some small and medium-size enterprises (SMEs) can deal with some kinds of contamination, as they may not always have X-ray machines or metal detectors installed.

Even so, the smallest, one-person food business still has a legal responsibility to protect its consumers from harm, if only by staying alert to what is in food.

Routes

There is just one good thing about physical hazards: usually they tell a story. While it may be immensely difficult to trace the contamination routes of microbiological hazards, by comparison, physical contaminants provide hard evidence. You can use that evidence to discover what went wrong. For example, if you find a metal screw in food, you may suspect that a piece of equipment has been poorly maintained, whereas a false eyelash will point you in a rather different direction.

Methods of detection

Even so, you may find yourself involved in something akin to hide-and-seek as physical contaminants do not always turn up in the most obvious places. Detection methods for physical contaminants include:

- visual inspection
- metal detectors, magnets
- base and side scanners of bottles
- X-raying.

Visual inspection

This form of detection can take place in most food businesses during many stages of food handling. It is the first-line control during the receipt of deliveries to your premises and should include random spot-checks when staff open some of the packaged goods.

Visual inspection can also be carried out, for example, during manual sorting from a conveyor belt when unwanted plant material can be separated from fruit and vegetables, and it is an essential part of general stock and pest control.

Do bear in mind that where staff are involved in on-line inspection or sorting processes, they may lose concentration at times, so additional methods may also be desirable where they are feasible.

Staff must know what they should do if they discover physical contaminants, and supervisors or managers should monitor visual inspections to ensure that the control deals adequately with any critical control points.

Automated processes

Detection equipment is designed to distinguish differences between the physical properties of the food or food product and the contaminant. Criteria for detection may be shape, size, colour, density, magnetic properties or opacity to X-rays. It is good practice (and a requirement for some certifiable industry standards) to make a note of incidents of contamination in a log book for automatic detection devices. The log could also include details of checks on equipment and calibration records. It is standard practice to run *dummy tests* with identifiable batches of food to ensure that the devices are working properly.

Magnetic devices and metal detectors

Magnets can detect and remove most metallic contaminants. Even so, the force by which magnetic materials are attracted is proportional to their size, so smaller particles, such as staples or swarf, are harder to detect than larger ones such as nails. The strength of the magnetic device also decreases with distance.

Two types of magnet are typically used. Plate magnets are usually used in pipelines conveying liquid. The pipes are usually narrowed over the plate to overcome the problem of distance from the magnet. Any metal present is drawn through the liquid by magnetic force onto the magnets. Rare earth magnets are usually used for powders falling though pipes. They have a series of cylindrical fingers, providing a high surface area that attracts any metal present. Even very fine metal filings and swarf are attracted to them.

Magnetic devices detect and *extract* metal contaminants from individual products, such as a batch of soup. In contrast, metal detectors detect metal in products, such as bread, and *reject* the entire contaminated item. As a consequence, metal detectors are usually positioned towards the end of a production process, often at the packaging stage. The crucial factors are not only the diameter of the metal particles, but also the speed of the conveyor belt – detectors can, for example, fail to detect contaminants if the conveyor belt goes too fast.

Magnets must be tested and, if necessary, re-magnetised at defined intervals.

Bottle scanners

Bottle scanners help to prevent physical contamination.

Bottle scanners work by sending beams of light through the bottles onto a photo-electric cell while the bottles proceed along a conveyor system.

Dirt or other physical contaminants interrupt the light beam, triggering the machine to remove the bottle from the conveyor. This not only prevents possible physical contamination, but also allows returnable glass containers to be cleaned thoroughly and re-used.

However, scanners cannot usually detect contaminants through the *base* of a bottle, which is usually thicker than the rest of the glass, unless the scanner has top and bottom light beams in addition to the side beams.

The efficiency of scanners must be checked and calibrated regularly by sending through contaminated dummy bottles.

X-raying

This method is especially useful for detecting material such as bone, glass, plastic and aluminium which are not magnetic. X-raying is practicable only for large-scale production and preparation and is often used in the production of supermarket convenience meals.

Procedures after detecting physical contamination

Ensure that everyone knows what to do if physical contaminants are discovered. Include the responsibilities and reporting procedures as well as the specific steps to be taken. Bear in mind that detection devices may not reveal every particle of a contaminant like glass and there may still be shards in the food. Your procedures are likely to need to include the following actions:

Stopping production
Food production must be stopped until the source of contamination has been traced and removed and production lines and equipment have been cleaned.

- stop production

- discard the whole batch of food that was under production or preparation

- identify and remove the *source* of the contamination

- clean and service any food equipment and utensils involved

- resume the process or preparation only after a supervisor or manager has checked that every possible action has been taken to avoid a recurrence

- record the incident, for example in a log book or production shift log

- review the system, critical control points and critical limits (see pages 188 to191)

- instigate any appropriate measures to prevent the contamination from happening again.

Making it easier for others

- Explain how physical contaminants are a cause of considerable customer dissatisfaction and distress.

- Point out that physical contaminants make food unfit for human consumption, even if they have done no physical harm.

- Emphasise the role that staff have in spotting physical contaminants in food.

- Encourage staff to report any situation that they feel could lead to physical contamination.

- Ensure that staff know what to do if food is physically contaminated.

- Encourage staff to watch out for signs of pest infestation and to report it to their supervisor or manager.

Allergen contamination

An increasing number of people have a food allergy or intolerance and they need accurate information to enable them to make informed selections from the many food products on offer. Every sector of the food industry has a legal duty to ensure that food is safe to eat – and that includes having suitable procedures to identify and control allergens and to provide consumers with adequate information.

There are four main steps involved: risk assessment, risk management, risk communication and risk review. The steps can be carried out as part of the company's HACCP-based procedures. Whether allergens can be eliminated altogether, or how they are dealt with at critical control points depends upon the sector and the individual business, but all food businesses must give accurate warnings and information to consumers.

Allergen risk assessment

The first step is to consider whether your product recipes contain any allergenic ingredients. As you saw on page 147, eight foods and ingredients made from them are responsible for most food allergies in the UK. They are milk; eggs; peanuts; tree nuts (such as Brazil nuts, hazelnuts, almonds and walnuts); fish; shellfish (including crab and shrimps); soya; and wheat. Other main allergens include sesame and other seeds, including pine nuts; fruit and cereals.

Unrecognised ingredients?
Some allergens are not always immediately obvious, but it is essential to identify them. Restaurants and take-aways in particular are often unaware of all the food sources in the ingredients they use. One survey found that 8 out of 20 take-away meals contained peanut, even though the person ordering the food had made it absolutely clear that the dishes must *not* contain peanut products for their safety. Examples of unexpected ingredients to watch out for include:

- salad dressings – these may be made from unrefined oil from sources such as peanuts, walnuts, hazelnuts or sesame

- Waldorf salad which contains walnuts

- satay sauce which is made with peanuts (which may be described as *groundnuts*)

- the sauces in many Chinese, Indian and Asian dishes – some ingredients used, such as 'almond powder', may also include peanut

- marzipan, praline and frangipane which are made with nuts

- pesto sauce which is made with pine nuts

- tahini, gomashio and hummus which contain sesame

- the dressing for Caesar salad which often contains anchovies

- Worcestershire sauce which contains anchovies

- some meat products, such as burgers, which contain a milk protein (casein) as a binding agent

- some sausages and hot dogs which contain wheat or cereals

- some types of pasta which contain eggs.

Unintentional ingredients

Some allergens end up in products accidentally, as a result of contamination or cross-contamination. The sources of contamination include people and poor personal hygiene, raw materials, shared equipment, packaging, shared storage and inadequate cleaning.

Allergen risk management – examples of controls

Allergens can be managed as part of your existing food safety systems – for example, through food safety prerequisites, HACCP critical control points, good hygiene practice (GHP), or good manufacturing practice (GMP).

Supplies

The ingredients and products you buy in to your company may be one of your main critical control points. Product specifications for individual products can help to eliminate the undeclared or accidental inclusion of allergens. In a small business you may have to rely on information provided by your suppliers, but you do need to check and confirm this information periodically because it may affect the information you give to consumers.

Ask suppliers for letters of guarantee that undeclared allergens are not present. Ask them to notify you of any change in the allergen status of ingredients used. Always check deliveries to ensure that there are no unexpected substitutions of products or ingredients that could affect allergy sufferers.

Preventing allergen contamination

The principles of good practice discussed for preventing other forms of contamination and cross-contamination are equally applicable to allergens, but, as allergens can cause illness or death in the tiniest trace quantities, additional, special measures may also be needed. The following list suggests just some of the issues that might be involved in your business.

- Separate allergens during delivery and storage.

- Separate allergens during production and preparation. It may not be possible to provide separate dedicated work areas, equipment, utensils and production lines for this purpose, but it may be possible to separate processes by *time*. This involves careful scheduling, a 'full chemical clean' between processes to remove the slightest trace of allergens, and analysis to confirm the absence of allergens.

- Prevent contamination and cross-contamination:

    by separation
    – do not use the same utensils and crockery for foods intended to be allergen free

    – do not use ingredients that have been cooked in unrefined groundnut oil because traces of nut protein may remain on the cooked food

– do not use any oil that has previously been used to cook nut products because it could contain traces of nut proteins that could be passed on to foods later cooked in the oil

by effective personal hygiene

– ensure that food handlers wash their hands thoroughly after handling known allergens

by effective cleaning

– ensure that all surfaces that could be contaminated by spills or air-borne particles are cleaned scrupulously after handling foods containing allergens.

Awareness and training

Every food handler needs basic training about allergens. Customer-contact staff in shops, restaurants, take-aways, nurseries, nursing homes and so on need additional training. As food eaten away from the home probably accounts for three-quarters of the deaths resulting from a food allergy, the people who take telephone orders for food should also be included. Customer-contact staff need to know how to *obtain* information about ingredients and how to *give* accurate information. Food presented as being allergen free must indeed be uncontaminated by even the slightest trace of an allergen. Food that fails to meet these basic standards could lead to criminal charges against the company for misrepresenting the ingredients. Civil courts can award damages to customers who were incorrectly led to believe that foods were safe for them to eat.

The training should bear in mind that some young people struggling to deal with allergies may not necessarily ask the right question about ingredients or may ask in a way that does not make the answer seem particularly important to staff. Ensure that staff appreciate that patience may be needed to help people to get the information they really need. You might consider designating particular members of staff to answer questions or to provide ingredient lists for all dishes prepared or sold on the premises.

Train staff to know what to do if they think that a customer is having a severe allergic reaction to a food.

Communication – consumer information

By law, pre-packaged foods, including alcoholic drinks, must list certain ingredients to which people may have an allergy or intolerance. Twelve foods must be mentioned:

- celery
- cereals containing gluten (wheat, barley, rye and oats)
- crustaceans (such as lobster and crab)
- eggs
- fish
- milk
- mustard
- nuts – such as almonds, hazelnuts, walnuts, Brazil nuts, cashews, pecans and pistachios
- peanuts

- sesame seeds

- soya beans

- sulphur dioxide and sulphites (preservatives used in some foods and drinks) at levels above 10mg per kg or per litre.

By December 2008, labels must also list lupin and molluscs (see page 147).

Labels also need to provide information about 'compound ingredients' that include the listed foods – a pastry glaze made from egg, for example. However, some ingredients made from these foods are so highly processed that they are not considered likely to cause an allergic reaction so do not legally need to be mentioned. They include refined soya bean oil and glucose syrups made from wheat or barley. As with any legal requirement, however, you must find out how your products and processes are affected and ensure that your company is complying.

Advisory labelling

Where allergens are not an *intended* ingredient in a particular product, manufacturers should include a statement to this effect (see page 287). However, such labels should be used only when a risk assessment has shown that there is a demonstrable and significant risk of allergen cross-contamination. They should never be used as a substitute for good manufacturing practices.

Review

Regular reviews of allergen risks, control and labelling should be carried out as part of your company's risk management system, such as HACCP. Additional reviews are likely to be necessary when, for example, there is any change to recipes, manufacturing processes, ingredients, packaging or cleaning procedures; or after a machinery break-down or a significant consumer comment or complaint.

Making it easier for others

- Make clear which foods and ingredients in your workplace could cause problems.

- Emphasise the important role that customer-contact staff have for finding out and providing accurate information to consumers about allergens.

- Ensure that staff know how to find out a product ingredient list or who to ask.

- Train everyone in the procedures that must be followed to avoid contaminating and cross-contaminating foods that should be allergen free. Don't miss out cleaners, maintenance staff and people who answer the telephone.

- Emphasise the importance of thorough handwashing and make sure that everyone understands the standards of cleaning required.

- Reinforce company requirements for separating allergens during production and storage, and not sharing equipment.

- Train staff to know what to do if someone seems to be having an allergic reaction to food in your workplace.

Feature

Customers as hazard?

No self-respecting food company would want its customers to know that it sometimes considered them to be a hazard.

The fact is, however, that customers are often a hazard to the safety of their own food and to that of others.

The big issue for managers is to find robust ways – discreet where necessary – to control the risk from the hazards customers sometimes create.

What is involved and what can be achieved depends largely on the sector you work in.

How, for example, can a manufacturer have any impact upon what happens to its food once it leaves the factory?

If you manufacture liquid chocolate, for example, and supply other manufacturers or caterers, it is fairly likely that the product information and advice you issue will be followed – and your clients are almost certain to have given you a product specification in the first place.

However, if your product – for instance, a ready-to-eat meal – sells to the general public, how do you know what will happen once it is in a consumer's hands?

After all, members of the public do not always read storage and heating instructions. Or, if they do, they do not always follow them.

As for *use-by* dates, some people seem to consider them merely as a marketing ploy to get them to buy even more supplies.

You cannot control their actions, but you can build in some safeguards.

Although it may sound unkind to say so, you should perhaps assume that a domestic consumer somewhere will consider doing something silly with your product, and you need to protect your brand as much as possible.

What goes on the packaging may be just as important as what is inside. As always, it is wise to consider consumer expectations.

Some years ago a pasteurized soup with a relatively short shelf life was being sold in cans. Many consumers assumed that it was *canned* soup and stored it like other canned foods for a longish period, even though the storage conditions and shelf life were clear on the label.

Consumers were less than happy to find that their relatively expensive soup did not have the shelf life they were anticipating.

The soup is now sold in cartons, like chilled milk or fruit juice. Consumers treat it like other chilled carton products and store it in the fridge, even if they don't read the label.

Labelling needs to be easily legible, but the type size on a lot of packaging is very small. Although it complies with legal requirements, it can be difficult to read even by people with perfect eyesight.

It should be easy to find the *use-by* date, so this needs to be taken into account when the packaging and labelling are designed.

The stated shelf life must be scientifically, technically and demonstrably correct, but should take into account, as far as possible, of some likely temperature and time abuse by domestic consumers.

Retailers and caterers dealing with hazards from customers often have to be both flexible and subtle. You cannot let customers feel that they are under intrusive surveillance, and you cannot humiliate them by pouncing to deal with problems they have created.

Of course, some preventive measures are relatively straightforward.

Customers, like staff, can spread bacteria by sneezing near open food or by handling open food by bare hand. Sneeze guards can be installed and an adequate supply of regularly replenished clean serving utensils can help to discourage customers from using their hands to pick up food.

Staff can be trained and encouraged to keep an eye open for customers who unintentionally move refrigerated and frozen foods out of their safe display conditions in a shop.

This often happens when customers select a product, place it in their trolley, carry on shopping, then decide that they do not want it. They may abandon the product on any shelf or return it to its original display. In either case, the product may have become too warm for safe sale to other consumers.

Similarly, shoppers may compromise the cold chain by turning over products in chillers and freezers as they look for a product with the longest shelf life.

Adequate training in shelf stacking, appropriate staffing levels and staff alertness can help, especially as customers often mix up the position of products with different shelf life dates.

In the end, however, you can only ensure that everyone is diligent, doing everything they reasonably can to keep food safe.

Management matters

Contamination marks the start of the route from hazard – the possibility of harm – to a food-borne illness. As a consequence, all your food safety systems must be geared to preventing contamination in the first place. To do so, you must carry out risk assessments, and establish and maintain systems of control that PROTECT food from contamination (including allergen contamination). Where microbiological contamination is possible, you must also establish and maintain procedures that PREVENT microbiological multiplication and DESTROY any pathogenic and spoilage microbes that could survive in food. There are various ways to establish such systems and to monitor their effectiveness and these are discussed in detail in the rest of Part 4.

As a manager, you must make yourself aware of the potential sources, routes and vehicles of contamination both within your premises and before food is delivered there. Knowledge of these factors will help you to implement the key controls for protecting food from contamination. To assess the risk of the multiplication of pathogens you also need to consider product attributes (intrinsic factors) and process qualities (extrinsic factors). Additional knowledge about the total composition of the microbiological flora may also help you to assess whether pathogenic organisms are supported or inhibited.

The prevention of contamination and the minimising of its consequences when it does occur depend upon dedicated teamwork throughout the company. Make sure that you:

- build a culture that values doing things the right way

- provide the right equipment for every task

- provide suitable protective clothing

- set clear rules for personal hygiene and habits

- organise appropriate supervision

- ensure that premises and equipment are kept clean and are maintained and serviced regularly so that they do not deteriorate

- do not expect people to follow rules unless they have been trained properly to carry out their jobs

- ensure that all food handlers understand the impact of their actions and omissions

- ensure that staff who do *not* handle food are also aware that they could cause contamination if they fail to follow company procedures

- make certain that managers and visitors do not break the rules

- set a good example yourself.

Managing resources

Key points

Under a suitable roof

Criteria for the selection of a site for food premises.

Why workflow is so important to food safety.

The significance of 'clean' and 'dirty' processes.

How the design and construction of food premises can contribute to the prevention of contamination and cross-contamination.

Why foods and processes must be segregated.

What to bear in mind for essential services and facilities.

Why separate facilities are required for personal hygiene.

Suitable materials for the construction of food premises.

Suitable materials for food-contact surfaces, equipment and utensils.

Factors affecting food safety in the design of food equipment.

What to consider in planning the safe storage and disposal of rubbish and food waste.

The part that the design and construction of premises plays in pest control.

The importance of an easy-to-access and easy-to-clean layout.

How design and construction affect transport vehicles, temporary and movable food premises, vending machines and the use of domestic premises for commercial food production.

Developing staff competence

Why food safety training and development are essential in a food business.

The benefits of effective training.

The management role in staff training in food safety.

The principles of training.

Who needs to be trained.

How to evaluate the training needs for food safety and how to draw up a training needs assessment.

Determining an appropriate training strategy.

Implementing, monitoring and evaluating the training strategy in comparison to food safety practice in the workplace.

Keeping training records.

Continuing the professional development of food safety managers.

Making learning easier

How adults learn.

Different methods of food safety training.

Checking the quality of training programmes.

Fit to work with food

The value of high standards of personal hygiene and personal habits.

How to manage this aspect of food safety.

What your company's personal hygiene policies need to cover.

Hazards associated with poor standards of food safety.

Staff responsibilities for personal hygiene.

The importance of suitable protective clothing.

Restrictions on food handling when staff are suffering from food-borne and other infectious illnesses.

Packaging for safety and promotion

The function of food packaging.

Product-specific risks.

HACCP principles.

Industry standards.

Key words

Ambient temperature
The environmental temperature, often used to describe normal room temperature.

Carrier
An infected person showing no symptoms of an infectious disease, who may transmit it to others.

Contaminant
Any unwanted material, object or substance in food.

Contamination
The presence in food, or the process of transferring to food, any unwanted material, object or substance.

Cross-contamination
The transfer of a contaminant from one contaminated product, such as raw meat, to another previously uncontaminated product, such as a ready-to-eat food.

Direct contamination
The route directly from the source of contamination to a food.

Due diligence
A legal defence where it can be shown that all reasonable steps were taken to avoid committing a food safety offence.

Extrinsic factors
External factors (such as temperature and atmosphere) that influence the growth and survival of micro-organisms.

Food safety policy
A company's written statement of its commitment to meeting its obligations towards customers and to producing safe and legal products.

Hazard
Anything, whether microbiological, chemical or physical, that might cause harm to the consumer.

High-risk food
A food that easily supports the multiplication of pathogenic micro-organisms.

Indirect contamination
Contamination due to the action of a vehicle of contamination or a vector.

Intrinsic factors
Inbuilt or inherent characteristics such as nutrients, pH and aw that influence the survival, growth and multiplication of micro-organisms.

Micro-organism
Any organism that is so small that it can be observed only through a microscope.

Multiplication
Microbial reproduction, such as by binary fission (bacteria) or budding (yeast).

Potable
Safe to drink.

Ready-to-eat food
A food that is either eaten raw, or is not prepared or treated (such as by cooking) in a way that would kill any pathogens present immediately before the food is eaten.

Risk
A measure, or scale, of the likelihood that a hazard will occur.

Workflow
The logical route organised through food premises for food, food handlers, equipment and waste throughout each stage of production.

From the ground up

Designing your own new premises is the ideal situation. Right from the choice of location to the last details of fixtures, fittings and decoration, you can plan for food safety every step of the way.

Even if you do not have this luxury, most of the principles are the same whether you are moving into an existing building or converting or refurbishing premises.

There are three main stages in the process: planning, design and construction.

The first consideration in the planning stage is the identification of a suitable site – a process that can involve feasibility studies and research into planning legislation and zoning requirements, transport links, environmental impact, market factors and financing.

Planning then boils down to four main aspects: access for delivery, distribution, market and customers; workforce availability; raw materials availability; and the 'orientation' of the site – that is, the potential effects of external pollution or contamination from the surrounding environment.

The order of importance of these factors depends on the nature of the business – access to bulk agricultural products, for instance, is not important to a small restaurant, whereas good access is vital for both workforce and customers, as well as for the delivery and distribution of products.

If the premises are sited within the business's main market or customer catchment area, you must take into account the food safety implications of walk-in customers.

In addition to general staffing, you may need to look at the availability of specialists. Will the area attract the people you want? What about suitable housing for your workforce? Will the commuting of staff create a nuisance or have an adverse environmental impact? Are raw materials readily available in the vicinity? If not, can they be easily obtained via road, rail, sea or air links? Will their delivery have consequences for food safety or the environment?

Pollution or contamination from the surrounding environment must also be considered. For example, care must be taken to ensure that air intakes are not downwind of likely contaminants, such as silage pits or landfill sites.

Finally, the provision of essential services (water, gas, electricity, waste removal) and the addressing of any potential food safety hazards, such as smoke, chemicals or flooding, also come into the planning stage.

At the design stage, you and the architect decide on the form of the building, its internal layout and the materials and finishes that will be used. Specialist companies and equipment suppliers may be called in to give additional advice on the design of the process flow. After detailed consultation with you, the architect makes drawings of the building and suggests the layout of equipment and fittings.

This is also the stage at which pest prevention measures and facilities for controlling the internal environment – through lighting, noise reduction, heating, cooling and air conditioning systems – are designed to suit your kind of business.

At last all the paperwork turns into reality – from the substructure right through to the installation of equipment and the application of surface materials, finishes and colour.

New or redesigned premises

Food premises must comply with laws governing construction, occupational health and safety and food safety. Bodies such as English Heritage and Cadw can influence plans likely to affect historic buildings and locations, while local authorities can impose restrictions in designated conservation areas. Legislation exists that affects building design and construction including aspects of planning, covering the volume of development, the appearance and layout of buildings; public health, imposing restrictions on noise, pollution and public nuisance; highways, dealing with roads and pavements; construction; and building regulations which set out material and design standards.

Under a suitable roof

Imagine it is your job to turn a derelict warehouse on a trendy waterfront into a state-of-the-art restaurant. As the walls are currently decorated with cobwebs and there are pipes hanging from the ceiling, it does not look as if food could ever be prepared there, let alone hygienically.

Alternatively, imagine that after years of happily running a combined convenience store and sandwich bar from a Tudor-beamed building, you have been quietly advised to improve your workflow and install food-safe work surfaces. Nothing has actually gone wrong, so you are loathe to spend hard-earned profit unless it is really essential.

Or, imagine yourself in the position of a newly appointed food safety adviser to the designers of a new canning plant: you have your best chance ever to influence food safety.

But would *you* know where to start in each of these three very different situations? What would be important, and how would you create and maintain premises that are fit for food?

The basics

Despite initial appearances, the principles are the same whether you are building from scratch, or renovating or improving existing premises. They apply equally, no matter which food sector you are dealing with, whatever the type, size or location of the food business or age of the building.

The principles are the same because the main aim in any food operation is to eliminate food hazards, or at the very least to minimise the risks from them. This involves:

- *protecting* food against microbiological, chemical, physical and allergen contamination
- *preventing* microbial multiplication
- *destroying* micro-organisms, their spores and toxins.

This chapter outlines the ways in which the design and construction of premises play a major part in:

- protecting food from contamination and cross-contamination
- helping staff to prevent microbiological survival and multiplication
- enabling staff to destroy micro-organisms.

All the principles are enshrined in law – in Annex II, Chapters I and II of Regulation (EC) No. 852/2004 on the hygiene of foodstuffs.

What is involved

Of course, *you* may not have much of a say, if any, in where food premises are located, and you may not be the person with the final responsibility for service and maintenance contracts for the building. Even so, as a manager with responsibility for food safety, you need to know:

- which materials are the most suitable for the structure of food areas
- which materials are the most suitable for food-contact surfaces

- which services (such as water, light and ventilation) should be provided and how many facilities (such as toilets and rubbish areas) are required

- how the design and construction can help you to keep pests out of the premises

- what to consider when purchasing and installing food equipment

- how easy, or otherwise, it is to clean the premises and its equipment to standards that are suitable for food preparation and storage

- how a linear workflow can contribute to the elimination of food hazards or can help to minimise the risks from them.

What might it cost?

Well-designed food areas help to prevent food contamination. In this catering kitchen dust and grease are likely to collect on the kitchen utensils hanging over the preparation area.

Time, effort and money invested in getting your premises up to scratch, and keeping them that way, will pay you back many times over.

Some food hazards, such as dust from utensils suspended over work areas, could be eliminated, while others, such as cross-contamination, could become easier to control.

An orderly work environment gives customers and clients greater confidence in your company. It could also help to improve staff morale and make some repetitive tasks, such as cleaning, more straightforward.

There is also the matter of legal compliance. After all, a food hygiene inspection is *not* the time to discover that mice are running riot in your dry goods warehouse or that your famous old copper kettle is slowly poisoning your regular afternoon tea drinkers.

In the end, perhaps the real issue is whether you can afford *not* to provide suitable premises and equipment. Although complete refurbishment may not be cheap, even making a few minor changes or re-organising your workflow could help you to enhance your operational efficiency, avoid an outbreak of food-borne illness and keep your company well within the law.

How safe for food?

Throughout the book we use the word construction in the usual way to mean either the process of erecting a building or the physical structure of a building. The word design is used in a broader-than-usual sense to cover the shape and external appearance (including landscaping) of the premises, as well as the internal layout, installations and fittings.

Designed to avoid contamination

Needless to say, premises need to be suitable for the kind of food operation you are running, but they must also help you to prevent food hazards from leading to food-borne illness – see the diagram on page 45. Effective design and construction of food premises can help to:

- prevent direct contamination by the:

  – use of appropriate construction methods

  – provision of appropriate surfaces and finishing materials

- prevent cross-contamination through:

  – a linear workflow (a logical way of working)

  – the separation of raw and other foods and the separation of various functions such as 'clean' and 'dirty' processes.

From here to page 248 we outline each of these guiding principles in turn, then discuss some specific points in greater detail. Before we do so, it may help to outline what we mean by 'clean' and 'dirty' in the context of design.

Clean and dirty

There are designated 'clean' and 'dirty' areas in many food premises. This does not mean that the clean area is never dirty, or that the dirty area is never cleaned. The descriptions refer to the state of the food or processes carried out in that particular area. Anywhere that raw food is handled or prepared is considered 'dirty' because of the possibility of contamination from the food. A 'clean' area is one where foods are being processed or packaged, or finished foods are handled.

So, air circulation and drainage need to flow from 'clean' to 'dirty' areas, and the workflow (see page 246) needs to prevent taking staff or food, or both, from 'clean' areas or processes back to 'dirty' areas or processes. To help to prevent contamination from 'clean' to 'dirty' areas staff in large food premises, such as factories and supermarkets, often have to wear different coloured protective clothing according to the area where they should be working: they are then easily spotted if they stray into the 'wrong' area.

Appropriate construction methods

Whether you are designing a building from scratch or converting or refurbishing existing premises, the following principles of construction should be observed to help to maintain food safety. Premises should be:

- windproof and waterproof

- equipped to prevent access by pests

- designed to make cleaning easy

- constructed from durable, impervious and easily cleaned materials (floors, walls and ceilings in food areas)

- designed to allow for a workflow that progresses from 'dirty' to 'clean', allowing for efficient working.

Outside the building

Circulation

Vehicles can include incoming deliveries of food and ingredients, incoming staff and customers and outgoing products, waste and rubbish. Ideally the incoming and outgoing routes should be separated: at the very least, they should be controlled.

Entrances

It is not always necessary or practicable to have separate entrances for staff who handle food and for those who do not, such as administrative workers. However, you might be able to provide separate corridors or routes through the building.

Delivery and loading areas

Although in many cases the same dock and entrance may be used for both delivery and loading, it is preferable to have segregated delivery and dispatch areas. For example, in abattoirs the fresh meat should not be loaded onto lorries in the same place where live animals are brought in. A double-entry system can help – food is unloaded and taken to a designated unpacking area before being moved to a temperature-controlled area, if appropriate.

Landscaping

Landscaping around food premises should:

- be easy to keep clean

- not encourage rubbish dumping or dirt collection

- not encourage or harbour pests.

There should be a strip of hardstanding, such as concrete or tarmac, around the building, directly against the outside wall, to discourage pests from nesting near, or gaining access to, the building. This has the added benefit of making obvious any hole in the building that might allow pests to get in.

Exterior waste storage and disposal

Food premises tend to produce a wide variety of types of food waste and other rubbish, including dry (such as packaging), liquid (such as drinks and waste water used for cleaning), food (including, possibly, food suitable for composting) and chemicals. Waste has to be stored outside until collection for disposal. If it is not removed immediately or automatically, then it should be kept separate from any incoming or outgoing deliveries of food. Controlled conditions, including refrigeration for some food waste, may be necessary to prevent microbial multiplication.

Disabled access

You should ensure that there is adequate access for disabled staff and visitors, according to the appropriate regulations.

Inside the building

The internal layout may be predetermined if you are taking over premises rather than building from scratch. Ideally, however, the internal layout should take into account the:

- circulation of people within the building – food handlers, other staff, customers and visitors

- workflow

- waste storage and disposal.

Customers and visitors should have their own entrances and separate circulation routes that keep them away from food processing areas. Areas to which customers have access should be designed to minimise contamination.

Circulation

Wherever possible, the paths of food handlers and other staff should not cross. This may be a matter of designating areas where individuals have authority to go and not to go, or it may entail structural separation.

Visitors, such as delivery drivers, and customers should be kept away from food processing areas.

Workflow

The flow of people and food through the building, and from activity to activity, must be planned with as few cross-over points as possible. See below for more information about workflow.

Waste storage within the building

Prior to its disposal, waste and rubbish must be collected and stored, initially inside the building. At no time should it come into contact with food products – for example, waste and rubbish should not travel through the building by the same route as fresh food, including movement by lifts, hoists, trolleys or vehicles.

Appropriate surfaces and finishing materials

All surfaces that come into contact with food should:

- be easy to maintain, clean and disinfect

- be made from a non-toxic material

- prevent the migration of chemicals onto food.

Surfaces that are *not* expected to come into contact with food should also be selected with care – for example, wall paint should be non-toxic and washable. The chart opposite suggests suitable materials for surfaces and finishes.

Linear workflow

Workflow is the sequence of stages or processes involved in creating a product. In the food industry the term usually refers to the various routes travelled by food, food handlers, equipment and rubbish during food production from the delivery of raw food right through to the dispatch, sale or service of the finished products.

Linear workflow is the ideal: you should aim to organise a clear and logical progression of tasks that safeguards food through all the process stages. Wherever possible, avoid points where people, food and equipment cross paths. The more cross-over points that exist, the more opportunities there are for contamination.

Right for the job

Characteristics	Examples of suitable materials
Work surfaces Non-porous Non-scratch Easy-to-clean	Stainless steel
Equipment and utensils Easy-to-clean Smooth finish Non-porous	Stainless steel, polypropylene and other synthetics
Shelving Easy-to-clean High-strength	Stainless steel or plastic
Walls Light-coloured to show up dirt Grease-resistant Heat-resistant Coved at base and top	Glazed tiles, smooth painted plaster, plastic laminate sheets
Floors Non-slip Easy-to-clean Weight-bearing Hard-wearing Sloped for drainage Water and chemical resistant if necessary	Epoxy resin, concrete with granite chips, vinyl sheet, non-slip ceramic or quarry tiles
Ceilings Smooth Easy-to-clean Coved Light-coloured to show dirt Fire-resistant Non-flaking	Metal, plaster

Separation of foods and processes

In addition to a linear workflow, it is an advantage to separate different foods, functions and processes to prevent contamination. For example, it would be unwise to prepare raw meat in the same area as salads.

Providing separate work areas

It is common in larger food businesses to have several preparation areas designated for particular foods or processes, each area with its own facilities and equipment. Dishwashing and laundry should be carried out away from food areas.

Keeping foods apart

Different groups of food need to be kept apart – root vegetables, for example, could contaminate cheese if stored in close proximity. You need to ensure that there is appropriate and separate storage for all the products and ingredients your company uses – for example, refrigerated, dry and frozen.

It may also be necessary to provide suitable storage areas at different stages of the workflow – for example, to store raw materials or finished products.

The most important points are to:

- provide suitable storage conditions, such as ambient, refrigerated and frozen
- keep raw foods apart from cooked and ready-to-eat foods
- segregate high-risk foods from each other and from cooked and ready-to-eat products.

Every effort should be made to ensure that these groups do not come into contact with each in storage or in transit between storage and other areas of the premises.

Other storage requirements

As well as keeping different types of food segregated, it is essential to separate food and non-food items. Cleaning materials and any other potentially toxic materials must be stored safely and separately, well away from food. More information on storage is provided on pages 349 to 356.

Machine service

Vending machines and other stand-alone facilities are subject to the same regulations governing the rest of the food industry. The law assumes that the food going into a vending machine has been prepared in food premises that meet all the relevant food safety and construction standards. In addition, the law views the vending machine itself as a food establishment, albeit on a miniature scale.

From outline to detail

Now that we have covered the basic underlying principles for avoiding food contamination through the effective design and construction of food premises, we examine certain aspects of the design of food premises in greater detail.

In position for cleaning and maintenance

According to the law, all food premises must permit adequate cleaning or disinfection or both. This means that the floors, walls, ceilings and work surfaces must be made from materials that can be cleaned and disinfected easily.

Avoiding dirt traps

The design, layout and location of equipment must avoid inaccessible nooks and crannies in rooms where dirt can collect unnoticed or where only microbe-sized staff could possibly reach to clean. Similarly, equipment should not have sharp-angled internal corners which are difficult to penetrate for cleaning.

Pipes and ducts

As everyone who has ever tried to clean behind a toilet knows, badly positioned pipes can easily become a dirt trap. Pipework and ducts in food premises need to be accessible for maintenance but should also be incorporated into the structure in such a way that surfaces are smooth and continuous for easy cleaning.

The mobile solution

Movable, rather than fitted, equipment gives better access for cleaning on all sides and underneath. The degree of mobility depends on the size and weight of the item, how much space there is for moving equipment, the services – such as water, electricity or gas – to which it is connected, and health and safety considerations for the staff who must move the equipment.

Keeping pests out

The design, layout and equipping of food premises should ensure that pests cannot simply walk or fly in. Insects and birds can get in through unprotected doors that are opened frequently. Birds can roost on unprotected window ledges, canopies and exterior architectural features, while insects and some rodents may be attracted to 'dead spaces' behind refrigerators and other equipment, or may find comfortable homes in ducting, cracks and crevices.

Research has shown that most insects enter food buildings through open doors, rather than open windows. External doors should be fitted with closers and, where necessary, with fly screens. The law requires fly screens to be fitted to windows 'where necessary', so a risk assessment must be carried out. A good starting point is to answer the following questions.

- Is there an occasional, frequent or constant problem from flying insects?

- What is the external environment – are the food premises near farms or animals, for example?

- Is the problem associated with the windows only or also with open doors?

If the risk assessment shows window screens to be necessary, it is important to ensure that the correct type are fitted. By law, the screens must be removable for cleaning. They should also allow the window to be opened. If inappropriate screens are fitted and staff cannot open the windows, ventilation problems and overheating can occur, or the staff may be tempted to remove the screens altogether.

Waste or refuse, such as packaging and pallets, that could attract or harbour pests should not be stored against the building. Exterior drains and gullies should be covered. Interceptor chambers can also be installed which include a vertical baffle to obstruct swimming rodents.

Traps, baits or fly killers used within the building should be positioned with great care so that dead pests do not contaminate food.

Utilities and personal hygiene

Food preparation cannot take place without access to water and the means to heat and chill food.

A safe water supply

Water that is safe to drink is described as being potable. By law all food premises must have an adequate supply of potable water. European food hygiene regulations (see page 165) also stipulate that potable water must be used whenever necessary to ensure foodstuffs are not contaminated.

Direct contact with food

Many recipes and drinks call for the direct addition of water. Water for this purpose should come from a drinking-water supply that meets legislated standards. When a product needs

Ice and steam

Water is not always used in a liquid state – it may also be used as ice or steam. If there is any chance of contact with food, only potable water must be used. This rule applies whether the ice or steam is added to food or drink directly – as crushed ice in a cocktail or as steamed milk in a cappuccino, for example – or whether it is used indirectly as in a chilled display, such as a fishmonger's slab.

Ice and steam machines should be treated like all food-contact equipment and kept free of contamination.

to include carbonated, flavoured, distilled, iced or cold vaporised water, you should ensure that it is prepared from drinking-quality water. To comply with the law and to protect food from contamination, make sure that only potable water is used for washing raw food.

Indirect contact with food

Because of the risk of indirect contamination and cross-contamination, only potable water should be used for cleaning food-contact surfaces and equipment and for supplying wash-hand basins.

Drains and gulleys must be covered to prevent contamination and access by pests. The drains shown here are not hygienic.

Separating potable and unclean water

You must ensure that potable water cannot come into contact with non-potable water, for instance waste water in the drainage system, rain, water that is part of a heating or cooling system or is kept at hand for fire fighting.

Where possible, stop staff from having access to water that is not of drinking quality. If this is not feasible, for fire-fighting supplies, for instance, make sure that the water is labelled clearly and that staff training sessions include warnings and explanations about the hazard to food.

Drains

Drains must have sufficient fall to allow all liquid and solid waste to be removed. The direction of the flow should be away from 'clean' areas. Where toilets are flushed into the same drainage system, the entry points must be *after* the food areas.

Gas and electricity

All food premises need a source of energy, usually electricity or gas. This energy supplies not only ancillary systems such as light, heat and computer power but also the energy for processing the food. This is mostly in the form of mains supplies but often food factories have an emergency back-up of bottled gas or electricity generators.

Facilities for personal hygiene

Food operations must provide adequate facilities for the staff's personal hygiene, and there should be wash-hand basins in toilet areas and also in strategic points that are readily accessible to food handlers from food areas.

Basins

In deciding where washing facilities are necessary, take into account the activity being carried out, the probable frequency of hand washing needed at that point or stage in the food flow, how close the next wash-hand basin is and how many people work in the vicinity.

Delicatessen counters, butchers' counters, various preparation areas in kitchens and locations between 'dirty' and 'clean' areas are some of the places where hand-washing facilities will be essential. The risk assessment in some businesses leads to them also providing basins between the staff changing rooms and the food area to prompt staff to wash their hands before starting work.

Staff should *not* use food preparation or washing-up *sinks* for the purposes of personal hygiene because of the risk of contaminating food or food-contact surfaces.

Wash-hand *basins* must have a good supply of hot and cold water. In some food premises, especially factories, hand-operated taps are replaced by hands-free taps that can be operated by knee, foot, elbow or proximity devices. These reduce the risk of contamination and cross-contamination from hands.

Toilets

You must provide adequate toilets for the number of staff employed, with separate toilets provided for visitors or customers. The suitable number is set out in legislation covering buildings and health and safety.

There are restrictions on where toilets are placed and how they are maintained. Toilets may not open directly onto a room in which food is processed and need to be separated by a ventilated space from any food handling area.

Hard though it may be to believe, this toilet was discovered by environmental health practitioners during an inspection of food premises. All personal hygiene facilities must be kept scrupulously clean to help to prevent indirect food contamination.

To prevent food being contaminated by the air from the toilets they must be ventilated, mechanically or naturally, to legislated standards (six to eight air changes per hour). Toilets must also be connected to a sealed drainage system through an effective trap. Facilities for women must include a hygienic means of disposing of sanitary towels and tampons.

Changing rooms and lockers

Food handlers should be provided with two *separate* lockers: one for street clothing and another for protective clothing. This is to prevent ordinary clothes from contaminating protective clothing that could then contaminate food.

The workflow should enable staff to get to 'clean' work areas without going through 'dirty' areas once they have changed into protective clothing.

A comfortable working environment

Food safety occasionally comes into conflict with staff and customer comfort. For example, some foods must be kept at below 8°C, but this temperature leaves most people feeling rather chilly. So, the provision of heating, cooling, lighting and ventilation needs to take both food and people into account. You should also remember that both lighting and ventilation can affect the ambient temperature.

Environmental temperature

In every food facility there are likely to be areas, such as kitchens, that generate heat and may need cooling and others, such as offices, that need to be heated for staff comfort.

A good layout will keep these areas separate from each other. A poor layout that places them close together can make fuel bills soar. You may need some local temperature control – for example, ventilation and extraction to dissipate heat generated by an oven or the back of a refrigerator.

Typical recommended ambient working temperatures	
Dining rooms and restaurants	18° to 21°C
Factories	
sedentary work	19°C
light work	16°C
heavy work	13°C
Toilets and cloakrooms	18°C
General offices	20°C
Warehouses	13° to 16°C

Lighting

Badly lit premises not only make working more difficult, but also make it harder to stay alert and active, so increasing the risk of mistakes. Where food is being prepared there can be numerous extra hazards – dirt could be overlooked, cleaning could be less thorough and the colour and general appearance of the product may be hard to gauge. For all these reasons good lighting is crucial.

Natural and artificial

There are two main kinds of lighting needed inside food premises:

- general background lighting to create a bright, pleasant environment without making people feel they are under a permanent spotlight

- task lighting to provide high and focused illumination for specific jobs.

There needs to be a balance between, on the one hand, the detrimental effects of direct sunlight on equipment, materials and food, and on the other hand, the well-being of staff who generally feel more comfortable when there is some natural light. Direct sunlight also increases room temperatures, particularly where there are many windows, and therefore increases both the demand on, and the cost of, running the ventilation system.

Light fixtures (including emergency lighting) must be:

- protected by shatterproof diffusers or sleeves so that there is little risk of physical contamination if a bulb breaks

- mounted in such a way – by incorporation into a sealed ceiling system, for instance – that there are no dirt-collecting spaces

- easy to clean.

What colour of light?

There is a surprising amount of variation, known as 'colour temperature', in what we generally regard as white light. It is crucial to get this right where processes require control of food colour. For accurate colour matching, choose 1A or 1B on the colour rendering index or 100 or 90 on the colour rendering groups specified by the CIE (from the French for International Commission on Illumination).

Typical illumination levels	
Offices	500 lux
General inspection	1000 lux
Corridors	100 lux
Emergency	0.1-1.0 lux

Ventilation

A good flow of air through the building is, of course, necessary to keep people breathing easily, carry away odours and prevent the build-up of condensation. In addition, dust, fumes, chemicals, odours, bacteria and other lightweight (often invisible) hazards can all reach food from the air, whether blown in from outside or wafted around the building through air conditioning and ventilation ducts.

The air circulation should be controlled – after all, there is little point in having clean and disinfected areas if the air itself recontaminates them.

Airflow in food premises should always be from 'clean' to 'dirty'. In many factory environments high-risk areas are put under positive pressure so that the airflow is forced towards the outside or 'dirty' areas.

While natural ventilation may reduce energy consumption and contribute to staff well-being, it often conflicts with the need to prevent contamination. Many food premises control the air temperature, humidity, air quality and number of air changes by mechanical means so that only purified air is supplied to 'clean' areas where food is being processed.

All filter systems in a mechanical ventilation or air conditioning system must be accessible for cleaning and replacement. For insurance purposes it is often necessary to obtain a certificate from a cleaning contractor stating that the system has been fully cleaned.

Air quality control

An air change does not mean merely recirculating the same old air. The law requires a steady supply of fresh air, but your ventilation system is only as good as the air that goes into it and how it is filtered before being circulated around the building.

It is important to ensure that the air inlet is not positioned where it could draw in air from the building's air outlet or from any other potentially polluted source.

Removal of hot or impure air from sensitive areas

There may be places where direct, local extraction is required to draw heat, smoke or polluted air away from a particular activity or piece of equipment. This usually means fitting a hood with an extractor fan.

Regular changes of air	
The number of air changes required varies according to the use of the space	
Restaurants and canteens	8 to12 air changes per hour
Industrial kitchens	20 to 60 air changes per hour
Toilets	6 to 8 air changes per hour

Keeping food hot and cold

To meet legal requirements all food premises must have enough suitable equipment to cook, heat, hot hold and refrigerate food, according to what is appropriate for the foods and processes at each workplace. The equipment must be able to hold high-risk foods at the temperatures specified – at 8°C or below or at 63°C or above – not only to meet legal obligations, but also because effective temperature control is a major weapon in the battle to prevent microbial multiplication and to destroy pathogens (see also pages 324 to 346).

Domestic premises used for food preparation

Just as with vending machines and mobile premises, commercial catering or production done from a home kitchen must comply with the same principles of food safety. The only difference is one of scale.

Making it easier for others

- Ensure that the premises are designed, constructed, equipped and laid out to make it as straightforward as possible for staff to produce food that is safe to eat.

- Train the staff how to use the facilities and equipment.

- Formulate company policies for dealing with malfunctioning equipment.

- Encourage staff to report defects in the building and equipment to their manager or supervisor.

- Supervise and review the workflow as part of your hazard analysis.

Equipment as hazard?

Food preparation and processing machinery can have a significant impact on the safety and quality of food, so you need to make a point of including it in your regular review of risks to food safety.

Unless you come from an engineering background or can call on the expertise of specialists within the company, where do you start? Are there some principles that can be applied to all electricity-powered (or gas-powered) equipment, from a coffee grinder to a bottling line?

An important first step is to ensure that all equipment complies with the minimum standards required by legislation.

Chapter V of Regulation (EC) No. 852/2004 on the hygiene of foodstuffs covers general requirements for the construction, installation, cleaning and maintenance of equipment and surfaces that come into contact with food.

Most powered food machinery with moving parts is also covered by the European Directive 98/37/EC, which is enforced in the UK by The Supply of Machinery (Safety) Regulations 1992 and its 1994 and 2005 amendments. The supplier (usually the manufacturer or the importer) has the main responsibility for compliance.

Suppliers of food machinery must carry out a risk assessment of their designs and supply equipment that will produce safe food, provided that it is installed, operated, cleaned and maintained according to their instructions. They must, for example, specify how to clean, how often to clean and with what.

Most new food processing machinery sold in the European Union must carry a 'CE mark'. This is the manufacturer's declaration that the equipment conforms to the legally specified design and construction standards. Fines, imprisonment and the removal of the machinery from the market can follow a failure to comply with the legislation.

In the past there have been some problems with equipment that falsely carries the 'CE mark'. Checking the precise reproduction of the 'CE' symbol with the Department for Business, Enterprise and Regulatory Reform website and checking the way in which the mark has been fixed to the machinery may give you some clues to the care with which the rest of the machine has been made.

In all cases, experts recommend that you also check whether new and existing machinery conforms to the the good practice standards for food equipment.

These are, for example, the certifiable standards of the European Hygienic Engineering and Design Group (EHEDG) and the British Standards BS EN 1672-2:2005 and BS EN ISO 14159:2004. The EHEDG produces a range of guidance documents and publishes a list of equipment that it has been certified by approved third-party test laboratories according to a reference cleanability test. You might also look out for the 'NSF Mark' on some equipment – a product certification by NSF International.

So, what can you expect from well-designed and constructed machinery?

The major hazards tend to be microbiological and chemical – usually linked to water, or moisture. So 'dead' spaces, recesses, sharp angles and rough or ridged surfaces must, for example, be avoided because they allow a build up of product debris and bacteria, and the retention of cleaning chemicals.

All liquids from food or cleaning fluids must drain away easily, with all discharges piped to a drain, not onto floors. Aerosols, condensation, ice melt and splashing should be avoided.

Ancillary substances, such as lubricants, must not be able to touch food.

It must be possible to clean and disinfect food-contact surfaces, if necessary, after dismantling parts. Insects must not be able to get into the machinery and organic matter must not be able to accumulate: there must be a seal between the floor and the bottom of any equipment that is not mounted on feet or castors.

Metal-to-metal joints should ideally be made by welding or continuous bonding, while screws and rivets must not be used except where technically unavoidable.

Even so, the responsibility for safe food equipment does not lie solely with its makers. There are also some important legal implications for you when selecting, adapting, operating or selling on food equipment.

One important step is for you to ensure that staff and contractors are following the equipment manufacturer's instructions. This is important both for the production of safe food and to ensure that liability remains with the machinery supplier.

Any changes, such as the use of different types of cleaning chemical, the use of ingredients unforeseen by the supplier, or the replacement of parts with a component that is not exactly the same as the original, may introduce new food safety hazards. A new risk assessment would be required and advice obtained from the supplier, possibly with written approval.

(Bear in mind when buying equipment that sales staff have been known to unwittingly accede to exceptions and bespoke modifications, without approval from their employer.)

If your company were to sell food equipment with unapproved modifications to another food company, then your would company become the legal supplier. If there were hygiene deficiencies, your company would be responsible.

Another important step is staff training, particularly for maintenance engineers. They need to be trained as food workers, treated as food workers and to operate like food workers. Their clothing, tools, practices and attitudes must all reflect the fact that they are dealing with food equipment and not the gearbox of a road vehicle.

Finally, always aim to anticipate and define as specifically as possible the processes, products, ingredients, processing speeds, changeovers and so on that your company needs now and in the future. This will help your own staff and equipment suppliers to ensure that you have the right machinery for the job, without needing inappropriate, or temporary, engineering fixes.

Developing staff competence

Staff can be a company's most valuable resource, but if they are in the wrong place at the wrong time, or if they do not do what they should be doing, staff can also be a shocking drain on company profit. Of course, people make mistakes for many reasons. Sometimes it is because they are under stress, feel insecure in their job or are not motivated, but usually it is because they do not know enough about identifying hazards, minimising risks and setting priorities – in short, because they are poorly trained.

Why training counts

Train for success
Training gives staff the competence and confidence to carry out their work to the highest professional standards.

As you might expect, there are *statutory* requirements for food safety supervision and training, but from a *business* point of view, it is impossible to rate the importance of staff training and development too highly.

Time and time again it has been shown that, besides making fewer mistakes, well-trained employees usually do a better job. On a personal level, they tend to get more out of their work, have more confidence and greater motivation. They may well take on more responsibility, encourage others to achieve even higher standards and may need less supervision. This all counts towards the bottom line.

So, appropriate training in food safety helps a food business to:

- assure the fitness of food for human consumption

- prevent food contamination, microbial multiplication and survival

- prevent food-borne illness

- reassure customers and clients (if they see the evidence of effective food hygiene measures)

- demonstrate due diligence (particularly when training records are thorough).

Why then are some food handlers poorly trained or not given any training at all? The short answer is: poor management.

Who is responsible for training?

It may be that *you* do not have the word training in your job title, or there may be someone else in your company whose role it is to take care of all forms of occupational training. Even so, if you have any kind of management responsibility for food safety, you are likely to have a responsibility for some aspect of food safety training. This could simply be to liaise with training staff within the company on food safety topics, to make reports to the board of directors, or to make the contractual arrangements with outside training consultants.

However, your role could also involve assessing the type and level of training required, arranging and running training courses and monitoring the effectiveness of all training activities within the workplace.

What you need to know

This chapter covers the main areas of management responsibility for food safety training and development. You may not be responsible for carrying out all the activities mentioned, but you need to know about them and consider how they fit in with your other responsibilities. The chapter is *not* designed to help you to train as a trainer, even though you may find some useful advice here. If you are going to run training sessions yourself, we strongly advise you to enrol on a course that deals specifically with training techniques and, perhaps, to study for a qualification such as the CIEH Professional Trainer Certificate (see pages 415 to 419 for educational, training and awarding bodies).

What do we mean by training?

Most definitions of training talk about preparing someone to achieve a desired level of skill or competence by the means of instruction and practice. Sometimes the development of certain attitudes and habits is also mentioned.

As you read through the rest of this chapter, you might wish to include some of the following words somewhere in your own definition – learning, understanding, confidence, responsibility, teamwork and professionalism. Let's take a brief look at two aspects of dictionary definitions of training – desired level of skill or competence, and instruction and practice.

Desired level

Effective training starts with clear goals. It is essential to know what you want staff to achieve by the end of any food safety training activity ('the outcomes') and that the goals are indeed achievable and are measurable.

The expected outcomes should be easy to understand and should be as precise as possible, whether they are a change in behaviour (such as more frequent hand washing) or a demonstration of knowledge (such as being able to state the causes of food poisoning).

Putting it into practice

Training usually needs to include information that helps staff to understand *why* they must do things in certain ways – the chain of contamination and the ideal conditions for microbial multiplication, for example – and firm guidance on *what* to do, *when* to do it and *how* to carry out the task.

Formal, classroom-type training is just one possible step, however. Any new knowledge needs to be constantly reinforced in the workplace by a manager or supervisor – perhaps by you.

A vital part of food safety training is to ensure that staff are shown and told what to do in their own workplace.

It does not end there: after all, the best training in the world will be useless if staff are not given the materials and support required to work hygienically.

If, for example, there are too few hand basins, or the liquid soap runs out, or the hand towels are fabric ones that are replaced only once a week, how can staff implement all they have learnt about the importance of hand hygiene?

Similarly, if there are too few staff on duty at peak times or managers set a bad example, it is foolish to expect staff to achieve high standards.

The scope of responsibility

The management of food safety training encompasses action to:

- identify all the jobholders in the organisation whose actions or inaction could affect the safety of food
- evaluate the *training needs* for each jobholder
- create a written *training needs assessment*
- devise a strategy for delivering training
- ensure that the strategy is implemented effectively
- monitor and evaluate the training programme
- keep training records
- stay abreast of the company's training requirements.

Identifying the jobholders who could affect food safety

Matching the job
Anyone whose actions or inaction could affect consumer health must receive food safety training that matches their tasks and responsibilities.

Employers in the food industry have a legal responsibility to ensure that everyone who works with food has adequate preparation. Regulation (EC) No. 852/2004 on the hygiene of foodstuffs (see pages 163 to 167) states, 'Food business operators shall ensure that food handlers are supervised and instructed and/or trained in food hygiene matters commensurate with their work activity, and that the employees responsible for the development and maintenance of the procedures based on HACCP principles have received adequate training in the application of the principles.'

What does the rather vague requirement of the first part of that sentence mean in practice? Simply that food handlers must be competent to work hygienically with food. There is not a standard syllabus: instead it is up to every organisation to determine what kind, and what level, of training is required by each individual to achieve that competence. The expression *food handler* should not be taken to refer just to people like butchers, bakers and chefs who have direct contact with food, but to anyone who works with food or whose actions or inactions could affect food. This list gives examples of the range of jobholders who may need food safety training:

- administration and secretarial staff
- cleaners
- delivery drivers
- food preparation staff
- food retail staff
- kitchen porters
- maintenance engineers
- marketing and public relations staff

- packaging staff

- senior managers and directors

- supervisors

- waiting staff

- warehouse staff.

Evaluating training needs

Training needs describes what people need to learn and to carry out in order to do their jobs properly. Determining training needs is not always straightforward and you may need to draw on various sources of help.

Written job descriptions and job specifications should provide a good framework for defining what a particular job involves. Separate interviews with staff and managers or a round-table discussion with the people who are doing a particular job should help to reveal what actually happens day to day. It should also give staff a chance to take an interest in their own professional development and to avoid any concern they may have that training is a disguised form of criticism of their personal professional performance.

Finding out what people know and still need to learn

Proof
Staff should be able to prove that they have undertaken training by producing an attendance or an examination certificate.

The staff in your organisation probably come from many cultural, social, ethnic and educational backgrounds, with a variety of experience of the food industry. Some will have had formal training away from their workplace while others may have learnt everything on the job. Some training activities will have covered hygiene comprehensively, while others will have done the bare minimum – and it may all have been a long time ago.

Before you can plan specific training programmes, you need to know people's training history. There may be company records you can consult and you may need to ask people to describe the training they have had, including the level.

You can find out a lot by talking to people and making your own observations. Do this sensitively – people often find it difficult to admit to gaps in their knowledge, especially if they are professionals with many years' service under their belt. And nobody likes to feel watched. Some ground rules are:

- talk about training as a wonderful opportunity, never a judgement on someone's ability

- emphasise that everyone needs to be involved in the training programme, including the managers, and that no one is being singled out

- ask for staff opinions before you present your own ideas

- make observations discreetly – don't walk around with a clipboard.

Commensurate – measuring up to the job

Food safety training needs to match what staff actually do as closely as possible. It is most likely that the people who prepare or serve food need to understand more food safety topics and practise a wider range of food hygiene activities than those who transport food in sealed containers. Some people will need thorough general training, whereas others may be well served by one or two short sessions on clearly defined subjects. Everyone benefits from refresher training.

It is worth repeating how vital it is for *everybody* who could influence the safety of a product – whether by practical action or inaction, or by management decisions or advice – to take part in food safety training. This could even include administrative staff if they enter the production area – for example, a secretary who delivers a sales note. Supervisors and managers are not exempt as they need broad training in all aspects of food safety so that they can make sure that the rules are implemented correctly throughout the organisation.

At the right moment

When to train
New staff, new responsibilities, hygiene problems and changes in legislation, machinery or procedures all warrant some form of training session.

In broad terms, some kind of food safety training needs to take place whenever:

■ new staff join the company – staff must be aware of the most basic food safety dos and don'ts from day one and such training must be included in their general induction training, even if they have been trained by a previous employer

■ staff have new responsibilities – the topics and level depend upon the particular job and should equip staff to do their jobs professionally

■ there has been a lapse in food hygiene standards or a new food hazard is identified – the topics and level could be new, or could be designed to refresh jaded memories

■ procedures or systems change or new machinery, equipment or products are introduced

■ food safety legislation changes or new rules are introduced.

As you can see, training is not a one-off exercise but needs to take place continuously – to motivate and develop staff, to maintain desired standards and to comply with the law.

Drafting a training needs assessment

All the information you collect about training requirements for different tasks in the organisation should be recorded in a document that is usually described as a *training needs assessment*. The assessment should be circulated throughout the organisation to encourage comments from staff and managers and to ensure that the senior management team (and the board of directors, if there is one) endorse it formally. This endorsement commits the organisation to providing and supporting the necessary training.

The assessment is not a once-and-forever activity and the training needs analysis should be reviewed regularly and updated in the light of changing circumstances.

Provided that the training does actually take place, the endorsement could be used as legal evidence that the organisation has taken its food safety responsibilities seriously – a point worth making to any management team that seems reluctant to give food safety the priority it deserves.

Devising a training strategy

The next step is to plan and implement a programme that fulfils the requirements you have identified: in the jargon of trainers, this is often described as delivering the needs or delivering the training. Depending on the nature and size of the organisation, the training needs you have identified and the resources to which you have access, there are many different ways in which training can be 'delivered'.

It is likely that you will need to use several methods. If, for example, there are a number of new staff who need basic-level training and a few who would benefit from a refresher course in the near future, you might decide to book the new staff right away onto a one-day external course, then discuss the running of refresher training with in-house trainers or external consultants. How can you decide what is best? Some options are outlined below and on the next two pages.

Learning in the workplace

Informal workplace learning
Practical and related directly to the workplace.
May be unthreatening to nervous learners.
Inexpensive.
Likely to be incomplete.
May pass on bad habits.
Little quality control.
May disrupt production.

Learning by copying skilled and experienced people is a time-honoured and highly effective method that almost everybody uses at some time in their life, whether deliberately or not. Skills and attitudes can be shaped by structured on-the-job training, such as a demonstration, or by ad hoc advice or simply by following what others do.

Although this is an inexpensive method of training, it is unwise to rely on this alone, as staff could pick up some bad habits and there is no guarantee that the underlying knowledge – the reason why the rules are as they are – will be grasped without some formal instruction.

In-house courses

In-house courses
May be truly commensurate with activities.
May be cheaper than external courses.
Possible quality control issues without any external accreditation or validation.

If your company employs suitably qualified staff, you can organise your own training courses within the organisation. Provided there is space enough to run the theory part of the course, there is likely to be less disruption than when staff attend an external course. An in-house trainer can tailor the course precisely to people's jobs and may be able to assist with follow-up – for instance, by monitoring and assessing the outcomes.

Despite the cost of the trainers' salaries, an in-house programme may be cheaper than sending staff on an external course. However, staff may miss out on hearing about the experiences of employees in other organisations if they do not attend an open external course. If the trainers are not accredited by an awarding body and the staff do not take an externally validated exam, it may be difficult to monitor and control the quality of the training that they receive.

Using external providers

Some organisations rely on consultants to deliver the bulk of their formal training, whether on the premises or outside. The consultants may be local environmental health officers, employees of independent companies or one-person consultancies.

External providers
May have wide-ranging experience.
May offer tailored courses and workplace follow-up.
Could provide a more objective view of training needs.
May be inflexible.
May cost more than in-house solutions.
Possible quality control issues.

Experienced consultants can train large numbers of people quickly and can offer a variety of tried and tested courses. Particularly where an organisation's training needs vary greatly over time, making it difficult to provide all the in-house instruction required, external courses may offer a cost-effective solution even though the cost of staff travel and meals may need to be added to their time away from the workplace. Some consultants offer to shape courses to your company's own requirements and they may provide a follow-up service in the workplace. If not, you will need to ensure that the training translates into behaviour at work.

Making some basic checks

Before you sign a contract it may be a good idea to interview two or three consultants and to compare them. Here are some questions to consider.

- Do they seem interested in your organisation and its specific needs?

- What qualifications do the trainers have themselves?

- Will they visit your premises to see what you do and will they adapt their material and delivery accordingly?

- Can you see some of their teaching aids? Do you find them easy to understand, and will your staff?

- Do they offer to provide follow-up and implementation, or must their involvement end with the last training session?

- Will they put on a sample session or let you sit in on one?

- Is the consultancy an accredited training centre?

- What do previous clients say about them?

Open learning material

Open learning
Usually inexpensive.
Provides consistent quality.
Allows learning at a suitable personal pace and 'in private'.
Unthreatening.
May help those with poor English.
May not be related to the workplace.
May not be recognised by awarding bodies.

Open (or distance) learning packs aim to provide a self-contained programme. They are usually cost-effective in comparison to face-to-face taught courses and, as they are not dependent upon the varied skills and experience of particular trainers, can provide a consistent message in a consistent way.

Staff can learn at their own pace, so high-flyers can get ahead while those who take longer than average to absorb information can take all the time *they* need. Open learning material is also often beneficial to people with low self-confidence who do not wish to be seen making mistakes. Curious though it may seem at first, some people whose first language is not English also get on better with open learning materials than with courses taught in English, because friends or family can translate for them.

Open learning may not, however, always be suitable as a stand-alone method because most people benefit from being able to ask questions and obtain specific work-related advice. Not all open learning materials are recognised by awarding bodies as a suitable necessary preparation for their exams, so staff may not be able to sit a nationally accredited exam.

Implementing the strategy

To be successful, training cannot be a one-off event. As well as dealing with immediate needs, your strategy should incorporate plans for regular follow-up sessions and annual refresher courses. Additional refresher training may need to be arranged if any food safety problem arises.

Some staff may need, or want, more advanced instruction or instruction on particular aspects of their job. Make sure everyone knows what training opportunities are available. Often people battle on, without realising that training could make their working lives more straightforward. You need to encourage an open, non-blaming company culture where people feel free to speak out about any difficulty they are having and to report any concern they have about food safety hazards or hygiene practices. If people cannot tell you what's wrong, you have little chance of designing training to improve the situation.

Management commitment

Keep the rest of the management team up to date with activities and progress. If necessary, remind them that all the effort, time and money spent on training will be wasted if staff cannot act on what they learn, or if managers set a bad example.

Monitoring and evaluating success

There is little point in running any kind of training if you do not check how successful it has been in helping staff to work hygienically – how well, for example, it helps to prevent food-borne illness, comply with the law, avoid court cases, prevent food from being wasted and create a favourable impression among customers. The basic questions you need to ask are:

- what evidence is there that staff have met the training objectives?

- are the outcomes appropriate to your company?

- what, if anything, in the training programme needs to be changed?

Feedback

You will probably have your own ideas about answers to the questions above from observing the way in which staff carry out their work, but it is also important to know what the staff feel about a course and what their supervisors perceive to be the benefits or failures. It is good practice to ask for comments immediately or shortly after any structured training and also at about six monthly intervals, if not more often. This allows for the so-called halo effect of a course to wear off and for staff to put the training into practice.

Questionnaires

Questionnaires are a popular way to obtain comments because they provide a written record, allow for anonymity and, provided they are written in simple language, are quick and easy to complete. You can use either open questions, where staff have plenty of space to write comments, or multiple-choice answers where staff tick their choice of answer or respond according to a scale of satisfaction, or a mixture of the two. In either case it is always a good idea to leave a blank space for comments not covered by the questions. Although questionnaires can provide a great deal of insight, they do not provide objective standards or enable water-tight comparisons between teaching methods or practitioners.

Verbal comments

You can ask people, either singly or in a group, for verbal feedback. If you do, bear in mind this advice:

- let a speaker finish, however long-winded or tortuous

- encourage everyone to have their say

- explain, but avoid becoming defensive

- thank people for their comments

- remember that you don't have to accept every piece of advice.

Management feedback to staff

You need to keep other managers and supervisors informed of what staff have learnt and to make sure they recognise the efforts staff have made. Managers who notice and comment positively on improved practices reinforce the training message and increase motivation: those who do not can rapidly destroy the investment of time and money. Some managers and supervisors will do this without thinking, but it is still a good idea to make it explicit, as it is all too easily overlooked in the daily rush of work. You may be able to give encouragement by talking regularly to staff, listening to their comments, helping to resolve any problems and praising their efforts.

Keeping training records

Checking
During a food safety inspection EHPs may ask to see training records, exam certificates or course attendance documents. They may also question staff to check how much they understand about food safety.

There is no legal requirement to keep records of general training but it makes legal and business sense to do so. Records can hold information that, once analysed, can help you to plan, review and revise your company's training activities. If the worst happens, they can be produced as written evidence that appropriate food safety training has been given.

The information you write down is likely to include information about the:

- names of people who have received training

- date of the training (day/month/year)

- type and level of the training

- duration and phasing (for instance, 36 hours' trainer-led training over seven days)

- training subjects covered and practical activities undertaken

- form of training (such as, trainer presentation, group discussion, workshop, case study, demonstration)

- use of training aids and media (such as books, acetates, slides and videos)

- formal outcome (such as the name of any qualification achieved and the results of tests, exams or work-based assessments).

You may also wish to include the name(s) and qualifications of the person (or people) responsible for the training content, the training schedule and the training review.

Specific HACCP training

Under Regulation (EC) No. 852/2004 on the hygiene of foodstuffs companies must give specific appropriate training to employees who have responsibilities for the development and maintenance of the procedures based on HACCP principles. The legislation also requires documents and records to be kept that are appropriate to the type and size of the food business to demonstrate the effective application of CCPs and the other required measures. It would be prudent to include the specific HACCP training in those records.

Staying abreast of requirements

Managers also need to keep up to date. There are many ways of doing this, including joining one of the professional organisations listed on pages 415 to 419, subscribing to food safety journals or magazines and attending seminars.

Training for qualifications

There is no legal requirement in the UK for food handlers or their managers to obtain a food safety qualification. Even so, many organisations encourage staff to do so because courses and examinations provide a recognisable standard of achievement which helps to safeguard consumer health, provides reassurance to customers and clients and may benefit the professional status of staff.

Qualifications are usually at three or four levels. Depending on the level of study and the awarding body involved (see pages 415 to 419 for the main ones), obtaining a qualification usually depends upon both a specified period of study at an accredited training centre and the successful completion of an exam, or assignments and an exam. Some qualifications are recognised internationally.

Making it easier for others

- Lead by example, and ensure that other managers do too.

- Create conditions in which it is easy for staff to learn.

- Shape training programmes to your workplace and to the jobs that staff do.

- Remember that people learn in different ways.

- Provide the right equipment, so staff can practise what they have learnt.

- Supervise and follow up training – it is a continuous process.

- Ensure that anyone who works in a food-handling area is trained in the essentials of food safety, personal hygiene and requirements for reporting illness.

- Consider whether a willingness to learn would be an important criterion for selecting and appointing staff to work with food.

Making learning easier

Whether your role is to run training courses yourself or is limited to choosing consultants or outside courses, it is worth understanding the principle training methods for food safety, their possible advantages and disadvantages and the circumstances in which they are most suitable.

The learning process

Adults do not learn like children – they are usually more self-directing and independent, and they may demand to know why they need to know certain things.

Learning happens in a number of distinct steps and a good training course takes account of this. First comes the stage of receiving new knowledge, whether through observation, words or practice. Then the knowledge needs to be discussed with others and interpreted in the context of the workplace. Finally it needs to be applied in practice and, if the outcome is good, passed on to others. Remember, though, that bad experiences as well as good ones are shared. Poor training can be worse than no training at all, undermining key messages and perhaps prompting staff to lose interest.

Different methods of training

Scheduling training Tired people make poor students. Try to schedule training at the beginning, rather than at the end, of a work shift.

There are many different methods available to trainers. Suitability depends on the subject and time available and on the people receiving the training. Good trainers recognise that different people respond to different methods and try to use a variety of approaches, which can range from a formal presentation to a highly informal discussion or role-playing activity.

All methods have advantages and disadvantages, but people usually learn better when they see something as well as hear about it, better still when they have the chance to discuss it, and best of all when they are required to tackle a task themselves. Most good trainers use a mix of methods so that staff do some listening, watching, discussing and hands-on practical work. This helps to vary the pace and maintain interest, as well as improving the learning process.

Presentation

In a presentation the trainer gives information to those being trained. The interaction is essentially one-way, with the trainer doing most of the talking and the students taking notes and asking questions. The technique is useful for communicating complex or abstract material that needs the full attention of the audience. It works best when combined with more participatory methods, such as a demonstration or discussion, and when followed by some kind of student activity such as an exercise, question and answer session or case study. The possible advantages are that:

- a lot of information can be conveyed in a short time

- the presentation and its timing can be prepared thoroughly in advance.

Among the possible disadvantages are that:

- students may need to be prompted to ask questions, otherwise there may be little feedback, making it hard to gauge just how much they have understood

- it may be difficult to get the pace right for all the students

- students may not have time to formulate their own thoughts

- the material may not be remembered.

A message from the bored

We, the long-suffering business men and women of Britain, are fed up with boring, badly prepared presentations that send us to sleep. High on our list of bad marks are poorly laid-out rooms.

Next comes waffling (why can't presenters get to the point quickly and stick to it?)

Followed by unfunny or embarrassing jokes. Who needs them?

Equally unpopular are presenters who waste time apologising for being 'no good at presenting'.

And who likes to sit there while a speaker sweats, stammers and dries up?

Or, speaking of which, who raises their voice? Droners, whisperers and squeakers all have a hard time holding our attention. Knowing how to speak is one thing. Knowing when to shut up is another.

Why should we stay put for a moment longer than scheduled? Of course, punctual ending begins with prompt starts. (Take note all presenters who like to learn how the equipment works in front of the audience.)

Discussion

Discussion is a good technique for encouraging people to develop their thoughts and find solutions to problems. Discussion methods include the formal 'platform' approach in which the trainer encourages individuals to speak; the informal, open discussion in which everyone contributes as they wish; and the unstructured, free session (sometimes referred to as an 'idea shower') in which the only rule is not to criticise anyone else's idea. The subject, composition and size of the group, and the goals of the training session all have a bearing on which is most appropriate in any given situation.

Among the possible advantages of discussion are that:

- participants are active and involved

- everyone is encouraged to make their own suggestions

- individual suggestions and solutions may make the topic more meaningful (staff may 'take ownership' of the issue), so they are more likely to remember what they ought to be doing in their daily tasks

- communication and understanding are promoted, which may improve workplace co-operation.

The possible disadvantages are that:

- the method is time consuming

- discussions may degenerate into disputes, if the trainer is inexperienced

- contributions may wander off the point, unless the trainer guides the group gently

- less assertive people may not have a fair say.

Demonstration

Most skills or techniques benefit from a practical demonstration. This could be in the workplace if time, space, hygiene and health and safety considerations permit, or it could be a classroom mock-up of a real situation, or it could be on a video.

A simple demonstration in the workplace can help staff to relate theory to everyday good practice.

The possible advantages are that:

- the students get information by both seeing and hearing, so they are more likely to remember what they have witnessed

- it is easy, particularly with a live demonstration, to explain details and answer questions as they arise.

Possible disadvantages are that:

- the preparation may be time consuming

- the demonstration may not be suitable for large groups, unless you have a camera and screen

- the students may lose concentration because it is a passive experience.

Case study

In a case study the trainer presents the group with a story, or scenario, that raises some important food safety issues. The story can be taken from real life, made up, or a combination of the two.

If good real-life material is available this is often the most interesting – although the details of a well-known incident should be disguised so that trainees do not recognise the case immediately.

Among the possible advantages are that:

- the students can imagine themselves in a real situation instead of a hypothetical one

- the focus is on facts and causes

- independent thinking is encouraged.

Possible disadvantages are that:

- good, ready-made, appropriate cases can be hard to find

- preparation can be time consuming, as solutions must not be too easy or too difficult

- the case study may be suitable only for small groups, to give everybody a role, and where a larger group is divided into smaller groups, the feedback in the plenary session may be time consuming

- some students may take an inflexible stance, creating group tension.

Checking the quality of courses

Before you authorise training, it is a good idea to discuss with the trainer which approaches will be used. A variety usually works best. Trainers should be able to explain why they consider their techniques appropriate for the audience, the designated outcomes and the time and facilities available.

It can also be useful to see the training aids and materials that the trainer will be using, such as books, handouts, acetates, computer-based presentations or videos. These should have clear learning benefits and be of a professional standard.

Finally, it is reasonable to ask trainers specific questions. How will they relate their teaching to the actual workplace experience of the students? What will they do to make sure students understand and that everyone keeps up? How will they keep students interested? What will they do to help students to put their new knowledge into practice? What goals will the training have and how will they be measured?

Fit to work with food – health and hygiene

Is your workforce clean, tidy and well groomed at all times? Do staff take pride in their appearance and in high standards of personal hygiene? These things may sound trivial, but few issues are so important in an industry where many processes are literally hands-on and lapses in personal hygiene can lead to cases of severe food-borne illness.

In contrast, a smartly turned-out, hygiene-conscious workforce is a good form of insurance. As well as safeguarding food from contamination, it sends out a powerful message of professionalism and trustworthiness to customers, clients and the general public. In turn, this maintains your company's business standing and may help to boost the team spirit and morale of employees. Perhaps best of all from your viewpoint, it helps to make the manager's job easier!

The management challenge

Personal hygiene is not a difficult subject. There is no complex theory to learn and no long list of facts to remember. Managing it is quite another matter, however.

People often resist changing their behaviour, especially when they have ingrained habits. Some employees find it difficult, embarrassing or offensive to discuss aspects of personal hygiene. *You* may find it difficult too. As everyone comes to the subject with different attitudes and standards, you need to respect these differences while ensuring that everyone lives up to the same high standards. So, even though this is the most personal of all the food safety topics, you need to ensure that the subject does not appear to be aimed at a particular individual, but is seen to apply equally to all – staff and managers alike.

Your four-point plan

Despite the difficulties, personal hygiene can be managed successfully. There are four key things you need to do:

- implement a personal hygiene policy as part of your general food safety policy (see page 373)

- provide suitable and effective training

- create a hygiene-focused working environment

- monitor personal hygiene.

The personal hygiene policy

Your organisation should have a clear written statement setting out the standards it expects its staff to follow for personal hygiene and habits. Such statements are usually included in a document known as the company food safety policy or the company food hygiene policy. The document should be as detailed and unambiguous as possible and should be circulated to everyone.

Once you have a general policy, you can draw up simple, specific rules based upon it and post these in appropriate places to remind people about issues such as washing their hands before entering a food preparation area. When such notices identify the instructions as company policy, they tend to carry extra weight.

Training

Do *you* follow instructions blindly? Probably not. So why should your staff? Training should *explain* the reasons for the rules – a much more effective means of getting people to comply than lecturing or threatening them.

A hygiene-focused workplace

Clean toilets and basins; a good supply of hot water, soap and hand-drying equipment; protective clothing; and an appropriately stocked first aid box readily available – all these things make a difference by making it easier for staff to maintain high personal standards. After all, rules that are hard to follow are hardly ever followed.

Monitoring

Not all aspects of personal hygiene are on show! But many can be observed and managers and supervisors should stay alert to ensuring that rules are being followed. The ideal, however, is to promote self-monitoring by encouraging people to take a pride in their own and one another's hygiene habits and personal presentation. Part of the written policy might be that each employee is expected to take responsibility for his or her own health and hygiene.

Key aspects of a personal hygiene policy

There are a number of crucial subjects that should be covered in the personal hygiene section of your food safety policy. Firstly, there are factors relating directly to the human body: hands, skin, mouth, nose and throat, and infectious diseases. Then there are body adornments and applied products, such as jewellery, toiletries and sticking plasters. The rest of this chapter discusses each of these in turn.

Hands

Of all bodily parts, the hands are the most likely to come into direct contact with food. How many processes can you think of in your business that require someone to touch food with their hands? Not even the most automated of industrial processes is likely to be completely hands-free. Unsavoury though the thought may be, just consider what people might do with their hands regularly every day. These are just a few possible answers:

Unwashed hands can easily carry pathogens from a source of contamination, such as raw meat, to ready-to-eat foods and food-contact surfaces.

- handle non-food items, waste and bins

- scratch their head or rearrange their hair

- stroke their chin, scratch an itch or wipe their mouth

- stifle a cough or sneeze, or blow their nose

- massage aching feet

- handle money

- open doors

- shake hands with others

- use toilet paper

- touch their genital area

- handle raw and cooked food.

Each of these actions has the potential to contaminate the hands and consequently any food that is handled. As any textbook will tell you, there is a simple solution: hands must be washed after each of these actions, before entering a food room and before handling food. Real life, however, is not quite so straightforward.

Solving the great hand-washing mystery

Surveys show that almost everyone knows that they ought to wash their hands after going to the toilet, but that surprisingly few actually do so. One possible reason for this discrepancy comes from PhD research carried out by Lisa Ackerley in the 1990s into what she calls 'health benefit analysis'. Her findings suggest that people will do something only if they are convinced it brings a direct health benefit. In other words, unless people believe that dirty hands really do cause disease, there is very little chance of encouraging thorough hand-washing habits.

In a way this is good news because it means that you can use information about food-borne illness to change behaviour, perhaps by discussing or pinning up dramatic stories of real incidents of disease caused by poor hand hygiene. The downside, however, is that you will probably not get far just by sticking up more and more lists of rules or by introducing fines and penalties.

Teaching good technique

Even if your workforce is thoroughly convinced of the need for hand washing and is committed to doing so at every appropriate moment, individuals might still not be washing their hands thoroughly. You can supply water at the correct temperature (usually 45°C to 50°C), copious amounts of an approved unscented soap, nailbrushes and hygienic methods of hand drying – but there is no guarantee that all parts of the hands will be washed properly.

Might a visitor to your workplace from another planet be forgiven for thinking that the process more or less involved showing the hands to water, stroking them together once and wiping them down the front of clothing? It may seem petty and tedious, but even adults often need to be helped to understand that the soap and hot water do only part of the work and that rubbing hands together vigorously and using a nailbrush really do help to prise microbes from the skin surface. As for wiping hands down clothing, staff often need to be reminded of the sources of microbes and the possibility of cross-contamination and recontamination.

Examples of when to wash hands
Before
- starting work

- working with any open, raw or high-risk food

- wearing food-grade gloves during any work with food

- when switching from handling raw to cooked food

After
- handling raw food

- visiting the toilet

- wearing food-grade gloves

- handling raw eggs in their shell

- coughing or sneezing into your hands or a handkerchief

- touching the hair or face

- carrying out cleaning jobs or touching containers of cleaning chemicals

- dealing with rubbish/waste and bins

- eating or drinking (in designated areas) or smoking (in an unenclosed area outside).

In brief, hands must be washed as often as necessary to keep them clean.

How to wash your hands

You need to ensure that the following basic points are second nature to all food handlers. If your company asks for a double-wash procedure or the use of bactericidal hand preparations, ensure that the rules are clear.

- Always use a hand basin provided exclusively for this purpose. (Never use a sink designed for washing food or for washing up.)

- Use comfortably hot water and soap. Liquid soap is best because a bar of soap may carry bacteria left by the last person who used it.

- Work the soap into your hands by rubbing them together vigorously. The agitation helps to remove bacteria. It is suggested that you take 15 to 20 seconds on this. Don't forget the areas between your fingers and around your wrists.

- Rinse your hands thoroughly before drying them.

- Dry your hands thoroughly, using the method approved by your company. Never dry your hands on your overalls, apron, a tea towel or oven gloves.

- Apply a hand disinfectant if it is your factory procedure to do so.

Skin complaints

Cuts, boils, septic sores and other skin problems and infections can all harbour pathogenic bacteria, such as *Staphylococcus aureus*, which can cause food poisoning. In a way, these problems are easier to manage than hand washing because they are often easily visible.

Treating skin conditions

People may continue working with minor cuts, sores and so on, provided that the skin condition is covered with a brightly coloured waterproof dressing. The rule about dressings should apply to both visible areas of the body, such as the face or forearm, and to covered areas, such as the torso – although in the latter case you will have to rely on staff co-operation since you will seldom know about the problem. Even if you do know, you may not ask to monitor treatment as this could be an infringement of personal liberty.

Mouth, nose and throat

The mouth, nose and throat can all harbour pathogens, particularly *Staphylococcus aureus*. When people sneeze or cough, they spray out tiny water droplets which can land on food, utensils or preparation surfaces, so transferring pathogens. Another route of transmission is, as already mentioned, via the hands when people touch their mouth or nose, then handle food without first washing their hands.

What managers can do

There are two things you need to do to prevent contamination from the mouth and nose: keep people with coughs and colds away from food and stop people scratching or picking their nose or touching their mouth.

Dealing with sneezes, coughs and colds
Coughs and colds are minor infections in themselves, which is part of the problem because people still come to work. In the food industry, however, they are a serious issue and need to be dealt with in a similar way to that of reporting infectious diseases (see below).

An unrestrained sneeze can project bacteria-laden droplets of moisture through the air at 100 metres a second (more than 200 miles an hour). A sneeze, shown here in a high-speed photograph, may have between 10,000 and 100,000 droplets, each containing one or two bacteria that can settle on food or food-contact surfaces.

Preventing contact with hands
It is extremely difficult to stop people from touching their mouth or nose, since it is usually a completely unconscious action. Even when people do become aware of what they are doing, you still need to persuade them to wash their hands after doing it.

Hair

Apart from touching the hair, which we have already mentioned, the main problem of contamination is from loose strands that may fall out and contaminate food.

Not all aspects of personal hygiene are immediately noticeable, but managers can easily monitor whether food handlers and visitors are wearing suitable protective hair covering.

What managers can do
Hats and hairnets are the best way of preventing stray hairs from entering food, so ensure a good supply is always available. If possible, find a style that people are happy with. Include instructions on headgear in the written hygiene policy and give training so that people understand why the policy is as it is. Monitoring and enforcement are relatively easy, since few things are more obvious than wearing or not wearing something on your head.

Infectious diseases

It is illegal to allow people to work with food when they are suffering from, or are a carrier of, a disease that could be transmitted through food or could cause microbiological contamination. The illnesses that fall into this category (under Regulation (EC) No. 852/2004 on the hygiene of foodstuffs) include any disease likely to be transmitted through food, infected wounds, skin infections, sores and diarrhoea.

Other specific illnesses (covered by various pieces of British public health legislation) include typhoid, paratyphoid and dysentery and infection by Norovirus or Rotavirus or by parasites such as *Giardia lamblia* and *Cryptosporidium* species.

People working for a food business have a legal duty to report their illness or symptoms to the company immediately they become aware of the situation. The staff affected must not work with food until they are cleared as being safe to do so and they must not enter any food-handling area in any capacity if there is any likelihood of direct or indirect contamination.

Carriers

Food handlers who are, or may be, suffering from a food-borne illness and those who have been in contact with them are also obliged to report this to their manager or supervisor. This, however, is only one part of the story as many people are carriers of a disease – they do not suffer symptoms themselves but can pass the disease on to others. The role of these carriers in causing outbreaks is still not fully understood because, unlike Typhoid Mary (see page 91), not all carriers excrete the organisms responsible for the illness.

Carrier status will become known either to the person involved or to others only when a positive result is indicated for a particular organism as a result of analysis of either a stool or blood sample. The possible detection of carriers may be one of the few positive arguments for pre-employment medical checks in the food industry although, even then, there is no guarantee that carriers will be detected or, indeed, that their carrier status is necessarily a barrier to employment.

What managers can do

Juggling the issue of illness can be difficult. The manager's primary responsibility is, of course, to ensure that anyone who could genuinely pose a hazard to health is either excluded from the premises altogether or is given work well away from any food handling operations. Some managers take the view that the risk from a carrier who works with food may be too great to allow, even if the person is not excreting the organism.

Managers must also ensure that staff do not report an 'upset stomach' every time they want a day off work. As with hand washing, there is a certain degree of trust involved. You need to be confident that people will report symptoms of a food-borne illness when they have them and that they will not fake symptoms. Some companies analyse their sickness records and if people consistently take Mondays or Fridays off for 'diarrhoea', they may, as a matter of routine, ask the company doctor or the employee's doctor to investigate.

Checking it out

If a food handler suspects symptoms of food-borne illness, advise him or her to consult a doctor and explain that he or she may need to provide a faecal sample. If an infectious illness is confirmed, the health service will inform the Consultant in Communicable Disease Control (CCDC) who, in turn, informs local authorities if it is a notifiable disease or food-borne infection.

Absence and return to work

Food handlers with a food-borne illness or certain other conditions (such as skin infections and other septic and bronchial conditions which could contaminate food) can be excluded from work by the local authority. If this happens, the employee may apply to the local authority for compensation for loss of wages.

The big question is how long do they need to be excluded from work? The Department of Health guidelines *Food Handling – Fitness to Work* issued in 1995 and updated in 2004 recommend in most cases that there should be no return to work until at least 48 hours after the last episode of vomiting and diarrhoea and even then only if the strictest attention is paid to personal hygiene.

The table on page 394 outlines the criteria for when a sufferer or carrier may return to work after he or she has become free from symptoms.

Seeing a doctor

Many management policies require employees to seek medical advice for any severe or long-lasting health problem. The advice may be from a company doctor, if there is one, or the person's own general practitioner. The policy may also require the doctor to state that the person is fit to work as a food handler before he or she is allowed back to work after illness. This can make the manager's job easier and prevent the need to ask intrusive questions that could infringe rights to personal privacy.

Jewellery

Most organisations prohibit food workers from wearing jewellery because of the risk of bacterial and physical contamination. While most customers would probably not mind finding a diamond ring in their breakfast cereal, the hard gemstone could cause physical injury – and you can imagine how many pathogens might be lurking in the gem setting. Sometimes exceptions are made for a plain band wedding ring and some companies permit staff to wear sleeper earrings, nose studs or religious jewellery only if they are fully covered by coloured sticking plasters. You should assess such hazards and their risk in your business, formulate an appropriate policy and make it clear to all.

Clothing

Some items of protective clothing are designed to protect the wearer from burns, scalds and knife or impact injuries, but most items, such as overalls, hats, hair nets, footwear, gloves and aprons, are to protect food from contamination.

Protective clothing may include hats or hair coverings (above), heat-proof gloves (centre), overalls and even beard snoods (below).

Many food handlers mistakenly believe that the purpose of protective clothing is to protect their own clothes from food. Training should correct this misconception.

Most management policies insist on protective clothing being worn by everyone who works directly with food. Garments are usually supplied by the company. Light colours are preferable because they show dirt more easily, prompting staff to put on fresh clothing.

Sometimes garments are colour-coded by work area to help to maintain the separation of staff working with raw and cooked food, for example.

All protective clothing should be either washable or disposable. There should be no pockets or only internal pockets (to prevent items falling out of them and into food).

Fastenings should take the form of studs that could be detected by metal detectors if they got into food, or hook-and-loop strips. Name labels should be sewn into uniforms or embroidered.

Staff need to be trained to put on their hats and hairnets *before* putting on overalls or tunics so that any loose hairs that drop, when they put on the head gear, do not go onto clothing that is exposed while they are working with food.

If your company provides food-grade gloves, ensure that staff wash their hands before and after putting them on and that they change the gloves whenever they could have become contaminated – when switching between working with raw and cooked foods, for example.

Toiletries

Toiletries can cause chemical contamination to food. Some foods – especially milk, milk products and tea – are particularly susceptible to taint by strong-smelling substances. You may wish to ban food handlers from using perfumed toiletries and personal grooming products altogether, or to encourage restraint in their application. Nail varnish should be prohibited because it can chip and flake into food.

Bandages and plasters

Sticking plasters and other dressings should be waterproof to prevent leakage. They should also be brightly coloured (usually blue) so that they can be seen and retrieved if they come off, and appropriate further action taken (such as disposing of that batch of food). Some types of sticking plaster also contain a thin metal strip so that they can be picked out by a metal detector if they fall into food.

Making it easier for others

- Lead by example. If you break the personal hygiene rules, no one else will respect them either.

- Apply the rules equally to all, including top management and visitors.

- Explain carefully and sensitively. Don't just issue orders. People will not change their behaviour unless they know there is a good reason for doing so.

- Keep the explanations simple. Whether it is in a training session or on notices on the wall, all messages should be unambiguous, easy to understand and easy to remember.

- Repeat messages often but in different ways. We all have our own ways of learning, so varying your techniques will get through to more people. Try notices, cartoons, videos, refresher training and so on.

- Ensure that everyone understands their legal responsibility to keep themselves scrupulously clean.

- Ensure that food handlers wear clean uniforms or protective clothing.

- Make the procedure for reporting illness and for not working with food as simple as possible.

- Encourage staff to ask questions about any aspect of personal hygiene or personal habits that could affect food safety.

- Consider asking everyone to sign a copy of the hygiene rules. It is common policy to print a booklet of hygiene rules and to ask each member of staff to sign that they have read and understood it. This prevents people saying later that they were not told or did not understand the rules. It may also help to provide evidence of due diligence should the company ever need to do so.

Management matters

If you have ever worked in a badly planned building or one that has been poorly maintained, you will know what a difference it can make to your attitude and your ability to do your job. A well-designed building makes work activities more straightforward and may help to promote feelings of pride, self worth and well-being among staff. In contrast, a poor design may sap energy and lead to demotivation, absenteeism and a range of complaints, such as the so-called sick-building syndrome. Bear in mind that the working environment your company provides may influence the standard of the finished product that staff produce. Of course, many companies have to make compromises to the ideal, but those should never be compromises to the safety of food. Deficiencies that are often highlighted during inspections include inadequate working space for the processes being undertaken, inappropriate workflow and insufficient contamination control because of poor separation of foods and tasks.

When it comes to staff training, we make no apology for repeating that the process is a continuous one and not a one-off event. When you run a car, you expect to have to put in fuel and to take it to a garage for regular servicing. Intermediate-level (level 3) and advanced-level (level 4) training sessions, as well as regular refresher training for everyone, including you and the other senior members of staff, help to ensure that the food safety 'tank' stays topped up. Supervision and motivation help to ensure that the food safety 'engine' is properly tuned.

Acknowledge employees' work experience and always give credit where it is due. Make connections to familiar experiences to make food safety more meaningful – for example, mention domestic situations or remind staff that what happens in a food business can also have consequences for partners, children and friends. The message that everyone is a customer can also prove to be helpful.

Sometimes even the words you use can help to nurture the corporate food safety culture. Use 'we' and 'our' rather than always saying 'the company'. Try to make everyone feel part of the team: your hygiene standards are only as good as the team members who support it, and every team is only as good as its weakest member.

Consider whether motivational awards or rewards might help. Well-tried possibilities include in-house certificates or shields, bonus systems, commendations in the house newspaper or on the news board and proposal systems which reward staff who propose helpful ideas. Watch out for local and national competitions and campaigns that include points awarded for hygienic practices and knowledge of food safety. What simpler route could there be into tackling the sometimes tricky matter of managing standards of personal hygiene?

Packaging for safety and promotion

The design of packaging plays a big part in selling foods and individual brands to consumers.

Did it ever occur to you that it is impossible to see a lot of the food you intend to buy? You have a clear mental picture of what you want to buy, but what you actually see is printed paper, cardboard, plastic, films, bags and so on. Some food is completely hidden, such as fruit in a can or soup in a pouch. Other food – such as fresh meat in a film-covered tray or jam in a glass jar – can be glimpsed through transparent packaging. Even so, shoppers have few chances to really examine and touch much of the food on offer, so they have to base many of their supermarket selections on packaging alone.

You may like it or loathe it, but packaging is an integral part of the food industry. Packaging of many types is introduced right at the start of the food chain and, as a consequence, is an aspect of food safety that food managers cannot afford to ignore.

This chapter puts food packaging in context and outlines the functions of packaging and some of the key considerations for safe materials.

Shopping trends

Only a few generations ago people would have found it strange to have to rely so heavily on packaging rather than on their own direct assessment of a food. So what has prompted the change?

Today's shoppers rarely walk to a small local shop each day for a few purchases. Ninety-two per cent of Britons say they shop at a supermarket – some once a week, but others only monthly for the bulk of their purchases. They expect food to keep its flavour and stay safe to eat until they go shopping again. Most people expect all kinds of food to be available throughout the year, and this often involves moving food right around the globe. The food must also survive being moved from the supermarket shelf to the shopper's trolley, from the trolley to the car (usually) and from the car to the kitchen. Many people say they do not have the time to prepare meals from scratch using fresh raw ingredients: they welcome and depend on convenience foods that bring together all the elements of a complete meal and can often be heated in some of their original packaging. The demand for packaged food has also increased because there are now far more one-person households.

For all these reasons the packaging industry needs to produce suitable receptacles to allow food to be handled, transported and stored in ways that both retain the quality of the food and keep it safe to eat.

The function of packaging

The earliest forms of food packaging were probably a big leaf, a piece of bark, an animal hide or a basket woven from plant stems or fibres. These simple, natural, renewable and biodegradable materials are still used in some parts of the world to carry and store food.

There are now three main categories of packaging:

- primary packaging or sales packaging – the materials in which the food is placed on sale to the final consumer: any materials in direct contact with the food must be approved as safe

- secondary packaging or grouped packaging – materials, such as cardboard cartons, used to group together a quantity of a particular product

- tertiary packaging or transport packaging – to prevent damage during physical handling and transport.

The packaging needs to:

- contain food and make it easy to transport

As well as promoting brand s, packaging has to fulfil many other requirements, including protecting food from contamination and damage, helping to maintain the right atmosphere and temperature, safeguarding the food quality and shelf life, and providing essential consumer information.

- protect food from outside influences – contamination and atmospheric conditions

- maintain the quality of the food

- extend the shelf life

- provide information for the purchaser and the person storing and preparing the food

- promote the brand.

Containing and transporting food

All food packaging needs to be suitable for the type and shape of the food, the method of preparation/manufacture, the type of storage conditions needed, the distance travelled and the use by the final consumer.

Food being transported usually requires packaging that resists physical damage from crushing, dropping or penetration. The level of resistance depends upon the material chosen. You would not, for example, expect a glass container to be unbreakable, but plastic materials should show resistance to breaking, tearing, bending and cracking, and abrasion.

All the materials need to be suitable for the storage condition required for each food, such as refrigeration or freezing.

Other considerations include the ability to stack and pile large quantities of the product in a safe and economic way, and the use of the food by the consumer – packaging needs to resist tampering and may need to be re-sealable.

Protecting food from outside influences

So far as is possible, all packaging needs to be a barrier to:

- microbial, chemical and physical contamination of any kind

- physical conditions, such as moisture and dryness that could damage the food quality by encouraging the growth of pathogenic or spoilage organisms

- storage pests

- taint from other foods or products.

Some foods may need packaging with specific properties. For example, beer needs protection from ultraviolet light; foods in modified atmosphere packaging need to be sealed against oxygen in the air around us; and food intended for cooking in its original packaging needs to be suitable for the specified cooking or reheating method, such as by conventional or microwave oven, directly in water in a saucepan or surrounded by water in a bain-marie.

Maintaining the quality of food

Although the quality of food cannot last forever, packaging needs to retain a food's typical characteristics – moistness, dryness, flavour, aroma and colour, for example – at least until the stated date for safe consumption.

Different types of packaging have properties that offer different benefits. These include laminated films that provide aroma protection for coffee; papers with grease and moisture imperviousness for wrapping pizzas and other greasy products; and special barrier properties, in the plastic bottles holding cooking oil for instance, to prevent food from discoloring or losing its vitamins.

Extending the shelf life

The combination of modern processing methods, packaging techniques and packaging materials can keep food fresh beyond its natural shelf life, without changing its intrinsic factors – the typical characteristics of a particular type of food, such as its moisture or nutrient content (see pages 60 to 62 and 66).

Fresh and minced meats, for example, can be kept fresh for several days in modified atmosphere packaging (MAP) (see page 344) before it needs to be cooked. The technique involves changing one of the extrinsic factors (see pages 63 to 66) – in this case, the oxygen level of the atmosphere surrounding the packaged food.

Providing information

Packaging has to carry all the information about the product that is required by law, together with any information that may help the buyer to store and prepare the food so that it is at its best and safe to eat. (See pages 287 to 288 for an example of labelling.)

Promoting the brand

In a retail outlet it is the packaging that really sells the product. The colour, design or shape of the packaging itself – think of distinctive brand packaging such as Coca Cola or Toblerone – can have a so-called trigger-function that enables the consumer to recognise the product even without a label. The design and information on packaging – such as 'fair trade', 'organic', produced by a named farmer, and 'luxury' – can also help consumers to choose between brands and to feel good about the choices they have made.

Selecting the packaging

So far in this chapter we have looked at the main functions and benefits of packaging. We must also consider some of the adverse influences of packaging, such as migration of chemical components into the food and microbiological or physical contamination.

Contamination

Many primary processes for packaging, such as plastic extrusion, glass melting, thermo-forming and paper-making, involve high temperatures that more or less sterilize the material, so there are few microbiological hazards to foods from the original material. However, temperature changes and high humidity can create conditions that favour the multiplication of micro-organisms, such as moulds, on paper surfaces.

Any materials coming into direct contact with food must be free from harmful chemical substances that could be passed on to the product by migration (see page 284). Chemicals used during the production process (such as solvents, inks, glues and lubricants) must also be food safe.

The major food hazards from packaging arise while the packaging is being made. This is particularly so where there are long open process lines, because of the risk of physical contamination from machinery, lubricants used on the machinery, people and the surrounding process environment.

Product-specific risks

Paper and paperboard

Paper and paperboard (commonly known as cardboard) is usually composed of plant fibre, almost exclusively from cellulose fibre derived from wood. The composition of paper may be fresh fibre only, a mixture of cellulose and recycled paper, or 100 per cent recycled materials. Production processes include bleaching, coating and laminating.

Cellulose-based packaging materials are prone to pick up unwanted odours, especially during long storage periods in moist conditions or during transport. Paperboard is also vulnerable to mould infestation which can produce a visible stain and make the packaging smell mouldy. This smell can then be transferred to food.

The processing environment of paper and board factories provides favourable conditions for mould spores and for spore-forming bacteria that can survive the production process. This is an understandable reason why moist, protein-rich foods should *not* come into direct contact with primary paper or cardboard packaging materials.

Plastics

Plastics are synthetic materials made from petroleum and can be formed into desired shapes. They are used for a wide range of packaging products from flexible bags to rigid yoghurt tubs.

Strictly speaking, the plastic polymers, such as polyethylene, polypropylene and polyvinylchloride that make up plastic packaging, are organic chemicals (see page 119). Even so, they are much less reactive to external influences than paper or paperboard.

Plastic films can become contaminated by microbes if air used during the processing is uncontrolled. When the films are wound on to reels some films are sprayed with starch flour which, if contaminated, can create a serious safety risk to food in contact with it.

Another problem is the electrostatic charging of plastic films which attracts dust particles from the surrounding air.

Migration

Food and beverages can interact strongly with the materials they touch. Whenever food is placed in contact with packaging, there is a risk that chemicals could migrate into the food. These chemicals may be harmful if eaten in large quantities, or they may taint the food, damaging its quality.

The increased demand for packaged products increased concern about the level of risk to consumers from the release of chemicals into foods – from plasticizers, for example.

Plasticizers

Plastics have various additives such as catalysts, lubricants, mollifiers, antistatics, antioxidants and stabilizators. Some of these could end up in food, either by 'global migration' when a combination of substances migrates from the packaging to the food, or by 'specific migration' when a particular additive is involved.

Some cling film contains the liquid plasticizer di-(2ethylhexyl) adipate (abbreviated to DEHA) to make it flexible. This can be harmful when consumed in high quantities. Numerous studies have confirmed that DEHA can leach out of the film into food. Of particular concern are foods, such as cheese and cold meats, that are high in fat and can absorb large amounts of DEHA. Oily foods, such as those in soya bean oil, in jars with a PVC lining to their lids are also particularly susceptible to plasticizer leaching.

There are legal safety limits for plastic additives and all plastics used for food must be of food grade. A plastic film, usually known as 'food wrap', is available that is safer to use in contact with some foods.

Metal cans

Modern cans are usually provided with a protective coating of varnish, such as epoxy-resin, to avoid interactions between the tinplate or the aluminium and the food. This coating also often has preservative functions, as some fruits bleach or change colour in direct contact with tin.

Glass

Glass is an inorganic substance, usually composed of silica sand, sodium carbonates and other mineral components, such as lead, aluminium or cobalt compounds. Normally we would not expect any *chemical* risk from glass containers. There is, however, a risk of chemical interaction between the different surface coatings applied to glass vessels at different stages of processing.

These surface coatings are usually watery dispersions of waxes and synthetic compounds and are meant to coat the exterior surface of the glass container to reduce friction with other bottles and the guide rails of the conveyor line. Depending on the spraying mechanism, it would be possible for these substances to reach the interior of the container, where they would be a contaminant because they would be unwanted matter in food.

It is a legal requirement for surface coating formulations applied at the 'cold end' stage of processing to be food grade, but excessive concentrations of even food-grade coatings inside glass containers have to be regarded as contamination.

HACCP for food packaging

Many food manufacturers now ask their packaging suppliers to maintain HACCP-type systems. These help the food companies to audit and verify their supplier's standards and to extend their own due diligence to a logical conclusion. So, even though it is not a legal requirement, many packaging manufacturers have introduced food hygiene standards and HACCP-type systems rather than risk losing major customers.

The approach to product safety following the principles of HACCP is the same for food packaging manufacturers as it is for food processors. The individual business must undertake a hazard analysis of its operations, assess the potential risks to consumers and have critical control points to deal with those risks.

Here the packaging manufacturer has some advantage. The food manufacturer starts with a potentially contaminated product that then needs to be kept at or below the acceptable risk level (by controlling intrinsic and extrinsic factors, for example). In contrast, the manufacturer of food packaging usually starts with a perfectly safe material that must not then become contaminated as production proceeds.

Like any other business implementing HACCP principles, the packaging company must devise ways to ensure that hazards are eliminated or the risks from them are reduced to an acceptable level. This means the implementation and monitoring of important key elements such as food safety training, personal hygiene policies, documented cleaning schedules, pest control, food safety incident reports, glass and blade registers, customer complaint statistics and so on.

Industry standards

A number of technical and industry standards have been developed. Currently the BRC/IoP Global Standard (developed by the British Retail Consortium in co-operation with the Institute of Packaging) could be regarded as a leading document for packaging manufacturers. This allows different levels of hygiene and contamination control depending on the risk level for the food.

Other sector-specific standards, such as the FEFCO standard (developed by the Fédération Européenne des Fabricants de Carton Ondulé and the European Solid Board Organisation), define specific requirements for individual parts of the industry – the manufacture of corrugated paperboard packaging, for instance.

It is expected that the ISO 22000:2005 standard will have a considerable impact on the packaging manufacturing industry as it will support the integration of the packaging manufacturer into a food chain controlled by a joint guideline.

Integrated approach to food safety

Protective shield or Trojan horse? Food packaging can be both. It depends not only on its safe production, but also on its safe use. As you can see, packaging manufacturers making products for food must take as much care as food companies to ensure the safety of food.

Genetically modified organisms

Genetically modified organisms (GMOs) are controversial, with some people regarding them as a hazard and some not. Regardless of opinion, companies must by law alert consumers if genetically modified ingredients are used in any of their products. This can be done by, for example, labels on packaging or displaying notices.

Many major retailers insist in their supplier specifications and industry hygiene standards on the absence of GMOs from their own-brand products. This can cause a problem for cereal farms that are adjacent to a licensed GMO cereal farm. It can also pose a problem in proving that animal feed is free from GMO products.

For anyone who thinks this far fetched, bear in mind the following true story.

One of the many uses of starch powder is as a binder for the inks in offset printing. Starch powder derives mainly from maize, which in mainland Europe has been so extensively subjected to genetic experimentation that it is often difficult or impossible to separate GMO maize from other maize. Offset printing is normally used in the food packaging industry for secondary packaging which does not come into contact with the food itself. Even so, some food manufacturers insist that all food packaging materials and inks be guaranteed GMO-free.

Safety through labels

1 Added ingredients:
Peach (10 %). Raw cane sugar,
modified maize starch

2 (!) Allergy advice
May contain nuts

3 Nutrition information
Typical values 100g

Energy	245 kJ/58kcal
Protein	4.6g
Carbohydrate	7.2g
of which sugars	6.5g
Fat	1.2g
of which saturates	0.2g
Fibre	0.2g
Sodium	0.1g

4 Use by: see date on lid

5 KEEP REFRIGERATED
Once opened, consume within 3 days

Delicious Foods
Peach yoghurt
Low fat live yoghurt

6 (v) Suitable for vegetarians

8

7 Gluten free

9
10 Made in the UK

11 Delicious Foods
11-12 Great Sutton Street,
London EC1V 0BX

12 UK
QQ999
EC

13 350g e

Food labelling requirements come under a variety of pieces of legislation. This feature looks at typical packaging information that is designed to give consumers the details they need to select, store and use products that are safe to eat. Additional information can be found on the Food Standards Agency's website http://www.food.gov.uk

1 Ingredients

The ingredients must be listed in descending order of their weight, with the greatest first. The percentage of the ingredient must also be provided if the ingredient is part of the product name, such as 'peach' in Peach yoghurt, or if it is a traditional essential ingredient, such as lamb in shepherd's pie. Any ingredient that is derived from specified foods that often cause allergic reactions must, by law, be included in the list of ingredients with reference to the source allergen (see page 230). The information is crucial to help allergy sufferers to avoid foods and ingredients that could make them seriously ill or even kill them.

2 Advisory panel – allergens

In addition to stating them in the statutory list of ingredients, manufacturers can choose to emphasise the presence of allergens in the intentional ingredients, or to state that a product is not suitable for people with a particular allergy. Sometimes a risk assessment indicates that, despite all precautionary measures, there could be an accidental addition of traces of an allergen, such as nuts in this yoghurt. In such cases, the product label should make this clear in a separate statement – for example, 'may contain' a particular allergen. The warning concedes that the named ingredient is not an *intended* part of a particular product, but its absence cannot be guaranteed because the ingredient is used on the same production line or in the factory for other products.

3 Nutrition information

This panel provides information about the typical food values of the product for energy, protein, carbohydrates, fat, fibre and sodium. The information must be given for a 100 gram portion. Manufacturers often also choose to give the values for a typical serving.

4 Date marking

Most packaged foods must, by law, have a date mark. Highly perishable or high-risk products, such as yoghurt, must have a *use-by* date. Other products must be marked with a *best-before* or *best-before end* date. Dates indicating display periods are optional.

5 Instructions for storing or using the food

Information about storing or preparing a food, or both, helps manufacturers to ensure that their product is eaten when it is safe and at its best.

6 & 7 Dietary guidance

This information is voluntary. If, however, a manufacturer makes a claim about a food, it must not give false information or mislead consumers. The manufacturer should also ensure that it can prove any dietary claim. Products must fulfil various requirements to be permitted to use various logos, such as that of the Vegetarian Society.

8 Product name and description

The name and description of a product must not be false or misleading. A peach yoghurt, for example, must be made from yoghurt that is completely or mainly flavoured with peaches. A few traditional names are exempt. Toad-in-the-hole, for example, does not contain toads and Eccles cakes do not have to come from Eccles.

9 Recycled material

There are no binding rules for the use of this symbol. It could indicate that the packaging is made from, or partly made from, recycled materials. Alternatively, the symbol could indicate that the package can be recycled.

10 Country of origin

The country of origin should be included whenever anything on the packaging, such as photographs, illustrations, maps, flags or even colours, could suggest that the product comes from, or has been made, somewhere other than the true place of origin.

11 Contact details

Contact information should be included for the manufacturer or packer or seller so that consumers can seek information or make complaints should they need to do so.

12 Traceability codes

Products must carry information to ensure that the product is traceable. The code could be on the individual item or on the outer packaging around the product. It is not necessary for consumers to be able to decipher the codes.

13 Weight or volume

The 'e' symbol indicates that the weight or volume shown varies slightly from packet to packet, but is an accurate average for the product.

Managing systems

Key points

Clean enough for food

The need for, and the benefits to be gained from, effective cleaning and disinfection.

What clean means in a food safety context.

What needs to be cleaned and what needs to be disinfected.

The differences between detergents and disinfectants.

Optional uses of the terms sanitizer and sanitizing.

Avoiding confusion between the meaning and effect of disinfection and sterilization.

Types of disinfection.

The sequence of cleaning and disinfection.

The importance of contact time.

How to evaluate the most appropriate methods of cleaning, including the consideration of the types of soiling, scale of the task, choice of equipment and cost.

Factors to consider in the choice of cleaning chemicals and disinfectants.

The importance of training and following manufacturers' instructions.

The principles of cleaning.

Encouraging staff to follow a clean-as-you-go policy.

How to evaluate the effectiveness of cleaning.

Managing the process, including the use of cleaning schedules.

Pests under control

The significance of pests to food safety and the loss of food stocks.

The characteristics and habitat of typical food pests in European countries.

How the design of food premises; cleaning, disinfection and refuse disposal practices; and personal hygiene habits can affect pest control.

Environmental, physical and chemical controls.

The limitations and precautions needed for some forms of control.

Working with specialists.

Types of pesticide.

Safe food at its best

The overlap between the management of time and temperature for the purposes of food safety and preservation.

Significant temperatures for food safety and preservation.

Controlling time and temperature

The significance of the danger zone.

Time and temperature as inseparable controls.

Measures involved in time and temperature control. Rules of thumb.

Measuring and recording temperatures.

Procedures for non-conforming temperature readings.

The use of low and high temperature controls.

Legal and recommended temperatures for refrigerated/chilled storage.

Why food must be cooled and chilled rapidly.

Safety during thawing.

Good practice for cooking, reheating and hot holding.

Maintaining quality over time

Causes of spoilage.

The effects of enzymes and spoilage organisms on food.

Which temperatures control enzyme and bacterial activity in food.

Delaying spoilage.

High and low temperature methods of preservation and the times and temperatures involved.

The difference between sterilization and commercial sterilization.

Why a botulinum cook is necessary in canning.

Chemical, physical and dehydration methods of preservation.

The debate about irradiation.

Stock control, storage and display

The value of safe food storage.

How to provide and maintain suitable conditions for the storage of food.

The principles of storage that minimise contamination, decomposition and infestation.

The continuity of care from the receipt of goods into storage.

How to control stock, including the function of date marks.

Dealing with a crisis

Why it is important to plan for an event you work hard to prevent.

Dealing with bad publicity.

Co-operating with investigating authorities.

Managing complaints of food poisoning.

Creating procedures for a product withdrawal or recall.

Managing the threat of bioterrorism.

Learning from a crisis.

Integrated management

Policies to consider for the success of the business.

Key words

Ambient shelf stable
A description for foods that can safely be stored at ordinary room temperatures for a specified period.

Ambient temperature
The environmental temperature, often used to describe 'normal' room temperature.

Audit (food)
A systematic examination of a company's food activities and results to determine whether they comply with the company's documented procedures and standards.

Best before
A date that indicates the period within which food is at its best.

Botulinum cook
A method of high temperature preservation designed to kill the spores of *Clostridium botulinum* and to reduce the spores of spoilage organisms to a level accepted as being safe for human health.

Carrier
A person (or other organism) infected by a pathogen who can pass it on to others, but who does not experience symptoms.

Case
One incidence of illness.

Catalyst
A chemical that initiates or accelerates a chemical reaction without changing itself in the process.

Clean
Free from dirt, marks or soiling.

Clean as you go
The recognised good practice of cleaning up throughout food preparation tasks and immediately after completing the task.

Cleaning
The process of making something clean; usually a combination of mechanical, chemical and thermal energy.

Cleaning schedule
A management plan for effective cleaning and, where appropriate, disinfection, detailing what, how and when something is to be cleaned.

Cold chain
All the stages in the handling of food that requires refrigeration from farm to sale.

Commercial freezing
The rapid freezing and storage of foods at temperatures below -18°C, typically at -22°C or colder.

Commercial sterilization
A method of high temperature preservation, also known as appertizing.

Contact time
The period when a disinfectant must remain on, or must surround, a surface in order to achieve disinfection.

Core temperature
The temperature measured at the centre or the thickest part of the food.

Critical control point (CCP)
In HACCP, a stage in the process of handling food at which a food business can eliminate a hazard or minimise the risk from it.

Critical limit
The border between safe and unsafe (HACCP).

Danger zone
The temperature range (5°C to 63°C) at which most food-borne micro-organisms multiply easily; the temperature range to be avoided for high-risk foods.

Date mark
A date or code indicating the period within which food should be consumed. Legally recognised date marks include *use by* and *best before* dates.

Detergent
A chemical formulation that helps to dissolve grease and remove food particles or other soiling.

Disinfectant
A chemical formulation or the application of heat (as steam or hot water) to achieve disinfection.

Disinfection
The reduction of micro-organisms to a level accepted as being safe for human health.

Due diligence
A defence that every practicable measure was taken to avoid breaching food safety legislation.

Enzyme
Proteins (chemicals) produced by cells; they act as catalysts in biochemical reactions.

Food safety policy
A company's written statement of its commitment to meeting its obligations towards customers and to producing safe and legal products.

Hazard (food)
A source of danger: anything microbiological, chemical or physical, or any condition or circumstance that could cause harm to the consumer.

Hazard analysis
A systematic process for identifying, assessing and controlling hazards and risks associated with food and drink; a simplified system of HACCP.

Hazard Analysis and Critical Control Point (HACCP)
A system for identifying, assessing and controlling hazards associated with food and drink.

High-risk food
A food that easily supports the multiplication of pathogenic micro-organisms.

Hurdle technology
Controlled manipulation of factors essential to microbial survival and multiplication to increase shelf life.

Infestation
The presence of food pests, usually in large numbers, in any kind of food or domestic premises.

Integrated pest management
A style of pest management based on co-operation between a food business and a specialist pest control company, dealing mostly with preventive measures.

Intrinsic factors
Inbuilt characteristics, such as nutrients, pH and a_w that influence the survival, growth and multiplication of micro-organisms.

Organoleptic
Involving the use of the senses.

Outbreak
A cluster, in time or place, of cases of illness caused by a particular organism.

Pasteurization
A method of heat treatment that destroys tuberculosis pathogens and reduces other pathogens to accepted safe levels for human health.

Pest (food)
A creature that contaminates or destroys food intended for human consumption.

Pest control
Measures including the prevention of infestation to safeguard the fitness of food for human consumption.

Pesticide
A collective term for chemicals designed to kill pests and noxious plants and protect crops and stored products.

Prerequisites
Essentials of good hygiene practice that must be established and carried out before any system of risk management, such as HACCP, can be carried out effectively.

Preservation (food)
Treatments designed to delay the natural processes of decomposition and extend the period within which food is good to eat.

Product recall
Publicity asking consumers to return a contaminated or suspect product to the supplier for a replacement or refund.

Product specification
A food company's detailed description for its suppliers of the content, design, composition and intended use of the product to be supplied.

Product withdrawal
A public health protection measure in which contaminated or suspect products are traced to purchasers and removed from the food chain before they go on the market.

Quarantine
The separation, isolation and labelling of contaminated or suspect foods until an informed decision can be made about what to do with them.

Ready-to-eat food
Food that is not prepared or treated (such as by cooking) in a way that would kill any pathogens present immediately before the food is eaten.

Risk
A measure, or scale, of the likelihood (or probability) that a hazard will occur.

Sanitizer
The name in the UK for a chemical formulation that combines the properties of a detergent and a disinfectant.

Sanitizing
Another term for disinfection; American-English for disinfection.

Shelf life
The period within which food is both safe for human consumption and at its best.

Spoilage
Any undesirable change in food that make it unacceptable for eating, including natural deterioration and physical damage.

Sterilization
A process destroying all living organisms.

Stock rotation
The practice of using a product with the shortest shelf life before using a similar one with a longer shelf life.

Stored product pest
An insect associated with foods such as grain, flour, herbs, spices and nuts that are often stored for long periods.

Temperature control
All aspects of food safety in which temperature is used as a measure to stop a hazard or reduce the risk from it. Combined with time control, temperature influences the survival and multiplication of microbes.

Traceability
Procedures enabling ingredients and products to be identified and followed through all the stages of production, processing and distribution.

Ultra heat treatment (UHT)
A method of high temperature food treatment, usually applied to milk, designed to reduce spoilage organisms and extend the shelf life.

Unfit food
Food that is not safe or suitable, as defined by law, for human consumption.

Use by
The date indicating the last day on which food is safe to eat.

Vector
Animals, including insects and birds, serving as vehicles of contamination.

Workflow
The logical route through food premises for food, food handlers, equipment and rubbish at each production or process stage.

Clean enough for food

Most adults know something about cleaning and disinfection, however reluctant they may be to do their fair share of the household chores. As a manager with responsibility for food safety, you need to know more about cleaning methods and cleaning chemicals than you know already from your everyday experience. The problem is that you may be faced either with banal statements – such as 'mix with water and apply to surface' – or with mind-numbing detail that is almost incomprehensible to all but the specialist – for example 'this product contains sodium sesquicarbonate, polyphosphate and metasilicate which have more buffering power than products containing sodium carbonate and trisodium phosphate'.

Prerequisite
Clean and, where necessary, disinfected premises and equipment are an essential of good hygiene practice.

This chapter aims to steer you between the two extremes. It offers down-to-earth information to help you to comply with the law and enhance your company's business reputation. There is general information about cleaning methods and groups of chemicals to help you to choose the best forms of cleaning and disinfection for the type of food operation you manage. (Detailed material about cleaning chemicals is provided on pages 301 to 304 and 391 to 392.)

The business context

In Part 1 we said that the success of a food business is inextricably linked to the effectiveness of food safety measures. Thorough cleaning and, where appropriate, disinfection, play a central part in this success by:

■ controlling microbiological, chemical, physical and allergen hazards – for example, by removing microbiological contaminants from surfaces and food environments, removing food scraps that could attract and nourish pests, disturbing areas where pests could hide and breed, and making it easier to see damage to the packaging of stored food

■ preventing food-borne illness

■ maintaining the operational effectiveness of utensils and machinery

■ complying with food safety legislation.

Benefits

Legal requirements
Food premises and food rooms in particular must be kept clean. The general environment of food premises, such as yards and forecourts, must also be kept clean. Any attempt at a defence of due diligence is unlikely to succeed if the food premises concerned are dirty.

In turn, these measures are likely to help a food business to:

■ maintain a pleasant working environment which may improve staff motivation and productivity

■ reinforce food handlers' hygiene awareness and motivation

■ create a better impression for customers

■ reduce the amount of food that has to be thrown away

■ minimise the cost of maintenance, repair and replacement of equipment, utensils and facilities.

In addition, clean and tidy food premises help to reduce workplace accidents caused by slipping or tripping.

What do we really mean by clean?

So far we have used the word clean in its everyday sense, but what does it really mean in the context of a food business? The word derives from an Old English word meaning pure or clear, but it is far easier to define by referring to its opposite – dirty. So most dictionaries state something like 'free from dirt, marks or soiling' or 'without dirt or filth' or just 'unsoiled'.

Clean for food

Most people recognise when something is physically clean because a surface is free from dirt, soiling or residue – there is nothing to be seen or touched.

Chemically clean means that all the residue and deposits from cleaning and disinfecting materials have been removed, usually by rinsing the item in water of drinking quality.

Microbiologically clean means that the number of micro-organisms on a work surface or equipment has been reduced to a level that current scientific knowledge deems acceptable for human health. This usually involves the use of disinfectants, which we discuss on pages 298 to 305.

It is, of course, one thing to check whether something is physically clean and quite another to confirm whether something is chemically or microbiologically clean. That is why it is suggested that you have equipment and surfaces checked scientifically from time to time – see pages 67 to 69. (There are, of course, legal limits and recommended maxima for chemicals such as mycotoxins, naturally occurring toxins and agricultural and veterinary residues.)

The process of cleaning

Cleaning (sometimes termed cleansing) is the *process* of making something clean. The process is necessary to control chemical, physical and microbiological contamination of food by keeping food premises, equipment and food-contact and hand-contact surfaces free from soiling, whether visible or not.

Energy for cleaning

There are many methods of cleaning but they all require energy in one form or another. The energy is generated by one or a combination of:

- movement (known as mechanical or kinetic energy) provided by:

  - personal physical effort (sometimes described as elbow grease), such as wiping, sweeping or scrubbing

  - the action of mechanical and electrical equipment, such as dishwashers or floor polishers

  - water agitation (turbulence), as used in many clean-in-place (CIP) systems involving pipes and spray balls

- temperature (thermal energy) – from hot water or steam

- chemicals (chemical energy) – in detergents, disinfectants and sanitizers.

Combining energies

The balance between these forms of energy depends upon factors such as the nature of the cleaning task being undertaken, the frequency with which the task is carried out, the equipment used and the time involved. The time is not merely the time to complete the task but also, and more significantly, the time required for a chemical to work effectively or for hot water to be in contact with the item to be cleaned. These diagrams indicate very roughly the significance of the different forms of energy in a selection of cleaning processes.

Cleaning a work surface by hand

chemical energy

thermal energy

mechanical energy

time

Sweeping a floor with a broom

mechanical energy

time

Using a pressure hose

chemical energy

time

thermal energy

mechanical energy

Washing crockery in a dishwasher

chemical energy

mechanical energy

time

thermal energy

What should we clean, or clean and disinfect?

Everything in food premises must be kept clean and the immediate area surrounding food premises must also be kept clean. It is as simple as that. However, as you well know, this is not the end of the story as there are many surfaces in food premises that could be microbiologically contaminated to a level that could cause food-borne illness or spoilage.

The use of detergents – chemicals that help to dissolve grease and remove dirt – combined with mechanical and thermal energy (as in washing dishes) removes dirt and may remove some microbes. Even so, many micro-organisms and their spores can survive this treatment, so a more lethal approach is required – disinfection.

Disinfection

In the British Standard 5283 disinfection is defined as 'the destruction of micro-organisms, but not usually bacterial spores; it may not kill all micro-organisms but reduces them to a level which is neither harmful to health nor the quality of perishable goods.' In other words, disinfection reduces microbiological contamination to an 'acceptable' level – one considered low enough to be safe for human health.

Surfaces and equipment that must be disinfected after cleaning include:

- food-contact surfaces – such as preparation or cutting boards, knives, work surfaces, mixing bowls, serving dishes and slicing machines

- hand-contact surfaces – such as taps, door handles (including those on refrigeration units), light switches, telephones, toilet seats and nail brushes

- cleaning materials and equipment – such as mops, cleaning cloths, scrapers and brushes – and waste disposal equipment – such as bins and their lids.

Types of disinfection

Disinfection can be carried out by:

- heat (as steam or hot water)

- chemicals

- a combination of thermal and chemical energy.

Ultraviolet radiation is used in some bakeries and at some water processing plants because it is particularly good at killing protozoa which can survive chlorination. The most common methods of disinfection in food premises use either heat (thermal energy) or chemicals (chemical energy).

Thermal disinfection

Hot water disinfection is usually limited to the use of a machine, such as a dishwasher, as the temperature is too high for comfortable skin contact. The temperature reached is around 88°C with a variable contact time of between one and 20 seconds.

Steam disinfection is usually used for areas of equipment that are inaccessible by hand. The process can corrode or otherwise damage materials and equipment and some specialists question whether it is effective for food safety and safe enough for staff to use without scalding themselves.

Chemical disinfection

Chemical disinfection is a second stage process: it must always follow cleaning and rinsing, otherwise the disinfectant may not work properly. Thermal and chemical disinfectants need to be in contact with the surface for a specific time in order to work properly, and this contact time is specified by the manufacturer. Cutting short the contact time will stop disinfection from taking effect, but prolonging the contact time may also have undesirable effects. It is possible, for instance, for a few bacteria to develop resistance to chemical disinfectants if the products are not used in accordance with the manufacturer's instructions, so it is unwise to leave cloths, mops and so on to soak in chemical disinfectants overnight.

Sanitizing and sanitizers

In some parts of the world it is more common to talk about sanitizing (also spelled sanitising) than disinfection. These two words mean the same thing but, just to make life a little more complicated, sanitizers are *not* the same as disinfectants! In the UK sanitizers combine the functions of a detergent and a disinfectant. They clean and disinfect in one go.

A common confusion

Never confuse disinfection (or sanitizing) with sterilization, which means the destruction of all pathogenic organisms. Sterilization is a routine process for medical equipment, but is rarely achievable, or necessary, in normal food operations, although commercial sterilization is used as a method of *preservation* (see pages 338 to 340).

Sanitizers
When we talk about sanitizers in the UK we mean a chemical formulation that combines the functions of a detergent and a chemical disinfectant.

Colour coded

Many hand-held items of cleaning equipment, such as brushes, mops and cloths, can be bought in a range of colours that you can designate for use in a particular area of the premises – for example, red for raw meat preparation and storage areas, green for areas where vegetables are prepared and stored and blue for washrooms and toilets. The colours help to distinguish which equipment should be used in certain areas of the premises, so helping to reduce the possibility of cross-contamination.

Which method is the most appropriate?

Perhaps this question seems a little patronising at first. After all, you would not dream of asking staff to scrub an oven with a bottle brush or to try to disinfect a floor mop in a bratt pan with cooking oil. Even so, from time to time it is worth reviewing how cleaning is undertaken in your workplace. By considering what is being cleaned, the material the surface is made from, the type of soiling and the amount of soiling, you may be able to improve efficiency or reduce costs. Questions for you to answer include:

- what is the surface to be cleaned – for example, a wall, floor, work surface, toilet, piece of equipment – and what is it made from?

- what kind of dirt must be cleaned – is it organic, such as animal fat, butter or blood; or inorganic, such as rust or limescale?

- how dirty is it – heavily or lightly soiled, or likely to be microbiologically contaminated?

- what is the condition of the dirt – for example, long-standing encrustation, fresh soiling, stained (soaked in) or burnt?

- how clean should the surface be when cleaning is finished – physically, chemically or microbiologically clean, or all three?

- what equipment could be used – for example, a hand-held brush, electrical rotary mop, dishwasher, washing machine, jet wash?

- which chemicals would best achieve the level of desired cleanliness – for example, a detergent alone or a detergent followed by a disinfectant?

- how would the pH or hardness of the local mains water affect the efficiency of a chemical?

- how cost effective is the method chosen – for example, can the dilution be controlled, can a cheaper product do the same job, does a more expensive product use less personnel time?

- how can you monitor and test the effectiveness of the method chosen?

Water hardness
A characteristic of water caused by salts of calcium, magnesium and iron that causes soap to curdle and increases the consumption of soap or detergent and the deposition of limescale. The hardness is not necessarily related to a high pH.

Scale of the task

The size of the job should play a part in your decision-making. A small floor area, for instance, may be most effectively cleaned with a mop and bucket and the application of 'elbow grease' whereas a large floor area may be more effectively cleaned by using an electric machine that combines the functions of sweeping, vacuum cleaning and polishing.

Cleaning in place (CIP) is a method used in industrial-scale food premises for cleaning equipment and pipelines without having to dismantle them every day for manual or machine cleaning. The design of the equipment must ensure that the circulation of cleaning chemicals and rinsing water is continuous and is not disrupted by spurs or dead-ends in the pipeline. (Part or all of the system should be dismantled for inspection and manual cleaning from time to time.)

Cost-effective hygiene

While some items, such as cooking pots and trays, may be best washed by hand, a dishwasher probably offers a better standard of hygiene, coupled with savings in cost and time for cleaning crockery, glasses, utensils and cutlery.

The choice of cleaning equipment

Brushes

Commonly used for sweeping floors and scrubbing stubborn dirt, they should be kept clean and in good repair so that bristles are not shed onto food. Sweeping can raise dust and contaminate food, so the use of brushes should ideally be restricted to times and places where food is out of harm's way. Many specialists prefer the use of damp mops to clear up both food debris and spills during food preparation and production periods and in food stores.

Cloths

The use of cleaning cloths (particularly dishcloths, wiping cloths and drying-up cloths) should be limited as they often cause more problems that they resolve. Many studies have shown that cloths are the most heavily contaminated items in a food preparation area. Single-use paper may be preferable for cleaning a work surface and drying up. If reusable cloths must be used, they should be replaced with fresh ones frequently during the work period and cleaned thoroughly before being soaked for the appropriate contact time in a frequently changed disinfectant solution. Service cloths and oven cloths (or gloves) could also become hazardous if they are used for cleaning tasks or for drying hands.

Dishwashing machines

They have the advantage of disinfecting as well as cleaning, while freeing staff for other activities.

Floor mops and floor cloths

They should be cleaned and disinfected after use.

High pressure hoses

These are often used to clean the walls and floors in food processing plants. Some specialists advise against their regular use in food areas as they can spread isolated pockets of contamination throughout the food premises in air-borne droplets. The use of low-pressure hoses is sometimes advised.

Sinks

The use of double sinks is often advocated, with one sink used for cleaning and disinfection and the other used for rinsing. It is also usually recommended to provide, where space permits, separate sinks for food preparation.

Steam hoses

These should generally be used only in special circumstances, such as deep cleaning, and by specially trained personnel as they can cause steam scalds. They are often used for cleaning the walls and floors of abattoirs and for reaching awkward corners of equipment or premises.

Vacuum cleaners

These include the domestic type and sit-on models and may include functions such as brushing, vacuuming and washing. They can usually clean large areas in one go, with less chance of causing dust, but may be difficult to use in restricted spaces.

Washing machines

Many premises, especially hotels and restaurants, have laundering equipment. Care should be taken to position the equipment away from food areas and air conditioning inlets.

Which chemicals are appropriate?

Cleaning products are available in many forms, including liquid, gel, foam, tablet, aerosol and powder. Before trying to answer the question of which is best for a particular task, we need to familiarise ourselves with a few technical terms applied to cleaning and disinfection materials. There are five basic groups of chemicals used by manufacturers to formulate detergents and disinfectants. A product often contains chemicals from more than one group, designed to suit particular examples of cleaning circumstances. The groups are:

- surfactants

- sequestrants

- natural soaps

- solvents

- inorganic builders.

These groups are outlined on the following two pages, and you'll find more detailed information in the Reference section.

Surfactants

Wetting agents
A wetting agent (surfactant) is a substance which lowers the surface tension of the water or the cleaning solution, allowing it to have better contact with all the surfaces and to penetrate the soil.

Surfactants reduce the surface tension of a liquid, so increasing the penetration of detergents. They are often referred to as wetting agents or, more technically, as synthetic surface-active materials.

There are many types of commercially available surfactant, almost all of which are petrochemical products. In the early stages of their development there were some environmental problems because sewage works could not easily treat the chemicals in the waste water, so foam formed on many rivers and waterways.

The problem has largely been overcome by formulating products that are more 'environmentally friendly' and biodegrade rapidly.

Types

They are usually classified according to their electrical charge when they are in solution, but we need not go into detail here!

Anionic surfactants

These are the most commonly used of the surfactants and can be found in most detergents including those in domestic use. They have very good wetting properties, are biodegradable and are non-toxic but they are not compatible with quaternary ammonium compounds (abbreviated to qats, quats or QUATS – see page 304) which are used as bactericidal agents.

Cationic surfactants

These are usually used for their bactericidal properties. They have some wetting properties but not as much as those of anionic surfactants. Their efficiency can be adversely affected by mineral salts and mineral-based soiling.

Amphoteric surfactants

These relatively costly chemicals are useful for removing grease – for instance, in ovens. However, they are unsuitable for use on food-contact surfaces.

Non-ionic surfactants

These are often mixed with the other surfactants because they are quite effective in removing oils and are not badly affected by hard water.

Sequestrants

These are chemicals that suppress or counteract the effect of other chemicals. They are used as ingredients in detergents simply as water-softening agents, so preventing the formation of scum or limescale.

Natural soaps

Most modern detergents are synthetic soap made from petrochemicals, but the original detergents – the so-called natural soaps – were manufactured by treating animal or vegetable fats with strong alkalis. With perfume added, these are still in use as toilet soaps and commercial laundry products. They do, however, form a scum in hard water.

Solvents

These are liquids, such as water and alcohol, used in products that remove oil and fat. Some also aid the rapid penetration of the detergent through layers of soil.

Inorganic builders

Neutral fillers

These are added to make it easier to measure and handle the product, although cynics might say that they are included merely to bulk up the product and make it more profitable to the manufacturer. Examples of the substances used are water, magnesium sulphate, sodium sulphate, sodium chloride and borax.

Oxygen-release agents

Some laundry products include sodium perborate and hydrogen peroxide that release the available oxygen which acts as a mild bleach.

Caustic soda

This is highly alkaline and therefore not normally used in manual operations because of the risk of chemical skin burns or respiratory problems. It has good fat-removing properties and is often used in automatic milk bottle washing. It can be very corrosive.

Silicates

These highly alkaline materials, although less corrosive than caustic soda, have good wetting and emulsifying properties. They also help to suspend dirt particles in the liquid, so they can be rinsed away more easily.

Emulsifying
An emulsifier is a liquid that holds another substance, usually fat or oil, in suspension.

Phosphates

These can suspend and disperse soil (break lumps or areas of dirt into particles) and have water-softening characteristics.

Carbonates

The most common of these detergents is sodium carbonate (soda ash) which also has water-softening properties.

Chemical disinfectants

The number of chemical disinfectants available for use in the food industry is restricted because products must neither taint the food nor cause chemical food poisoning when used properly. Such is the concern over the effectiveness of, and possible harm from the use of, such chemicals that in many European countries chemical disinfectants must have official approval before they can be used in food premises. Until the mid 1990s chemicals used in the British dairy industry also had to be approved, but there is no longer a system of approval.

As with all chemicals, great care should be taken when using and storing disinfectants. Staff must be properly trained before they use them and supervisors must ensure that the manufacturers' instructions are followed to the letter.

Alkaline attack
We cannot attack bacteria by making food more alkaline because the flavour would suffer, but bleach and other powerful bactericidal disinfectants work by having a high pH level (very alkaline) that destroys bacteria.

There are many trade names for chemical disinfectants. We outline a few by their groups.

Chlorine

Chlorine is relatively cheap and is effective against most micro-organisms, provided that the manufacturers' instructions are followed. The chemical is available in many formulations and dilutions, but it is the amount of 'available', or 'free', chlorine that essentially determines how effective it will be.

Chlorine-based compounds are probably the most commonly used chemical disinfectants. Sodium hypochlorite is used most frequently: it works by oxidising the protein in the microbial cell structure. Chlorine dioxide is being used more and more: it works by disrupting the movement of nutrients across the cell wall.

Iodophors

Although more expensive than chlorine-based disinfectants, iodophors are very effective. They also have some detergent properties. As the name suggests, iodophors contain iodine: this is held in an alcohol solution which makes it particularly effective in the dairy and brewing industries where moulds and yeasts can be a problem. As with all chemicals the manufacturers' instructions need to be followed or they may become corrosive.

Quaternary ammonium compounds (qats, quats or QUATS)

While these disinfectants have the advantage of being odourless and non-corrosive, they are relatively expensive and, unless modified, are not very effective against Gram-negative bacteria.

Per-acetic acid

This is used widely in the dairy industry because of its effectiveness at low temperatures and on stainless steel and glass surfaces.

Alcohols

Ethanol and iso-propanol, two types of this group of chemical compound, are often the disinfecting agent in disinfectant wipes which are used where there is light soiling and for disinfecting hands and temperature probes.

Factors in chemical disinfection

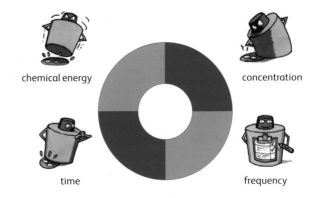

chemical energy

concentration

time

frequency

What does effective cleaning involve?

Whatever the type of cleaning task that needs to be carried out:

- all soil should be removed from the surface or item being cleaned
- the surface or item should be disinfected if disinfection is appropriate
- the contact time (for chemical and thermal disinfection) should be observed
- if chemicals are used in the cleaning process, all residue should be removed
- if the process involves wet cleaning, the surface or item should be dried or allowed to dry before it is used again.

Principles of cleaning

You could view the process of cleaning under the following general stages:

- task preparation

  - the process: selection of chemicals, materials and equipment, checking safety instructions, use of personal protective equipment (PPE) where appropriate

  - preparing the surrounding area: for example, by removing or covering food

  - preparing the surface to be cleaned, for example, by rinsing or sweeping to remove loose soiling

- cleaning – which may itself involve several stages (see the example of wet cleaning below)

- finishing

  - putting away clean items in the correct place so that they are free from hazards

  - storing chemicals safely and cleaning, repairing and maintaining cleaning equipment before storing it safely.

Wet cleaning and disinfection

Many cleaning tasks in food premises, such as washing large food storage containers in a sink by hand, may involve several steps within the cleaning stage.

1 Surface preparation – rinse to remove all loose and easily removed soil.

2 Washing – to remove, usually with the aid of a detergent, all the remaining soiling from the surface being cleaned.

3 First rinse – to remove all the detergent and loosened debris from the surface.

4 Disinfection – either with chemicals or hot water to reduce any remaining bacteria to an 'acceptable' level. (This stage is obviously applicable only when a reduction of micro-organisms is necessary, as with food-contact surfaces.)

5 Second rinse – to remove all trace of disinfectant.

6 Drying – to remove the residual water left from the second rinse. (Ideally allow the item to dry naturally. Otherwise, use a disposable cloth or a clean, dry fabric one.)

All the stages are not always necessary – for instance, to rinse items before washing them. When a sanitizer is used, several stages are combined because the chemical incorporates the function of both a detergent and a disinfectant.

When should cleaning be carried out?

The aim of cleaning is to remove contaminants and reduce the opportunities for microbial multiplication – in other words, to make items that come into contact with food as safe as possible for as long as possible.

As ordinary cleaning processes rarely destroy all the pathogens that could cause a food-borne disease or accelerate spoilage, the aim of disinfection is to reduce pathogens to a low level that is considered safe for human health and helps to prolong product shelf life. So cleaning needs to be carried out:

■ whenever there is a possibility that food has been contaminated

■ whenever food-contact or hand-contact surfaces could have been contaminated

■ as a matter of course to prevent microbial multiplication, chemical persistence or the build-up of dirt that could impair the way equipment or machinery operates.

In *addition*, disinfection needs to be carried out:

■ whenever there is a possibility of microbial contamination

■ whenever there is a change from raw to cooked processes within the same work area or using the same equipment, such as production lines or chopping boards

■ whenever there have been conditions, such as sufficient time and a danger zone temperature, for the multiplication of pathogens and spoilage organisms.

Before use

All utensils, equipment and facilities used for food must be clean and, where appropriate, disinfected before use. If a piece of equipment is used only occasionally, it may need to be cleaned after taking it out of storage and before use.

During use

Items and areas on which micro-organisms are likely to collect and multiply should be cleaned and disinfected throughout the work period. This is usually described as a clean as you go policy. It involves staff in clearing away and cleaning up as they work and immediately after completing a task.

If utensils and equipment are in constant use, they should be cleaned and disinfected frequently – for example, once every four hours, or at the end of every shift. Where the same equipment, work surfaces and food areas must be used for preparing different types of food, or for preparing raw as well as cooked or ready-to-eat foods, the equipment, utensil or surface must be cleaned and disinfected between different types of use.

After use

All food-contact surfaces must be cleaned and disinfected immediately after use and utensils and equipment should be stored in a clean area, protected from contamination, so that staff can have reasonable confidence that items are clean before they use them. Hand-contact surfaces should be cleaned at least at the end of the working day or the work period, or more often depending on the level of use.

Structural features, such as walls and floors, and installed items, such as extractors, should be cleaned regularly according to the cleaning schedule (see page 308).

Frequency

It is normally quite easy to decide how often cleaning should be carried out and to some extent the subject is covered by asking *when* cleaning should be undertaken. It would obviously be unacceptable to clean and disinfect a work surface only on the first Thursday of every month, but it would be unnecessary to wash the walls of a dry goods store once an hour of the working day.

The factors involved in the decision include microbiological, physical and chemical hazards – in other words, microbiological, physical and chemical contamination plus microbiological multiplication and survival. Your hazard analysis (see page 188) should help you to decide the frequency and this should be shown in the cleaning schedule.

Who should do the cleaning?

The jobholder who carries out the cleaning really depends on the circumstances. For example, in a clean-as-you-go area it should probably be the person who made the mess who cleans it up, or someone in that immediate work team. However, the cleaning could also be carried out by someone who is employed specifically as a cleaner or, in the case of scheduled deep cleaning, by an outside contractor, say every few months.

What is important is that the person who has been given the responsibility for a particular cleaning task should be properly trained for the job. They should also know:

- what they are responsible for cleaning
- how they should be cleaning
- which chemicals, if any, they should be using
- how often they should carry out the cleaning task
- what documentation they should be keeping
- why they should be cleaning and how it contributes to food safety.

How can you judge the effectiveness of cleaning?

It is all well and good to establish criteria such as how often, with what and by whom, but how can you know how well cleaning is being carried out and whether it is making a positive contribution to food safety?

Daily supervision should indicate whether cleaning is done when it ought to be, whether the process is carried out in the prescribed way and whether something appears clean. The re-ordering rate for chemicals at least suggests that cleaning products are being used, while log books for detection equipment should provide evidence of levels of some types of contaminant. It may well be appropriate, however, to use rapid microbiological test methods to check the effectiveness of disinfection or to arrange for laboratory testing of samples from time to time, or both.

It is an excellent form of insurance to make certain that staff involved in any cleaning activity, however minor, have been trained properly and are supervised so that they get it right first time, every time. It is also important that senior staff lead by example and help to motivate the staff to carry out what can be rather mundane tasks.

Cost

One of the factors in judging the effectiveness of cleaning is the cost of achieving an acceptable result. As we have seen, cleaning is basically the application of energy. All of these energies cost money, whether for the heating bills for water, for the purchase and maintenance of equipment and the purchase of chemicals, or for staff salaries.

Studies show that the labour cost of cleaning activities are up to 75 per cent of the total bill, so lowering this element of the cost by even five per cent would make a significant difference to your profit margins. It is for this reason that investment in equipment which cleans more quickly as well as more effectively than several human cleaners is often seen as a better option than using less detergent or cooler water. However, the effectiveness of good old-fashioned 'elbow grease' should never be underestimated.

When you review the cost of cleaning, make sure that any cost-cutting initiatives introduced still enable your staff to clean and disinfect surfaces, equipment and utensils thoroughly. Bear in mind the hidden cost of cleaning after a plant breakdown or maintenance work, and ensure that in periods of pressure time is not made up at the expense of time spent on cleaning.

How should you manage cleaning?

Cleaning and disinfection are very important components of a safe food system, and are one of the HACCP prerequisites, so it is essential that they are carried out properly. Cleaning schedules are documents that help managers to plan what needs to be done on an hourly, daily, weekly, monthly, quarterly and annual basis and to help to ensure that all is actually carried out according to plan. Every food business should have a cleaning schedule. It could have a variety of designs but it is advisable to carry out at least all the points suggested in the left-hand column of the chart below. Experiment with the layout, as it can make all the difference to how staff follow the schedule – grudgingly, willingly or perhaps enthusiastically.

Cleaning schedules

Point for inclusion	Examples and comments
What is to be cleaned	A mixing bowl.
How it is to be cleaned	Manually with a nylon brush.
Which chemicals should be used	A detergent followed by a disinfectant (and rinsing water).
What temperature the water should be	Optimum operating temperature for a particular chemical. For thermal disinfection, water needs to be above 82°C.
When it is to be cleaned	Disinfected before use and cleaned and disinfected after use.
How often it should be cleaned	Every time it is used, or weekly, monthly or quarterly depending on the item.
How long is required to complete the task	Between five and eight minutes. Ensure that sufficient time can be allocated.
Who must carry out the cleaning	Either the title of the jobholder or the name of the individual(s) responsible, or both. The name of the contracted specialist company.
The signature of the person who has carried out the cleaning	Personal guarantee that the cleaning has been carried out according to specification.
The signature of a supervisor to confirm that the standard of work has been checked	A safeguard giving a manager confidence that the work has been carried out to a required standard.

Making it easier for others

- Emphasise that effective cleaning and disinfection help to prevent illness and create a favourable impression on customers and clients.

- Explain the hazards that can arise from inadequate cleaning.

- Outline the group and individual responsibilities for carrying out cleaning.

- Mention that it is a legal requirement to keep food premises clean.

- Train staff how to clean effectively and safely, including occupational safety measures such as the use of rubber gloves and aprons where appropriate.

- Emphasise the importance of checking how to use chemicals, including the dilution and method of application, before attempting to carry out a cleaning task with them.

- Create an appropriate procedure for keeping refrigerated and frozen food at a safe temperature while refrigerators and freezers are being cleaned.

- Make sure that senior staff, such as chefs, lead by good example.

- Insist that staff always wash their hands after completing a cleaning task.

Pests under control

In some ways humans have made their own pests. The foods we grow, eat and store, and the environments we create often provide valuable food sources and refuge for a wide range of insects, birds and small animals. In return they are, at best, inadvertently destructive or troublesome. At worst, they can be dangerously harmful, destroying crops and essential food supplies, contaminating food, causing food poisoning, spreading other diseases to humans and livestock, and creating occupational safety hazards by, for example, gnawing through electricity cables. Small wonder then that pest control is a prerequisite for food safety management.

Miniature invaders

When we mention pest control we are mainly talking about preventing infestation – the presence of food pests, usually in large numbers – in food premises. Indeed, something like 90 per cent of effective pest management is concerned with *active* prevention rather than *reactive* remedial measures (or in dealing directly with pests). As a consequence, pest management is inextricably linked to four other crucial aspects of food safety management:

- the design of the premises
- cleaning and disinfection
- the safe disposal of waste and rubbish
- hygiene practices.

When any of these goes wrong – if the building is badly designed or poorly cleaned, or if rubbish piles up or people are careless – then one of the first consequences is usually pest infestation. So, pest management also involves raising the staff's awareness of the hazards from pests, specific training in preventing infestation and effective supervision and monitoring of all methods.

A timeless relationship

People, their health, food and pests have been closely linked ever since humans started to preserve and store food. Initially regarded as a nuisance to be tolerated, pests started to become a problem when stored foods were destroyed or rendered inedible, sometimes leading to human hunger or starvation.

The direct fight against pests probably began in earnest when the pathogenic potential of pests began to be realised in the eighteenth and nineteenth centuries. Pest control then gradually developed into the *prevention* of infestation rather than trying to kill the pests – a crucial move from reactive to proactive types of food safety management, which is demonstrated today by *systematic* forms of food safety management including HACCP.

Harm from food pests

Food pests create both microbiological and physical hazards – and food businesses have a legal responsibility to eliminate hazards to food or to reduce the risk from them to 'acceptably safe' levels. Clearly, pest infestation is a sign that a food business has not exercised due diligence in the management of food safety. The hazards from pests and the risk from those hazards depend largely upon the type of pest. Mice, for instance, can cause serious damage to stored foods and to food premises, but little economic damage is caused by houseflies. However, flies, which may have landed on rubbish tips and animal droppings, may be the vectors of serious diseases.

The main five plagues cited by the World Health Organization in 1999 – malaria, dengue fever, leishmaniasis, sleeping sickness and lymphatic filariasis – are all transmitted by insects or other vectors. Rats can carry a vast array of pathogenic bacteria that can become food-borne or water-borne and can cause potentially fatal conditions, such as leptospirosis (Weil's disease). Cockroaches are also laden with pathogenic micro-organisms, such as *Salmonella*.

Types of problem

Despite the variety of harm caused by pests, the problems can be divided into six main categories:

- direct damage to food

- consequent damage to food

- spoilage

- health hazards

- physical contamination of food

- physical damage.

You should also bear in mind that the inexpert use of pesticides can also cause chemical hazards.

Direct damage to food

Hazards
Pests create microbiological and physical hazards, while the inappropriate use of pesticides can cause chemical hazards.

Direct damage to food intended for people occurs in various ways. Rodents, for instance, consume all kinds of food. In contrast, stored product pests practice selective feeding, eating only a part of a food like a nut kernel but still making the whole batch of food unfit for human consumption. Another significant problem is caused by the larvae of some stored product pests which can destroy large quantities of food.

Consequent damage

Food can become unfit as a by-product of its infestation – for example, by becoming foul smelling or by losing its usual flavour or appearance.

Spoilage

Food starts to deteriorate as soon as it is harvested or slaughtered, and peeling, crushing or gnawing can accelerate the process. As soon as pests attack products like stored cereals their nutritional value also declines.

Health hazards

Insects, rodents and birds can cause food-borne illnesses, serve as vectors of cross-contamination and trigger skin ailments and allergies. The Indian meal moth, for example, can cause skin disease. Flour moths, grain weevils and cockroaches can provoke human respiratory problems.

Physical contamination of food

Every part of the body of every type of pest and every pest excretion and secretion has at some point been found in food products. Typical finds are:

■ droppings

■ eggs, larvae, insect exoskeletons, cocoons

■ cobwebs from spiders, web-like residues from moths and beetles

■ rodent hairs and bird feathers.

Physical damage

As well as causing health hazards, some pests cause significant structural damage to buildings and food packaging materials. They may also create a range of health and safety problems. Rodents must gnaw to wear down their incisors which continue growing throughout their lives. Rats gnaw almost anything, including electricity cables, hoses, pipes and pipelines. This can lead to short-circuits, fires, floods or mechanical failures.

Typical food pests

As food safety manager you need to establish appropriate systems of pest management. To do so, you need an underpinning knowledge of the creatures that are most likely to be a threat to your business and of where and why they are likely to 'invade'.

On the following pages, we summarise typical examples of food pests in the UK and Europe. Later in the chapter we look at proactive pest management.

Scientists often group pests according to their impact on humans. So, *storage* pests are a hazard to food in store, while *material* pests damage wood, textiles and so on. So-called *hygiene* pests may not be a direct danger to food, but their presence is objectionable, while *health* pests are injurious to human health as vectors and transmitters of disease. As some pests fall into more than one of these categories and as all pests are a hazard to food safety and hygiene, we have decided to consider pests under groups of animal.

Rodents

Rodents are a large group of gnawing mammals but only a few families, such as mice and rats, are classed as food pests. Rodents followed people into the towns and cities centuries ago and rodent populations do best by living near food premises, waste disposal sites and sewage works. Urbanisation and urban rubbish, among other things, have been blamed for an increase in rodent problems.

Signs of rodent infestation include droppings, gnaw marks, footprints and fur and tail marks. Rodents try to avoid crossing open spaces: where their fur touches walls or any other surface, such as pipes, sacks or containers, they tend to leave characteristic smear marks along well-established routes. Small numbers of rodents may be difficult to detect but you may find damaged food or food containers, destroyed packaging materials or other signs of feeding or nesting. It is important to encourage staff not to ignore damaged food containers or spilled goods as they may indicate rodent infestation.

Mice

Mice are vegetarian and prefer grain and cereals because of their high energy content. They can develop particular food preferences, for instance, for potato crisps. They usually live singly, but their immensely successful distribution is due to their reproductive ability – one female can give birth to about 45 young each year.

House mouse (*Mus musculus*)

Originally native in Mediterranean countries and the Asian steppes, the house mouse can now be found all over the world, usually near human settlements. Its favourite habitats are farm buildings, supermarkets and food manufacturing premises. As their preferred foraging range is no more than ten metres, mice try to live as close to their food source as possible. They can survive without drinking water, instead using the residual water in food.

Rats

Both the brown rat and the black rat are omnivorous, although they prefer cereals, meat, fish, nuts, eggs and fruit. The damage they cause is immense. Not only do they devour large quantities of food, but they can also destroy utensils and equipment by gnawing. They can cause serious physical contamination too, because each rat can produce about 200kg faeces and 55 litres of urine every year.

Disease spreaders Rats can cause an alarming number of serious and life-threatening food-borne diseases including typhoid, cholera, tuberculosis, cryptosporidiosis and listeriosis.

Their role as vectors is wide ranging and cannot be overestimated. They can transmit diseases including typhoid, cholera, tuberculosis, cryptosporidiosis, toxoplasmosis, listeriosis and other zoonoses and they are also associated with diseases such as tularaemia, leptospirosis and Hanta virus.

Since the Middle Ages they have had a significant role in distributing plague among urban and rural populations because the plague bacterium *Yersinia pestis* lives in rat flea and is spread by rats. Rats are very good climbers and swimmers and access through waterways and unsecured sewage pipes poses no problem for them.

Black rat (*Rattus rattus*)

This is darker than the brown rat and its tail is longer than its body length. It made its way to Europe from India via Africa. Preferred habitats include grain stores, where it is warm and dry. The black rat does not depend on water sources as much as does the brown rat.

Brown rat/Norwegian rat (*Rattus norvegicus*)

During the Middle Ages the brown rat began its spread from its native eastern Asia and is now distributed all over the world. Brown rats are social animals and prefer to live in groups of several hundred. They live in and outside buildings and use urine marks to define their territory.

In the urban environment they can be found in shops, storage areas, abattoirs and almost any food premises provided that there is access to a water source. They tend to be active at night and avoid people. If cornered, however, brown rats can be quite aggressive and may even attack humans.

Insects

Flies, cockroaches, ants and stored product pests come under this heading. Their small size, tough exoskeletons and large numbers make them difficult to eradicate and, as many are also highly mobile, they are often difficult to control.

Signs of infestation include seeing the insect itself and finding dead bodies, larvae, pupae, egg cases and, especially in the case of cockroach infestation, the exoskeletons left after casting. Storage moths and beetles leave web-like structures that are often mistaken for lumps of flour. Unusual smells may also indicate insect infestation. The adult form of most insects may be easy to detect, but as pests can enter your premises at earlier stages of their life cycles, it may be very difficult to identify the larval stage. They can be hidden inside some products and it is almost impossible to see the eggs.

Flies

Flies have always troubled humans, but it is only since the nineteenth century that people have appreciated that flies can carry and spread disease as a result of their habit of feeding on, and flying between, human food and human and animal faeces. The adult fly can feed only on *liquid* matter so the fly dissolves solids by regurgitating stomach acids onto the surface of the food then sucking up the resultant partially digested fluid. Flies are known to transmit typhoid, dysentery and microscopic parasites. Latest research suggests that they may also be vectors for *E. coli* O157.

Housefly (*Musca domestica*)

This is probably the most familiar and certainly the most widely distributed of all insects. It has followed humans everywhere, adapting itself to breeding and hibernating in various conditions. At a minimum temperature of 18°C the housefly can develop and multiply in any season of the year, with the female producing up to 600 eggs during its life. The development from egg to adult insect takes about three weeks in warm weather. In tropical latitudes, the housefly can be responsible for the spread of cholera.

Fruit fly (*vinegar fly, genus Drosophila*)

These very small flies are attracted to fermenting substances and they appear wherever fruit and vegetables are processed, for instance in the production of jams, jellies, juices, wines, beers, ciders and vinegar. Infestation accelerates fruit spoilage.

The flies can cause considerable nuisance in kitchens and canteens by flying around in swarms. They breed on overripe, decaying fruit and are a major problem in fruit and vegetable stores, canning factories and juice manufacturers. The female fly lays between 400 and 500 eggs during its life. The maggot larvae feed mainly on moulds and yeasts on the food material.

Whether fruit flies are also vectors of diseases is not known, although there is a strong suspicion that they are because they also settle on faeces.

Bluebottle (*Calliphora erythrocephala*)

With its characteristic iridescent blue body and loud buzzing, this fly is a member of a family that also includes greenbottles and flesh flies. They are sometimes collectively known as blow flies because of their habit of depositing ('blowing') their eggs on exposed meat, where they develop into maggots. Bluebottles are more likely than their close relatives to enter buildings in search of meat and they also frequent dustbins that contain meat and fish scraps. The female can produce up to 600 eggs in its lifetime.

Cockroaches

The two most common species in the UK are the German cockroach and the Oriental cockroach. They tend to infest premises where there is a constant ambient temperature and a reasonable level of humidity. Typical breeding areas are moist and dark and include beneath refrigerators, stoves or sinks, in and under cupboards, around plumbing and in factory service corridors. They are usually active only at night and seeing a cockroach during the day suggests an extremely serious level of infestation.

Cockroaches are omnivorous and are attracted to a wide range of foods, fouling what they do not consume and leaving a typical odour described as a 'roachy' smell: for those who recognise it, the smell is an unfailing indication of infestation.

They do not go through a complete metamorphosis from larva to adult (unlike a butterfly or beetle). A miniature cockroach, called a 'nymph', hatches from the egg with only slight differences to the adult form. As their hard exoskeleton (body covering) is very rigid and does not enlarge, cockroaches need to shed their exoskeleton in order to grow larger. The casts (the shed exoskeletons) indicate infestation and particles from them can cause respiratory allergic reactions (sometimes described as cockroach asthma). Cockroaches can also cause a number of food-borne diseases by carrying pathogenic bacteria from refuse or excrement to food. The bacteria may be carried on their feet and transferred to food or may be transmitted from the intestinal tract or regurgitated stomach contents.

German cockroach (*Blattella germanica*)

These are found in most parts of the world, usually indoors. Their life cycle depends very much on the ambient temperature: at 30°C it takes 50 to 60 days from egg to adult insect. The females are able to mate several times during their lifetime, every time producing an egg case containing 15 to 45 eggs. German cockroaches do not only attack foodstuffs but also packaging materials and textiles. This insect, which is only between 1cm and 1.5cm, is often carried into premises in cartons or other packaging materials.

Oriental cockroach (common cockroach, black 'beetle', *Blatta orientalis*)

This cockroach, measuring between 2cm and 2.7cm, is the more common in Britain. It deposits its egg cases in warm hidden places where they stay for about two months (unlike the German cockroach, which carries its egg case until a few hours before hatching). During their lives females can produce up to 18 egg capsules, each containing about 16 eggs, but the length of their life cycle depends on the suitability and abundance of food as well as on temperature and humidity: the Oriental cockroach does not need as much moisture as does the German cockroach.

Ants

Ants live in highly developed social organisations, taking distinct adult forms according to the tasks they perform in the colony. It makes little sense killing single worker ants by mechanical methods (such as squashing them): not only does the dying ant leave a chemical warning for others, but the infestation will persist as long as the queen ant remains unharmed at the centre of the colony. Ant nests are usually to be found outside buildings but the insects find their way inside through cracks and crevices in walls, doors and window sills. In kitchens and food premises ants are mainly a cause of annoyance, although food attacked by ants may become insipid and spoilage is accelerated. Most ant species are not known to transmit disease – the Pharaoh's ant (see below) is an exception.

Black garden ant (*Lasius niger*)

Black garden ants, which are about 4mm long, are found all over Britain. Worker ants enter buildings in search of food: when they find a rich source of sugar, they send out a scent message to attract more ants. They form a line to transport the food into the nest where it feeds the queen and the workers tending the larvae. Old-fashioned remedies against ants rely on disrupting the scent communication by scattering aromatic plants such as lavender and marjoram along the ant trail.

Pharaoh's ant (*Monomorium pharaonis*)

Native to India, these ants were probably imported to Britain over a hundred years ago and have adapted to an indoor environment where there are high temperatures and relatively high humidity. They owe their name to the first scientific description of the species, which was discovered during the examination of mummies of Egyptian rulers (or pharaohs).

At 2mm long, this ant is much smaller than the black garden ant. Its colonies take up only a tiny space in walls or floor crevices, behind broken tiles or cracks in furniture or wooden frames.

One colony usually hosts several queens. These ants do not swarm like other ants but from time to time some queens leave the nest, followed by a stream of workers, to establish a new colony. Worker ants are attracted to meat, fat, cheese, sweets, bread and pastry but they also carry dead creatures such as cockroaches and decomposing mice into the nest. Eradication of an infestation is possible only by detecting and destroying the nest.

Pharaoh's ants can access almost any building and are frequently found in kitchens, canteens and bakeries, as well as in hospitals where they can contaminate dressings, catheters, intubation drains and other sterile items with bacteria picked up from wound liquids, faeces, sputum and hospital waste.

Stored product pests

Ever since humans started to grow crops and store them from one harvest to another, storage insects have been a constant companion – one of the principal stored product pests, the biscuit beetle, was found in the tomb of Tutankhamen who died in about 1352 BC. For a long time the infestation of grain, cocoa, tobacco and other goods must have been regarded as almost inevitable.

The presence of insects associated with stored products usually involves an immediate or potential risk of a substantial loss of food – most damage is caused by the larval form of the insect which needs the food as a carbohydrate (or starch) source for its development.

As there are many stored product pests, we can mention only some of the principal representatives. As you will see, many pests are named after their preferred food – for example, *flour* moth and *grain* weevil – but this does not mean that you will never find them in another type of food.

Biscuit beetle (*Stegobium paniceum*)

This beetle, measuring between 2mm and 3.5mm long, causes considerable loss of products in dried goods stores. Although it feeds mainly on grain and flour, it can also be found in many other products such as dried noodles, rice, spices, chocolate, nuts, dried vegetables and even cork, leather and paper. The biscuit beetle is one of the very few pests that can live under extremely dry conditions and survives in a humidity of lower than eight per cent. In temperate climates, such as that of the UK, the biscuit beetle can produce about two generations a year.

Confused flour beetle (*Tribolium confusum*)

The common name of this beetle, which is found worldwide, comes from the Latin word confusum, which can be translated as *dark*, a description that helps to distinguish it from *Tribolium castaneum*, the chestnut-coloured flour beetle. In cooler climates it is restricted to warm stores of staples such as flour, but it also feeds on grain, pulses, pastry, chocolate, spices, dried fruits, nuts and animal feeds.

Flour infested by this beetle produces a sour, evil-smelling odour, making it unfit for baking. The terminal segments of the beetle's abdomen contain glands that produce chemical substances which may have a carcinogenic effect on humans.

Grain weevil (*Sitophilus granarius*)

This is a familiar pest to anybody who stores grain and cereals in large quantities. It causes serious infestations of grain in undeveloped regions of Asia, Africa and South America where millet or kaffir corn is the staple diet of poor people. The larvae can grow in wheat, rye, barley, rice and corn as well as in sunflower seeds, millet, oats and chestnuts – one larva usually infests each grain. As the adult insect comes out from the grain, it leaves a distinct round hole.

Indian meal moth (*Plodia interpunctella*)

This insect occurs in warehouses, silos, mills and food-processing plants as well as in catering premises and homes. The insect got its common name from the United States where it was a pest of maize or Indian corn meal. It also infests dried vegetables, herbs, dried fruits, nuts, cocoa beans, chocolate, powdered milk, seeds and grain products. In warm climates it attacks a wider range of products including sultanas, raisins, currants, figs, dried apricots and lentils. The insect, or its larval form, is usually imported into the UK in such products.

Mealworm beetle (*Tenebrio molitor*)

This is better known for its larval form, the 'yellow mealworm', which is bought as food for caged birds and lizards. It takes the larvae about 600 days to develop and its significance as a pest in flour in domestic premises has diminished in recent decades with the decrease of home baking. However, the beetle is often still found in mills, flour stores and bakeries where it may transmit bacteria to food and can be an intermediate host for several tapeworm species. Infection occurs when whole or crushed mealworms are eaten.

Mediterranean flour moth (*Ephestia kuehniella*)

This moth is a serious nuisance in mills where, if it is present in large numbers, its web-like structures may clog conveyor spouts and other parts of the milling machinery. The larvae feed on flour, bran, flakes, grain and nuts and, in warm environments, may produce five generations a year.

Saw-toothed grain beetle (*Oryzaephilus surinamensis*)

The larvae of this insect are increasingly prevalent in warehouses, silos, mills and food-processing plants. The larvae need high temperatures at around 30°C, so they are attracted to grain that has been stored before it has cooled properly after the drying process. At 3mm long, this insect can hide in crevices inaccessible to sprays and fumigants.

Birds

Food businesses often neglect to consider birds when they discuss pest management, even though pest controllers sometimes describe sparrows as 'flying mice' because of their potential for causing pathogenic contamination.

Wild birds, such as sparrows, starlings, seagulls, swallows and especially pigeons, are potential vectors of serious diseases. Feral pigeons, for instance, can spread toxoplasmosis and many other diseases. Birds can also be carriers of a number of parasites such as mites and lice. They can cause severe contamination through their excrement and large-scale infestation can produce offensive smells.

In urban environments birds have adapted to living around people and their waste. They feed on all kinds of rubbish including bread, fast-food leftovers, even mayonnaise and mustard. Birds roost in roof structures in and outside warehouses and other buildings and are hard to expel when they have found a suitable niche.

An additional problem is that people are often fond of birds, especially pigeons. This makes their control a sensitive and sometimes unpopular measure.

Apart from seeing the bird itself, droppings, feathers and evidence of nest building are signs of infestation. Sparrows use every possible material when building their nests, including waste, pieces of packaging materials and old tissues. Birds undergo seasonal moulting when large numbers of feathers are shed. These are not only potential physical contaminants but can also carry pathogens and mites.

Managing the hazards

Effective pest management requires preventive, monitoring and control activities. Prevention includes measures such as appropriate design and construction of premises, the use of pest-proof containers and diligent cleaning. Regular inspections, monitoring and reviewing are required – for example, deliveries of food must be checked before storing, and food stores and baited traps must be inspected frequently. There must be immediate remedial action if necessary.

Integrated

It is common to tackle these activities in partnership with professional pest controllers. Partnership is the key here, as an arm's-length relationship may not produce the desired results. By developing a mutual understanding, both parties contribute time, expertise and action to keep pests out. Such an approach is usually described as integrated pest management (IPM). The essence of IPM is best explained as follows:

- co-operation between the food business and the pest control consultant

- staff training in environmental pest control

- preventive measures instead of chemical pest control once infestation is eradicated

- prevention of re-infestation.

Methods of control

Pest control can be divided into three categories:

- environmental

- physical

- chemical.

Some methods of control should be used only by professional pest controllers, others can be carried out by the food company as a matter of course, while still others need the skill and diligence of *both* parties to be effective. Whichever is appropriate, the staff involved must be trained properly. As you will see, you should consider chemical controls to be a last resort.

Environmental control

Every food business should exercise environmental pest control measures, whether or not it engages external pest specialists. As you will see from the examples of measures given on the next page, environmental controls are really part and parcel of everyday food safety management. They involve denying pests the three things that make food premises attractive to them:

- access

- food

- shelter.

Access

To stop pests getting in to food premises, all possible points of entry must be sealed or restricted and controlled. So, for example, the brickwork around pipes should be sealed and kept in sound repair: remember that insects and even mice can get through tiny fissures and openings.

While it may be easier to deny birds and rodents access than it is to keep insects out of premises, screens on windows and strip curtains on external doors help considerably.

Mechanical devices can help to keep food preparation areas insect-free, as many stored product pests enter the premises in sacks of dry goods, in the folds and crevices of packaging materials or clinging to wooden pallets or vehicles.

This is where effective staff training and constant staff vigilance provide a form of access barrier – trained staff can recognise the signs of infestation in typical deliveries of food to your premises and follow the procedures for rejecting unfit consignments. Regular daily inspections and vigilance, with prompt remedial action if required, help to stop your external defences being breached.

Food and shelter

Clean, tidy, well-maintained food premises, the essence of 'good housekeeping', are core defensive measures against pests and the damage and contamination they can cause. Regular cleaning routines disturb areas where pests might otherwise be harboured in dimly lit, out-of-the-way corners and installations (such as pipes and refrigerator coils), while removing food scraps minimises the risk of microbiological and physical contamination. If your premises are clean and tidy, staff are far more likely to spot the signs of any infestation that does occur despite all your best efforts. After all, pests are great opportunists.

Outside the premises

Neglected maintenance and repairs can rapidly provide access to food premises and habitats for food pests.

Remove vegetation from the immediate area around the premises: it could provide cover and habitat from which pests could migrate to the building. Do not cut corners on external maintenance and service, but do make sure to eliminate potential breeding grounds such as open or damaged gutters and drains.

Keep rubbish areas and storage containers scrupulously clean and tidy to eliminate harbourage and food debris. If rubbish builds up or bins overflow, check whether you need to arrange for additional bins or more frequent collections.

Emphasise to staff the importance of keeping bin bags inside the containers with the lids closed securely: some creatures, such as foxes and seagulls, can be persistent and ingenious at retrieving poorly protected refuse. Ensure that food is delivered at times when the premises are open so that food is not left outside.

Inside the premises

Establish appropriate cleaning schedules, paying special attention to any parts of the premises that tend to be neglected, such as the shafts of service lifts; areas under staircases and spaces behind shelves, piles of stock and equipment; or machinery that is not in regular use.

Emphasise how important it is for staff to follow the **clean as you go** principle in order to remove food debris that could attract pests. Whenever possible, store food in rodent-proof containers with close-fitting lids. Where this is not practicable, ensure that paper and card packaging remains intact. Reusable food containers must be cleaned and disinfected before re-use.

Physical control

These methods accept that there are pests in the environment and are designed to catch them before they become a food hazard or to deter them from getting in to food premises. The methods available differ widely in their effectiveness – mechanical devices such as the mousetrap, for instance, prove effective only against individual mice and cannot deal with a large infestation.

Physical methods can usually be employed by trained food handlers as well as by professional pest controllers. However, it might be worth investing in professional advice before making a decision to use physical methods and before training staff how to deploy the devices, check them and dispose of trapped dead animals.

Examples of devices include fly-swatters, insect-catchers that use sticky paper, electronic fly-killers, which use ultraviolet light, and preventive installations such as mesh screens on windows and other openings. For trapping larger animals, such as mammals and birds, there are traps, snares and nets available. Spikes on window ledges, the upper levels of buildings and on porches and architectural features can be used to deter birds, but nets can also be effective.

Ultraviolet (UV) fly-killers

UV fly-killers (also known as electrocutors and insect zappers) can be used in any kind of food business. It is especially important to position them properly and to maintain them carefully if they are to work safely and efficiently.

If, for example, a fly-killer were installed right over a doorway, it might attract insects into the building. Alternatively, if one were positioned directly above areas where open food is prepared, dead flies could easily fall into the product. Even so, every fly-killing device needs a collecting tray that is large enough to catch even those parts of insects that would otherwise be quite widely distributed.

Models of fly-catcher with electrified grids can be replaced by ones that catch the insects on a sticky surface. In either case the fluorescent tubes need to be changed regularly (at least once every six months is recommended).

Chemical control

Chemical pest control should be adopted only as a corrective measure and your aim should always be to keep the premises permanently free of pests. The decision to use chemical methods of control should be made with considerable caution as any chemical substance in a food business creates a food hazard which needs to be monitored and supervised. Some substances may be directly harmful to human health and their application is best carried out only by professional specialists.

As we saw in Part 3, the word **pesticide** covers chemicals designed to kill pests. There are three main types, named after their intended target:

- rodenticides (to kill rodents)

- insecticides (to kill insects)

- acaricides (to kill mites).

Pesticides should not be confused with chemicals, such as pheromones and other attractants, which are *not* used to *control* an infestation but are used instead to monitor intrusion into an area.

Many pests have developed resistance to previously effective poisons. In addition, rats and cockroaches can learn to avoid particular bait formulations and 'teach' the rest of the population to do so too.

Application of pesticides

There are many different methods of applying pesticides – as bait pellets, in spray or gel form or dispensed by fumigation (smoke or gas in a controlled area). None of these methods should be attempted by untrained staff. It is vital, even where qualified contractors are employed, to alert *all* staff to the pest control measures and to warn them about the personal dangers and possible contamination hazards involved if they touch, move or tamper in any way with bait stations or other forms of pesticide.

Chemical danger
It cannot be stressed enough that the application of pesticides belongs in professional hands.

If pesticides are applied as a surface film, aerosol or gas, you must ensure that the area is decontaminated thoroughly before any work with food resumes. If an existing infestation needs to be treated, product lines may need to be covered, open food removed and instructions given about disposing of potentially contaminated products.

Chemicals against pests

Until about one hundred years ago most pesticides were inorganic materials, such as sulphur, lead, copper, arsenic and mercury, or occasionally botanical compounds such as nicotine and pyrethrum. The development and extraordinary effectiveness of highly toxic DDT (dichlorodiphenyltrichloroethane) changed the nature of pest control and slowed down the development of other, less toxic substances.

Only when research proved that the gradual accumulation of pesticides created a possibility of global contamination did scientists start to look for less harmful solutions – and there is still a great deal of confusion about the toxicity of, and the necessity for, pesticides. Easy decontamination and biodegradability have become critical factors in the development of new pesticides.

Because pests adapt rapidly by their behaviour and their resistance to pesticides, it is necessary to make constant modifications to the formulations of pesticides to try and keep one step ahead.

Keeping performance under review

Pest management acknowledges that pest problems can vary enormously and may change over time. If infestation has occurred then access, food and shelter must have been provided and a first step before using chemicals should be to ask the following questions:

- why could it have happened?

- which pest prevention measures have been neglected?

- is it possible to get rid of the problem by removing sources of food, water and shelter?

- if not – how can infestation be prevented from happening again?

Taking professional advice

As the professional responsible for food safety in your business, you may have to listen to some constructive comments and criticism from the pest specialists. You could, for instance, be told that:

- you should improve general hygiene practices

- staff need better general hygiene training or specific training in pest prevention

- faulty or badly-designed processing equipment is harbouring pests

- transport vehicles used inside or outside your premises are moving pests into, or around, food areas

- the layout of your premises needs to be changed to improve workflow and reduce contamination

- your waste disposal system does not work as it should.

Making it easier for others

- Explain the potential food and health hazards from pests.

- Point out that the law requires the business to be free from pests.

- Emphasise the devastating impact that pests could have upon customer perception of the business and on trade.

- Explain that pests can literally eat into business profits, so damaging the company's profitability and viability.

- Encourage everyone to follow the company procedures for preventing infestation and reporting signs of infestation.

- Emphasise the message, 'Keep it tidy – keep it shut'. It works to prevent most kinds of contamination!

Safe food at its best

It is difficult to draw a clear line between temperature control for the purposes of food preservation and temperature control for the purposes of food safety as the use of high and low temperatures are central to both.

Generally speaking, preservation methods are industrial or large-scale processes aimed at extending the shelf life of food (and may include controls other than temperature), while temperature controls designed to keep products safe to eat are essential to almost every food business in almost every sector of the food industry.

Practical divisions

In this book we have gathered together the time and temperature methods that are primarily used for food safety into the chapter 'Controlling time and temperature' (see pages 326 to 332). Most of these controls are are likely to be necessary in any food establishment in any food sector. However, the pasteurization of milk, which is usually an industrial process, appears in this chapter because it is mainly a food safety technique even though it does prolong shelf life a little.

Techniques mainly used to prevent spoilage and extend shelf life, including the sterilization and ultra heat treatment (UHT) of milk, are covered in the chapter 'Maintaining quality over time' (see pages 333 to 346).

Of course, storage conditions are important to both food safety and shelf life and these are covered in the chapter 'Stock control, storage and display' (see pages 349 to 356), which also deals with labelling, date marks, deliveries, handling and stock rotation.

Safety and quality

Temperature control to ensure food safety is a cornerstone of the Hazard Analysis and Critical Control Point (HACCP) system (see pages 182 to 196). Preservation processes are also a part of the HACCP system to ensure that food remains safe, as well as good, to eat.

Key temperatures

Different countries, industrial sectors and companies set slightly different rules for time and temperature control. The times and temperatures given below remind you of the danger zone temperatures and provide an at-a-glance reference to temperatures that are generally accepted to be good practice, or are legal requirements where stated.

Oven cooking (a typical baking temperature)	180°C, time variable
Ice cream sterilization	149°C for 2 seconds
UHT milk	132°C for 1 second
Canning	121°C, time variable
Milk sterilization	100°C for 15 to 30 minutes
Normal boiling point of water	100°C
Minimum recommended core cooking temperature	Good practice is at least 70°C for 2 minutes for prime cooking
Minimum reheating temperature	Good practice is a core temperature of at least 70°C for 2 minutes, or an absolute minimum of 75°C if no time recommended; by law in Scotland, not less than 82°C
High-temperature short-time pasteurization (HTST)	72.2°C for 15 seconds
Ice cream pasteurization	Variable, eg. 71°C for 10 minutes
Egg pasteurization	64.4°C for a minimum 2.5 minutes
Legal minimum hot holding temperature	63°C
Danger zone	5°C to 63°C
Human body temperature (average)	37°C
Legal maximum refrigeration/chill/cold holding temperature for specified foods	8°C (England, Wales and Northern Ireland)
Recommended maximum refrigeration/chill/cold holding temperature	5°C
Normal freezing point of water	0°C
Typical freezer temperature	-18°C
Typical commercial freezing and frozen storage temperature	-26°C to -40°C

Controlling time and temperature

What is the main reason for food poisoning? Poor temperature control is the simple answer. Research over many years in several countries pins the blame on sloppy temperature practices. As we saw on page 75, such practices include inadequate cooling of hot food, unsuitable cold holding temperatures, preparing food long before it is to be served then leaving it at ambient temperatures, and inadequate hot holding or reheating.

It is not difficult to keep food at a safe temperature for a suitable time. So, while poor temperature control is the main cause of food poisoning, the main cause of poor temperature control is ineffective management. It cannot be overemphasised how important time and temperature control is in any food safety management system. With proper management, the risk of causing a food-borne illness is significantly reduced.

Time plus temperature

Inseparable controls
Effective temperature control necessarily includes suitable time control.

You are familiar with the idea of temperature control, but you will see that in this book we take about *time and* temperature control because the two are usually inseparable in practice. Forgetting the importance of *time* destroys the value of temperature control.

Time and temperature control includes measures to:

■ restrict the time that high-risk foods are at a temperature likely to encourage the multiplication of pathogenic or spoilage micro-organisms (see Part 3, especially the bacterial growth curve on pages 55 to 56)

■ destroy pathogens – for instance, by heating food to an appropriate temperature for a suitable time

■ restrict microbial activity – for instance, by holding food at a low temperature until it is needed for preparation, service or sale.

In practice, it is often impossible to prevent high-risk foods from being in the danger zone at some stage. In fact, it may be unavoidable that some foods pass through the danger zone *several* times – for example, during thawing, cooking and cooling. This is where time becomes a crucial part of temperature management. It is essential to restrict the length of time that a food is at a danger zone temperature, for instance, by refrigerating a high-risk food *immediately after* preparation and *until* it is needed.

Before we look at the specifics, it is worth reminding ourselves of some rules of thumb:

■ restrict the time that high-risk foods are at a danger zone temperature (5°C to 63°C)

■ cook food thoroughly, right through to the core or the thickest part of the food

■ keep hot food really hot, at 63°C or hotter, if it is to be eaten hot

■ keep cold food really cold, ideally at 5°C or cooler

■ keep frozen food frozen, at -18°C or below

■ thaw frozen food thoroughly before use, unless the manufacturer recommends cooking from frozen

■ cool hot food as rapidly as possible if it is to be eaten cold or stored for later use

■ avoid reheating food; if it is necessary, reheat thoroughly right the way through the food.

Maintaining safe temperatures

Time and temperature control is one of the most effective ways of preventing food-borne illness and is essential for the defence of due diligence (see pages 28 to 29). It is therefore important to establish and maintain appropriate systems for measuring and recording temperatures: this is likely to be a part of your HACCP-based procedures. You need to train staff to know:

■ how and when to measure food temperatures or check the data-logger

■ how to record the readings

■ which temperatures are unsafe in specified circumstances and which procedure to follow

■ what variation, if any, is permitted from the standard and what action to take.

The temperature of high-risk food must be checked regularly and recorded. Staff must know exactly what to do if there is an unsatisfactory reading.

Types of temperature measuring device

Some equipment, such as refrigeration and freezer units, indicates the temperature automatically and continuously. Some produce a permanent record. Other devices measure the temperature of food or air. They include digital, infrared, probe and electronic thermometers. To prevent contamination and cross-contamination it is essential to train and monitor staff in cleaning and disinfecting recording devices thoroughly, particularly those with probes for inserting into food.

Calibration

The devices must be calibrated regularly to ensure that the temperatures they indicate are accurate. This may have to be carried out by a specialist company. If it is undertaken in house, then the staff involved must be given appropriate training.

All devices must be calibrated according to the manufacturer's instructions:

■ before they are first used

■ at regular intervals, as a matter of course

■ when there is damage to a device or an inaccurate reading is suspected.

There are three main ways of calibrating a probe thermometer – by comparing it against a reference thermometer that is confirmed to be accurate, by the ice method or the boiling point method. The ice method involves inserting the probe part of the device into a small container of crushed ice topped up with cold water. When the indicator has stabilised, the calibration nut may be turned until the indicator shows 0°C. The boiling point method involves inserting the probe part of the thermometer into boiling water and, once the indicator has stabilised, adjusting it to show 100°C (at sea level).

Reading temperatures

Corrective action
Your company's rules for dealing with non-conforming temperature readings should be included in the HACCP plan and management policies.

It is important to ensure that staff follow the manufacturer's instructions and use each device only within its approved temperature range. Whichever method is used, sufficient time must be allowed for the device to reach an accurate reading. For example, meat and poultry are best checked towards the end of their cooking time by inserting a clean probe into the centre or thickest part of the flesh (for example, into the poultry breast or thigh). An ideal way to check the temperature of food under refrigeration is to insert a clean, disinfected probe into the centre of a tub of a commercial test medium (a gel made for the purpose) that has been kept in that particular refrigerator. Freezer temperatures, if not recorded automatically, can be taken by hanging the probe in the freezer unit, making sure that it does not touch the room or cabinet walls, or by placing it between packets of food or by resting it on top of food.

Ensuring accuracy

When checking the temperature of solid food that is being cooked, reheated, cooled or thawed, it is important to check the core temperature – the temperature at the centre of the food or in the middle of the thickest part of the food. Liquid food should be stirred frequently before taking the reading to ensure that it is accurate for the temperature *throughout* the liquid.

Unsatisfactory readings

It is crucial to ensure that there are clear rules about target temperatures (or critical limits) and that they are written into the HACCP plan. Staff must know what to do if a temperature is incorrect. For example, the appropriate action regarding cooked food may be to continue cooking. However, if a refrigerated vending machine has two readings of 9°C or higher, the appropriate action may be for staff to report directly to you or to a supervisor so that checks can be made on the way the machine is operating and a decision reached on taking the machine out of service and possibly destroying the food it contained.

Keeping records

Accurate temperature records help the business to monitor and maintain safe temperatures. They are also valuable evidence of due diligence in the event of an allegation of food-borne illness. The records should be kept where they are easily available to an inspector or auditor during a food hygiene inspection. It is suggested that the records be retained for several years in case they are needed to answer an allegation or defend legal action.

When to take temperatures

Temperatures should be checked as often as appropriate to the types of product and operation.

Examples	
Deliveries of food	as soon as it arrives
Refrigerated units	daily and regularly; ideally within 15 minutes of the start of shift, then throughout the day
Freezer units	daily
Thawing food	towards predicted end of thawing period
Cooked and reheated food	towards predicted end of cooking or reheating period
Hot holding	frequently

Use of low temperatures

Refrigeration

Refrigeration, chilling and cold-holding are all terms for the technique of keeping food cold. Although refrigeration keeps food safe for only short periods, it is an invaluable temperature control that even the smallest food business can use. Refrigeration contributes to food safety because it affects one of the intrinsic factors for the survival and multiplication of micro-organisms.

The ideal temperature for the multiplication of most pathogenic bacteria is between 5°C and 63°C (the danger zone), with the optimum temperature for most being around 37°C. So, when food is kept above freezing point but below 10°C the multiplication rate of bacteria slows down dramatically and eventually, at a slightly different temperature for each species, stops altogether.

Even so, many bacteria can still survive for quite long periods at low temperatures. Multiplication at below 5°C is restricted to some specialist organisms, such as the psychrotrophs *Yersinia enterocolitica*, *Listeria monocytogenes*, *Aeromonas hydrophila* and *Clostridium botulinum* Type E. Although the multiplication rate is slow, these organisms are still of significant concern. Parasites may also survive refrigeration temperatures.

Safety margin
Good practice is to keep refrigerated food at below 5°C.

The law and good practice

Legal requirements for chilled foods differ from country to country. In England, Wales and Northern Ireland, for instance, the storage temperature of foods which are not ambient shelf stable is set at or below 8°C. The accepted good practice, however, is to hold refrigerated food at below 5°C: in practice, this is usually no colder than 4°C to stop the formation at lower temperatures of ice crystals in salad vegetables, such as cucumbers.

Maintaining the cold chain
It is a legal requirement to maintain the cold chain. It may be interrupted only for limited periods (to allow for preparation or display, for example) but only if this does not result in a risk to health.

By law food businesses must not interrupt the cold chain – the holding of high-risk and highly perishable foods under refrigeration through all stages from farm to fork. There is a limited legal defence of some upward variation from the 8°C maximum (see page 162) and to allow for the practicalities of processing, preparation and so on. The key issue is to ensure that the time and temperature combination does not result in a risk to health.

Refrigeration and chiller units and refrigerated transport

The design of these units should be suitable for the intended purpose and they must be constructed of easy-to-clean materials. In food premises units should be placed away from heat sources and draughts and out of direct sunlight. Food must not be crammed into the unit in a way that prevents cold air from circulating so that the temperature of stored food rises to within the danger zone. Managers should ensure that there are sufficient refrigerators and chiller cabinets to cope with peaks in demand.

Cold holding (or chilling)

This term usually refers to the practice of keeping food cool for a relatively short time in a display cabinet or vending machine, commonly in retail or catering premises, sometimes for customer self-service. The food should legally be kept at below 8°C and ideally at below 5°C.

This can be achieved in many ways and the most common is the circulation of cold air through the display. Ice is used for many displays, particularly for fish, shellfish and prepared salads: this gives the food a pleasing and appetising appearance as well as keeping it safe to eat.

Cooling hot food

Inadequate cooling is a major cause of food-borne illness, so it is important to reduce the temperature of hot high-risk food quickly so that it is at a danger zone temperature for the shortest period possible.

It is good practice to aim to reduce hot food to a refrigeration temperature within 90 minutes. This is best achieved by using a blast chiller.

Other methods include cooling food in shallow trays, cutting large joints of meat or poultry into smaller portions, or using an ice bath – either where a cold container of the food is placed inside another of ice and cold water, or by putting the food in food bags before placing them in containers of ice and water.

Multi-use refrigerators should *not* be used for cooling hot food, as this may raise the temperature of the other foods stored there.

Cook-chill and cook-freeze

Many food businesses use a combination of cooking and chilling methods every day, but 'cook-chill' is the title given to a form of mass catering. It involves the preparation and cooking of a large number of meal portions which are packed, blast chilled and stored at below 3°C until they are required. They are then regenerated for service. The preparation, cooking, chilling and storing is often carried out at a central production unit before the food is distributed to satellite outlets, such as hospitals, for regeneration and serving.

Cook-freeze is a similar operation but, as the name implies, it involves freezing the cooked and portioned product instead of chilling it. There are specific guidelines for these processes.

Thawing

The process of freezing is discussed on page 337. Some frozen products may be cooked from frozen following the manufacturer's instructions, but many must be thawed first.

If food, such as joints of meat or whole poultry, is not thawed thoroughly before cooking, ice crystals may remain at the centre so that, although the surface of the food will cook, the temperature at the core may remain within the danger zone, providing ideal temperatures for microbial multiplication.

Thawing should ideally be carried out either in a specially designed thawing cabinet or in a refrigerator set aside for the purpose. This keeps the food at a controlled temperature outside the danger zone during the period of thawing which can be several days if the product, such as a turkey, is large.

It is unsafe to thaw food in a kitchen overnight, or worse still over several days, because the ambient temperature is most likely to be within the danger zone.

Frozen food should ideally reach refrigeration temperature right through to the core before it is cooked.

If your premises are so small that you have only one multi-purpose refrigerator, it is advisable *not* to buy large frozen items that require thawing before use. Where *small* items are thawed in a multi-purpose refrigerator, they should be placed on the lowest shelf to prevent juices from dripping and contaminating other products.

Ensure that workflow is planned to take account of thawing times.

Use of high temperatures

Heating food is without question the best way to eliminate micro-organisms and it is a happy coincidence that the cooking of foods often makes them more palatable. One could argue that if everything were boiled and eaten immediately, the only food safety problems would arise from some of the bacterial toxins, notably those of *Staphylococcus aureus*, and from the naturally occurring toxins. However, as boiling everything is not a viable option, we must consider alternative forms of heat treatment.

The law requires hot food to be held at 63°C or above to help to control the growth of pathogenic micro-organisms or the formation of toxins. The temperature should be checked frequently.

Cooking

Most forms of cooking or baking involve temperatures that are high enough to destroy pathogens (although spores and toxins may survive), provided that the food is cooked for long enough. The rule of thumb is 70°C or above for two minutes, so that the food is cooked thoroughly and evenly right the way through to the centre, or to the thickest part of the food or the bone. To do so, it is advisable to cook poultry stuffing separately and not in the chest cavity.

Reheating

Inadequate reheating can provide an ideal temperature for bacterial multiplication and is a common cause of food-borne illness. If your business must reheat food, you must ensure that it is heated thoroughly and evenly. Ideally a core temperature of at least 70°C should be reached for at least two minutes, and in Scotland there is a legal requirement to reheat previously cooked food to a temperature of not less than 82°C.

Food should ideally be reheated immediately before consumption. However, if it must be kept hot before placing it on the market, it should be held at 63°C or hotter. The reheating of leftovers should be discouraged.

Hot holding

Hot holding is important for anything from a display cabinet for hot food in restaurants and shops to a bain marie in a kitchen to a pizza delivery bag. Food should be held at above 63°C – in other words, outside the temperature danger zone. As with any time and temperature management, the temperature should be checked regularly to ensure that it has not fallen below 63°C.

Pasteurization

This relatively mild form of heat treatment is applied to foods such as milk, eggs, fruit juice, ice cream, canned fruit, wine and canned ham. The time and temperature involved varies according to the product and the exact method of pasteurization that is chosen. Milk, for example, is usually heated to 72.2°C for 15 seconds – the method known as high temperature short time (HTST) pasteurization. This treatment was originally applied to milk to destroy tuberculosis pathogens, but it also reduces other pathogens in milk to accepted safe levels for human health.

Pasteurization is not, however, a process of sterilization (in which virtually all micro-organisms are destroyed), so a small number of organisms, especially spoilage types, survive the process and can survive in the milk even when it is correctly refrigerated. This is why pasteurized milk has a shelf life lasting days rather than weeks.

The main advantage of pasteurization over other forms of heat treatment is that the flavour and composition of the food is relatively unchanged. Milk loses about 25 per cent of its vitamin content but the remaining amount is still so high that this does not significantly affect its nutritional value.

Storing pasteurized foods
Pasteurized products should usually be refrigerated as the process is designed for safety not for extending storage times.

The pasteurized cheese debate

Some types of soft cheese are traditionally made with unpasteurized milk and there has been much debate about whether they are safe to eat. Those who favour compulsory pasteurization maintain that pasteurized cheeses are safer and that food-borne infections such as *E. coli* O157 and *Listeria monocytogenes* have such a low infective dose that heat treatment is the only way to reduce the risk of serious illness. Those opposed to compulsory pasteurization argue that consumers should have the right to choose and that pasteurization alters the flavour of cheese, increases costs and may even increase the risk to health because any bacteria that contaminate the product after pasteurization will have no competition.

It is legal to sell unpasteurized milk products, but they must be labelled as such. Some companies also voluntarily label unpasteurized foods with a warning to people in the 'at risk group'.

Making it easier for others

- Make sure that all food handlers understand the danger zone and essential controls, particularly:

  - keep hot food hot

  - keep cold food cold

  - keep frozen food frozen.

- Teach staff how to stack refrigerators to avoid cross-contamination and to allow cold air to circulate.

- Encourage staff to plan their workflow so that they open refrigerator doors as infrequently as possible and remove food from refrigeration just before it is needed.

- Ban staff from placing food above the load line in chest freezers or from storing unwrapped food in freezers.

- Ban the storage of food in ice-cream freezers (conservators) because the temperature will be too warm.

- Insist that everyone follows the house rules for approved methods of thawing frozen food and do not tolerate high-risk food being thawed at ambient temperatures, for instance, overnight.

- Insist that everyone follows the house rules for cooling hot food.

- Remind staff to observe the standing time, or to stir the food, when items are heated in a microwave oven.

- Train staff how to check and record temperatures.

- Train staff to follow procedures for corrective action if temperatures are unsatisfactory.

Maintaining food quality over time

In our additive-conscious age, when the words *natural, fresh* and *unprocessed* have become familiar marketing slogans, food preservation and especially preservatives are sometimes viewed with mistrust.

But storing food to prevent starvation is probably almost as old as the human species and can be seen as one of the first evolutionary adaptations distinguishing humans from other animals. Some rodents, such as squirrels, do store nuts and other foods but they are unable to treat them to make them last. Often they fail even to find their food stocks when they are needed. Only humans have found the secret of reliable food preservation and storage.

Keeping food palatable

The first methods of storage were determined by climate. People in cold parts of the world learnt to use ice and cold larders while those in warmer regions developed methods of sun-drying. Even so, treating the food was only the first step and they also had to discover how to keep it in excellent condition.

One of the first big breakthroughs probably came with the discovery that liberal applications of salt can preserve foods such as meat and fish for long periods, regardless of climate. So important was this that salt became an early form of currency. (Our word 'salary' comes from the Latin for salt and gives us the expression 'to be worth your salt'.)

We will probably never know whether it was the human liking for salty flavours that led to the discovery of its preserving properties, or its use as a preservative that gave us a taste for salt. (Some other animals, such as cows, seem to like salt, but they of course have no knowledge of preservation methods.)

Later on, other methods such as smoking, pickling and curing were discovered. More recent technological developments have given us a wide range of methods, including heat treatment such as canning and sterilizing; the addition of chemicals; and vacuum packing.

Preservation in the modern food industry

Our ancestors were probably more motivated by hunger than by food safety. After all, when starvation is the issue, even unpalatable food will be eaten. Today, however, when we talk about food preservation we are mostly concerned with preventing spoilage and extending shelf life – which is sometimes described as prolonging the 'eating quality' of the food.

Even so, preservation and safety are closely connected because most techniques for controlling spoilage are also methods for controlling pathogens. In law, too, there is no sharp distinction and legislation in most countries considers food to be unfit for human consumption if it has been spoiled. Of course in the food business, you need to consider both aspects when you are processing food for storage.

Why food spoils

Spoilage is simply any change in a food product that makes it unfit or unacceptable for its intended purpose: and that purpose is, of course, eating. All food eventually spoils but the process can be accelerated by bad practices such as careless handling and inappropriate transport or storage. The four main causes of spoilage are:

- micro-organisms

- enzymes

- oxidation

- contamination.

Spoilage by micro-organisms

Micro-organisms are present in all food unless it has been specially treated to eliminate them. The same principles that apply to controlling pathogenic micro-organisms also apply to spoilage micro-organisms, so preventing them from:

- contaminating food

- multiplying if they are on food

- surviving.

Food is exposed to some micro-organisms even in the cleanest, most hygienic conditions and does not come to you in a sterile condition. So you must have in place effective methods for preventing microbial multiplication and survival.

As you know from Part 3, most techniques rely on one or more of the following approaches:

- removing nutrients

- reducing water activity (a_w)

- reducing or increasing temperature

- controlling and managing temperature and time

- creating an inhospitable hydrogen-ion concentration (pH)

- removing oxygen

- using microbial competitors.

As well as these methods, chemical preservatives may be used. These function in different ways, for example by disrupting the functioning of bacterial cells.

Spoilage by enzymes

Enzymes are chemicals produced by living organisms. They act as catalysts in essential biochemical reactions. In other words, they set off, or speed up, a chemical reaction without altering themselves. Often designed for just one specific biochemical reaction, enzymes are usually large, complex protein molecules. We cannot live without enzymes as they sustain essential chemical reactions in our bodies. One estimate suggests that there may be as many as 3,000,000 enzymes in every human cell and there are others – such as those involved in digestion – which are found outside the cell walls.

Chemical trigger
A catalyst is a chemical that triggers off, or speeds up, a chemical reaction without itself being changed by the reaction.

Benefits

Enzymes are used extensively in food processing to speed up reactions within the food. Some of these uses are modern high-tech developments but others have been known since ancient times. Enzymes in yeast, for instance, have been used for thousands of years to help in the fermentation processes behind wine production, beer brewing and bread making.

Disadvantages

For all their usefulness, enzymes can also be destructive. Long after an animal or plant is dead, enzymes carry on precipitating chemical reactions which may produce unpalatable or even dangerous compounds – an example of the latter is a part of the process that leads to scombroid poisoning of fish. The longer you keep the food, the higher the concentration becomes of these substances – unless, of course, you do something to halt their action. Indirectly, enzymes can also be destructive by preparing the way for microbes, creating an environment that is favourable to their multiplication.

Controlling enzyme reactions

There are several ways of controlling enzyme reactions.

Temperature control

One of the most important and effective ways is by managing temperature. Most enzyme activity occurs between 20°C and 50°C, with 30°C to 35°C being optimal. Some enzymes are still active outside this range but they are much less effective.

Temperatures of 60°C to 70°C will destroy most enzymes. In fact the standard way of testing whether milk has been properly pasteurized is to check for the presence of the enzyme phosphatase. Correctly pasteurized milk should be heated to 72.2°C for 15 seconds. This destroys phosphatase, so any sign of this enzyme after the pasteurization process indicates that the milk was not properly treated.

Low temperatures also control enzyme activity by preventing their production. In scombroid fish poisoning, for instance, the enzyme histidine decarboxylase is produced by bacterial action in the dead fish. Storing the fish at below 4°C controls bacterial activity and so controls enzyme production.

Hydrogen-ion control

Another way of controlling enzyme activity is by pH. Most enzymes function best in the pH range 4.5 to 8, so acidic foods and those processed in such a way that the pH is low, such as pickling, are less likely to spoil due to enzyme activity.

Rancidity of fats and oils

Rancidity in dairy products may be caused by hydrolysis (a chemical reaction), resulting in free fatty acids, or by the action of naturally occurring enzymes called lipases, producing odours and tastes which are usually described as 'off'.

Spoilage by oxidation

Oxidation typically happens in the presence of oxygen – for example, when you cut an apple in half and leave it exposed, the oxygen in the air causes a reaction that turns the cut surface brown. Processes of oxidation, known as redox or the oxidation-reduction potential (and often abbreviated to O/R or E_h) also have a significant impact upon micro-organisms. These are described more fully in the feature on pages 347 to 348. For now, the most important thing to know is that one way of preserving food from bacterial deterioration is by altering the amount of oxygen in the atmosphere around a food.

Spoilage by contamination

Contamination, as we have already seen, can be caused by almost anything and does not have to pose an actual risk to health but simply to be objectionable to consumers. Problems commonly occur as a result of bad handling, transport and storage that leads to microbiological, physical and chemical contamination.

Reducing spoilage

There are many ways of delaying spoilage. As you would expect, they include:

- altering the pH
- altering the a_w
- altering the E_h
- removing air or altering the air composition
- applying heat
- storing at low temperature
- chemical destruction or inhibition of microbial cells
- appropriate storage
- introducing competitive organisms.

Manufacturers use **hurdle technology** to preserve foods – the manipulation of the factors essential to microbial multiplication and survival. Alone or in combination, these factors generally control the multiplication of pathogenic bacteria such as *Clostridium botulinum* but will not necessarily control moulds and yeasts.

Although the preservation techniques listed above are varied, they fall into one of five basic categories of food preservation which are described on the following ten pages – low temperature, high temperature, dehydration, chemical or physical preservation.

Low temperature preservation

Reducing the temperature of food is a traditional method of preservation. As refrigeration (or chilling) is a short-term form of preservation only, it is discussed in the previous chapter on pages 329 to 330.

Freezing

Freezing preserves the 'natural' freshness of foods over an extended period and for that reason has become extremely popular.

Keeping food at below 0°C (the normal freezing point of water) can eventually destroy some harmful organisms, particularly parasites. However, the main value of freezing as a method of preservation is that microbiological activity almost ceases due to the reduced a_w. Some moulds and yeasts can nonetheless still grow at very low temperatures. Although some bacteria die when they are first frozen and some subsequently die during frozen storage, most become dormant. Even so, their spores and toxins can survive freezing.

A block of commercially frozen fish being prepared for bulk storage.

Preparing food for freezing

All foods must be wrapped to minimise the loss of surface water and prevent irreversible damage from *freezer burn* (the formation of large ice crystals caused by the loss of surface water). In most cases this involves using plastic or foil wrappings, but some products, such as fish fillets, are sprayed to form a thin coat of ice before they are frozen in order to prevent dehydration.

Products that are susceptible to oxidation, such as fatty foods, benefit from vacuum packing before they are frozen. Vegetables need to be blanched beforehand to destroy enzymes that might otherwise cause deterioration during storage.

Freezing methods

There are several methods of commercial freezing depending on the type of food to be frozen and the speed of the process. The longer the freezing process takes, the larger the ice crystals that are formed, and the greater the likelihood of freezer burn.

Blast freezing

Food is passed on a conveyor belt through a tunnel of cold air. This is probably the most common method and is used for fish and meat products. The time taken to freeze the product depends on the type of food, its size and surface-to-mass ratio.

Plate freezing

Packaged foods such as blocks of fish are inserted between two metal plates and cold air circulated around them.

Fluidised bed freezing

The food moves along a belt on an air cushion, allowing rapid freezing of individual items, often vegetables.

Cryogenic freezing

Liquid nitrogen is sprayed onto products, such as prawns, for a quick freezing process.

High temperature preservation

As we mentioned in the previous chapter, heating foods is an effective way to destroy micro-organisms. In the following paragraphs we look at methods used primarily or exclusively to preserve foods.

Ultra heat treatment (UHT)

This method of heat treatment was developed to give milk a longer unrefrigerated shelf life without significantly affecting the flavour. The milk is heated to 132°C for one second, then aseptically packaged. Some people detect a small change in taste and smell but the use of UHT milk has increased dramatically over the years, especially in buffet-style and self-service catering, where it is often packaged in single portions. Ultra heat treated milk does not need to be refrigerated until after it has been opened.

Sterilization

True sterilization means the destruction of *all* micro-organisms. As this is both difficult to achieve and to verify in food, the phrase commercial sterilization (sometimes known as *appertizing*) is usually used to describe the process when it is applied to food.

Commercial sterilization

Commercial sterilization involves heating the food to more than 100°C for anything from 15 to 30 minutes, usually by the application of steam and pressure.

Milk is sterilized in this way. The process modifies the flavour and texture of milk and impairs the nutritional value, including the vitamin content.

Ohmic heating and canning are typical forms of commercial sterilization and are discussed below and on the following two pages. Pouches of food, such as sauces and soups, which have become popular in recent years, are also subject to similar treatment before being packaged aseptically.

Ohmic heating

This is a form of commercial sterilization in which food is heated by passing an electrical current through it. The method is suitable only for small particulate, semi-liquid foods which can be pumped, such as chilli con carne or bolognese sauce. After heating, the food is aseptically packed. It can then be stored at an ambient temperature for several months.

Canning

The term canning refers to the process of putting food into metal, glass or plastic containers which are hermetically sealed and heat treated until the food is commercially sterile. The process is designed to kill the spores of *Clostridium botulinum* – hence the phrase botulinum cook – and to reduce to an acceptable level the heat-resistant spores of spoilage organisms.

The time and temperature required are related to the pH of the food. Fruit and other products with a pH of less than 4.5 (acid and very acid foods) receive relatively less treatment than those with a pH greater than 4.5 which receive more robust heat treatment. The a_w of the food is also taken into account in determining the treatment.

The importance of destroying *C. botulinum* spores cannot be overstated because the botulinum toxin is the most dangerous substance to be dealt with. In practice it is assumed that all organisms present are spores and that they must be reduced to a level which no longer creates a human health hazard – in other words, so that the product is commercially sterile. This minimum sterilization process for *Clostridium botulinum* is known as a 12D reduction: this is simply a mathematical way of expressing that however high the initial contamination may be, the end product is safe to eat.

F values

The time and temperature combination depends on the kind of food to be processed. The temperature is always 121°C, but the time varies as some foods have a higher possibility of being contaminated with spores than others, some products are denser than others, some products conduct heat more readily than others and so on. The time is expressed as an equivalent F_0 value. The F is simply a mathematical symbol. When, for instance, a product requires heating for 3 minutes at 121°C to achieve sterility, it is simply stated as $F_0 = 3$. Other examples of values are canned salmon which has an F_0 of 7 and acid fruits, such as strawberries, which may be as low as $F_0 = 1$.

Stages of canning

Invert and rinse cans to remove any debris,

Stage 1: Filling

After preliminary cleaning, sorting and processing, food is added to cans. Liquid is usually placed in the can first, to prevent air bubbles.

Stage 2: Exhausting

Steam is blown into the top of the open container above the contents, causing a vacuum and, to some extent, removing oxygen.

Stage 3: Sealing

The top seam is hermetically sealed.

Stage 4: Processing

Cans are cooked to the time indicated by the F_0 value (above). Steam, hot water under pressure, or steam and air mixes may all be used as a heating medium.

Stage 5: Cooling

Cans are cooled in chlorinated water as quickly as possible. It is important that enough chlorine has been used during the water treatment to ensure that the cans do not become contaminated, but not so much that the chlorine corrodes the cans.

Stage 6: Labelling and storage

Cans must be dry before being labelled to prevent rusting.

Common problems with cans

Blown cans

Blown cans occur because of a build-up of gas – either hydrogen or carbon dioxide – as a result of microbial action. In the early stages a blown can is slightly swollen at one end and would flex under thumb-pressure. Reputable suppliers would withdraw such a can, known as a flipper, as it could quickly progress to a dangerous stage when the can becomes extended at each end so that it resembles a rugby ball (this is known as hard swell). At this stage, the can could explode if knocked or dropped.

Hydrogen swells

Dark stains inside a can are the result of acid foods acting on the internal surface where the lacquering has been damaged. Hydrogen sulphide forms in the can and reacts with the lining. The condition is not harmful but it does look unpleasant.

Damaged cans

Dents, corrosion, leaks and punctures can come about for any number of reasons – usually because of poor handling or storage. Damage of this kind can be dangerous to health as bacteria or moulds may enter the food through the punctured container and oxygen from the atmosphere may permit pathogenic or spoilage organisms to multiply to harmful levels.

Corned beef typhoid outbreak

When two cases of typhoid were first diagnosed in Aberdeen in May 1964 nobody predicted one of the largest food safety crises in the UK in the twentieth century, with 487 patients in hospital. The outbreak was eventually traced to just one catering-size can of Argentinian corned beef. The can had a flaw in its seam and the meat inside had become contaminated by untreated water used in the cooling stage of the canning process. When the corned beef was sliced in an Aberdeen shop, the slicing machine became contaminated and cross-contaminated other meats.

Television broadcasts played a new and significant part in the intense media coverage, for the first time providing a public health warning as well as widely airing public reaction. The lessons learnt from the subsequent public enquiry changed the attitudes and policies of public health professionals, politicians and others concerned with food safety. One of the main outcomes was the setting up in Scotland, and later in the rest of the UK, of methods of surveillance to give early public warning of outbreaks of food-borne illnesses and advice on the ways to avoid becoming ill.

Preservation by dehydration

Drying is one of the earliest food preservation methods employed by humans. It works by removing the moisture that bacteria need in order to be active. To be effective, the drying processes must reduce the moisture content or a_w to a point where the activities of both spoilage and pathogenic bacteria are inhibited.

Foods that have been subjected to a drying process fall into two categories: dried or desiccated foods, such as whole eggs, yolks or whites, and semi-dry foods such as biscuits, cakes and pastries. The former, known as low moisture (LM) foods, contain no more than 25 per cent moisture and have an a_w between 0.00 and 0.60. The latter are called intermediate moisture (IM) foods and have a water content of between 15 and 50 per cent and an a_w of between 0.61 and 0.85. The two types have different storage requirements and different shelf lives.

Instant coffee is a familiar application of freeze drying.

Methods of drying

There are several ways of drying food, some going back to ancient times and some involving advanced technology.

Sun drying

The simplest and oldest form of dehydrating food is sun drying, which is often used for fruits. Food is spread out under the sun and, provided the temperature remains high and the humidity is not too great, the process is usually successful.

Spray drying

Foods such as milk are processed into a pasteurized slurry which is then sprayed into a hot air stream. Moisture is quickly lost due to the small droplet size and the food ends up as a powder.

Tomatoes and other fruits are traditionally dried all round the world simply by exposing them to sunlight.

Drum or roller drying

A food paste is spread on a roller or drum which is heated, causing water to evaporate. When enough water has been lost the dried 'cake' is simply scraped off the drum. A variation known as tunnel drying involves placing food on trays which are passed through a tunnel of hot air.

Freeze drying

The product is subjected to rapid freezing, which draws out water but creates smaller ice crystals than normal freezing and therefore does less physical damage. After freezing, the food is heated in a vacuum, causing the ice to turn to water vapour which is drawn off, leaving behind a dehydrated product such as instant coffee or vegetables used in instant soup mixes. With this method of preservation, the reconstituted product tastes only minimally different to the original.

Chemical preservation

The main use of chemical preservatives is against spoilage organisms but they do also have an effect on pathogens. In fact, it would be dangerous to use a chemical preservative that was effective only against spoilage organisms, as the pathogens would suddenly find themselves free to multiply without any competition. This does not happen in practice, because the chemicals used affect spoilage and pathogenic organisms in much the same way. Chemical preservatives can also be quite effective against spores, either by preventing their germination or by destroying bacteria as they germinate.

The chemical reactions involved in this form of preservation are quite complicated and in some cases not fully understood. For the purposes of food safety management, however, it is not necessary to understand the chemistry fully, but only to know which preservatives are used and what effect they have on food.

Salt

As discussed earlier, salt is an early method of food preservation which is often used to preserve meats and fish. It works by producing a drying effect. When food is salted a process known as plasmolysis takes place in which water is drawn out of the cells, causing them to contract, stop growing and, in some cases, to die. In fact, in smoking processes (see page 346) it is usually the salt that causes the preserving effect rather than the smoking itself.

Sugar

As you will know if you have ever made jam, fruit can be preserved by the simple addition of sugar. Sugar preserves food in much the same way as salt: it reduces the a_w and so inhibits the growth of spoilage and pathogenic organisms. Much greater concentrations of sugar than salt are required to be effective, but most people have a sweet tooth and this method of preservation has found favour for centuries. Sugar substitutes such as saccharine do not have the same preserving action as sugar itself, partly because they do not combine so readily with free moisture. Dietary products such as low-sugar jams can develop surface mould more quickly than traditional jams and need to be kept under refrigeration.

Benzoic acid

Together with some of its derivatives (such as sodium benzoate), benzoic acid was one of the first chemical preservatives to be given official approval. It works by disrupting the activity of cell membranes at a low pH, so making it useful in high-acid foods but completely ineffective at a neutral pH. The main use is therefore in foods such as cider, soft drinks, tomato ketchup and salad dressings. Of course, a low pH inhibits the growth of bacteria in any case, but the main effectiveness of benzoic acid is in inhibiting yeast and mould. It does, however, also have an inhibitory effect against some bacteria at certain concentrations. The maximum permitted concentration is 0.1 per cent but, even at this level, benzoic acid can give a peppery or burning taste to fruit juices.

Sorbic acid

The action of sorbic acid is very similar to that of benzoic acid. It is widely used and is effective at a lower pH than benzoic acid. Sorbic acid is thought to inhibit the dehydrogenase enzyme system, which is involved in processing moisture in the microbial cell. It is particularly effective against mould and yeast growth although it also works reasonably well against aerobes such as *Salmonella* species and can prevent the outgrowth of vegetative cells from germinating spores. It is used mainly in foods such as bakery products, juices, salad dressings and cheese.

Proprionic acid

The main use of proprionic acid is to inhibit the growth of mould in bread, cakes and cheese, and rope (a soft, sticky texture) in bread dough, which are formed by *Bacillus subtilis*, the spores of which may survive baking. The acid acts in a similar manner to sorbic and benzoic acid and is also useful in low-acid foods.

Nitrites and nitrates

Sodium nitrite and sodium nitrate are used in curing meat because they stabilise the red meat colour, inhibit some spoilage and food poisoning organisms and enhance the meat's flavour. Their main use is against *Clostridium botulinum* although these chemicals are also effective against other organisms, particularly other *Clostridium* species. They are a useful preservative for fish but only for those in the low pH range.

The Perigo factor

For some time researchers were puzzled by the almost total absence of botulism toxin in cured, canned and vacuum-packed meat and fish products even when viable spores were present. Then in 1967 it was shown that if curing salts, such as sodium nitrite, were added *before* heat treatment – as in these forms of processing – the result was about ten times more effective against spore germination than when the chemical was added afterwards. This is known as the Perigo factor, or Perigo effect, after the surname of its discoverer.

Sulphur dioxide and sulphites

Sulphur compounds have been used as preservatives since at least the beginning of the nineteenth century. They are effective against bacteria although the exact mechanism is not known. The main use is in neutral or acid foods such as lemon juice, molasses, wine, fruit juice and meat products such as sausages and mince.

Antibiotics

Two antibiotics are used in food preservation. Nisin, which was first used in Swiss cheese to control *Clostridium butyricum*, is added to cheese to inhibit spoilage. Natamycin is used as an antifungal agent, mainly for the control of surface mould and yeast, for instance on fruits and salami.

Fermentation

The chemist Louis Pasteur was the first to connect yeast to fermentation. He originally defined fermentation as 'respiration without air'.

Fermentation is the chemical conversion of carbohydrates into alcohols or acids as a result of the natural action of certain bacteria and fungi. Fermented foods are a good example of how microbes can be put to good use, and, like dried foods, have been with us a long time. Humans have been taking control of the process since prehistoric times – there is, for example, evidence of fermented beverages and milk products in Babylon in about 5,000 BC, and 7,000-year-old jars of wine have been excavated in Iran.

The process is prompted by the natural action of:

- certain bacteria that produce lactic acid, including the *Lactobacillus* species used to make some yoghurts

- yeasts, such as *Saccharomyces cerevisiae* used to make some breads and beer

- moulds used to make foods including soy sauce, rice wine and a mycoprotein product retailed in Britain as 'Quorn'.

The fermentation enables fruit juice to be converted into wine; grains into beer; carbohydrates into carbon dioxide to leaven bread; sugars in vegetables into preservative organic acids; and sugars in milk into yoghurt or cheese.

Other products from around the world that depend upon fermentation include cider, vinegar, cheese, cultured buttermilk, sour cream, preserved vegetables such as sauerkraut and kimchi, fish sauces, some sausages, coffee and chocolate. The steps involved in producing these products vary enormously and may also involve brining, drying or smoking.

Most fermented foods have prominent flavours and an extended shelf life. The preservative effects include reduced available moisture and increased acidity, both of which reduce the multiplication of spoilage organisms, and competition by lactic acid bacteria that inhibit other undesirable microbes.

Physical preservation

Several very different processes fall into this category. They involve manipulating the atmosphere around food, irradiation and smoking.

Altering the atmosphere

Three techniques are used – vacuum packing, modified atmosphere packaging (also known as gas flushing) and controlled atmosphere packing. They all work by changing the normal proportion of gases surrounding food (typically by decreasing the amount of oxygen), in order to inhibit the multiplication of spoilage organisms. The precise level of an individual gas or a combination of gases is manipulated depending on the food to be preserved. Oxygen, carbon dioxide and nitrogen are the main three gases involved.

To maintain the altered atmosphere necessary for a product's shelf life, it is important that the packaging is sealed properly during processing and remains undamaged during storage, transport and display for retail sale. In keeping with the principles of hurdle technology (see page 336), most of the products are also refrigerated.

The techniques cause few organoleptic changes to most food, so products are usually attractive to consumers. Some people dislike the dark-red appearance of vacuum-packed raw meat, but this disappears shortly after unwrapping the meat.

Vacuum packing

A wide range of foods is now sold in retail vacuum-packs, including delicatessen (cooked) meats, some raw meat joints, fish, some prepared salads and wine in 'wine boxes'. The product is typically placed in a plastic or aluminium bag and the air is sucked out by a vacuum-packing machine so that the packaging collapses on to the food. The bag is then heat sealed. Not all the oxygen is removed from the package, but the little that remains is quickly used up by any aerobic organisms present, so limiting their growth. Even so, it is always advisable to keep vacuum-packed products under refrigeration: the chilling creates another hurdle for the microbes to jump!

Clostridium botulinum is a potentially high-risk hazard in cooked vacuum-packed products because of the possible persistence of its spores and because of their ability to germinate without oxygen. However, products contaminated with *C. botulinum* often undergo organoleptic changes that make them so unpalatable that it is unlikely that anyone would eat them.

Vacuum packing is sometimes referred to as *modified atmospheric packaging*, not to be confused with modified atmosphere packaging (see below).

Small-scale food preservation is often carried out by restaurants by the process of sous-vide, a form of modified atmosphere packaging.

Sous vide

Sous vide, or cuisine sous-vide, is a form of vacuum packing and heat treatment used by some restaurants, caterers and manufacturers of chilled foods. The product is vacuum-packed, then pasteurized before being stored in a refrigerator.

Modified atmosphere packaging (MAP)

In MAP the air is flushed out of the packaging by a mixture of other gases, usually including high levels of carbon dioxide and nitrogen. The reduction of oxygen affects spoilage micro-organisms in a similar way to vacuum packing and quite a long shelf life is achievable, especially when the food is then refrigerated. Retail packs of red meat usually contain a higher proportion of oxygen to maintain the meat's typical bright red appearance. Other products preserved by this method include cured and processed meat, fish, cheese, pasta, bakery products and sandwiches.

Controlled atmosphere packing (CAP)

This form of preservation is used mainly for the bulk storage and transport of foods such as apples, pears, vegetables and raw meat. Typically, raw fruit and vegetables are stored at a cool temperature in atmospheres containing a higher than normal level of carbon dioxide. This slows the development of mould and counteracts the ageing effect of ethylene gas, which is naturally produced by plants.

Irradiation

Subjecting food to low levels of ionizing radiation is a reasonably effective way of destroying pathogens, bacterial spores, spoilage organisms, parasites and insects.

Irradiation is approved for use at specified doses for a limited range of products in Britain including fruit, vegetables, mushrooms, cereals, fish, shellfish, poultry, bulbs and tubers. So far, however, only one licence has been granted – it is for herbs and spices. All irradiated food must be labelled as such.

Although the process is strictly controlled and all the current scientific evidence suggests that there is no significant risk to human health, irradiation is still controversial and the subject of public concern. One of the perceived problems is that, as there are few perceivable changes to irradiated foods, it is therefore difficult to detect whether food has been treated or not. Consumer resistance in the UK suggests that there is unlikely to be any substantial increase in the use of irradiated foods in the near future.

The process

Food irradiation involves bombarding food with a form of energy – ionizing rays with strong penetration abilities, such as X-rays, gamma rays, microwaves and ultraviolet waves. In general, the shorter wavelengths of X-rays and gamma rays are the most powerful, with the lethal dose depending on the individual organism. Non-spore-forming bacteria, and yeasts and mould spores are killed at lower doses than spore-forming bacteria. The highest irradiation values (which are measured in rads) are needed to inactivate viruses and enzymes. The nature and consistency of the food is also taken into account when calculating the rads required.

Possible advantages and disadvantages

The process can be employed to treat solid and packaged foods. Not only is this convenient, but it also helps to prevent the recontamination of the product. There are some organoleptic effects which may be considered to modify the quality of the product – for example, colour changes and alterations in smell and taste. At high dosages some foodstuffs may undergo a change in structure. Some other concerns have also been raised, including:

- the possibility of decreased nutritional value – some vitamins may be affected but in general there is little cause for concern as radiation doses are low

- carcinogenic effects – none has been demonstrated to date

- residual radioactivity – doses are considered to be too low to pose a significant risk

- microbiological problems – it has been suggested that sub-lethal doses of radiation may allow micro-organisms to survive, possibly with genetic mutations, but no significant problems have ever been found

- altered flavour and smell – it is reported, for example, that doses at the higher end of the approved range may give chicken a 'wet dog' smell

- inappropriate use – fears have sometimes been expressed in the media that irradiation could be used to clean up microbiologically contaminated or spoiled foods before sale.

Smoking

This is a centuries-old method for treating food for storage, even though its value as a preservative is limited. It is thought that chemicals known as phenols, which are produced by the smoke, may have some preserving effect. If this is indeed true, then the effect can apply only at the surface.

Fish and ham have traditionally been smoked, but in recent years the process has been extended to a much wider range of products including many types of meat, sausages and cheese, although this is often done more for flavour than for preservation purposes. There are two types of smoking – hot smoking and cold smoking. The methods vary only in the time and temperature combinations.

The process

Smoking takes place in a kiln where food is suspended for a specified time over smouldering chips of oak or other hardwood. Modern kilns allow for careful monitoring and control of both time and temperature. Before smoking, the food is often left for up to eight hours in dry salt or in a brine solution, sometimes with additional marinades. It is probably the salt rather than the smoking that has the main preserving effect: unless the food is of uniform thickness, the salt profile varies significantly and so does the preservative effect.

The hot smoking process is essentially a form of cooking. The time and temperature combination is typically around 82°C for 30 minutes or 60°C for two to four hours. This form of treatment is used when smoking trout, kippers and some haddock and salmon. Cold smoking is carried out at much lower temperatures for a much longer time, typically 32°C to 38°C for 15 to 18 hours. The food is not actually cooked but merely cured and flavoured. Smoked salmon is prepared in this way.

Making it easier for others

- Train staff to understand and follow the rules for time and temperature control as they apply to methods of preservation undertaken on your premises.

- Ensure that suppliers' and manufacturers' instructions for storage and handling are observed.

- Emphasise the importance of observing *use by* and *best by* dates.

- Train food handlers to recognise the signs of spoilage.

- Make certain that staff understand that some 'preserved' products, such as pasteurized canned ham and vacuum-packed products, still need to be refrigerated.

Finding the energy

Why does manipulating the intrinsic factors of microbes work so well in many food safety and preservation techniques? One reason is the redox reaction or potential, also known as oxidation-reduction.

It is not essential to know about the redox reaction to pass a food safety course at managerial level. But a basic grasp of it, even if some of the explanatory terms we must use are unfamiliar, will help you to understand the importance of pH and why some organisms are aerobes, some anaerobes and some facultative anaerobes.

The redox potential indicates the ease with which a substrate (in this case, the food) loses or gains electrons. A substrate that loses electrons is said to be oxidised while a substrate that gains electrons is said to be reduced. You may come across this expressed as E_h.

The E_h is strictly dependent on the pH. It can change due to the multiplication of certain bacteria on the food or because of technological influences during storage and preparation.

In turn, micro-organisms display varying degrees of sensitivity to the redox potential of the food they contaminate.

Like every living thing, the growth of micro-organisms requires energy. Microbes obtain the necessary energy by degrading, or using up, the nutrients present in the food.

One of the most relevant using-up processes is respiration – the scientific term is catabolism.

In this context, respiration does not mean breathing, as microbes do not breathe. It is an oxidation, or using up, process, of which familiar examples are the rusting of iron as it reacts with moist air or the browning of the cut surface of an apple.

In food the chemical process involves a hydrogen transfer from reduced substrates (such as sugars) to oxygen or other oxidised compounds.

All micro-organisms that are able to transfer hydrogen as H+ to molecular oxygen (O_2) are known as aerobes. They can therefore live in the presence of air.

If they can grow *only* in the presence of air, they are described as *obligate* aerobes.

The process of oxygen reduction leads to the formation of superoxide free radicals which are very toxic. Aerobic organisms contain a specific enzyme (superoxide dismutase or SOD), a catalyst in the reaction, which binds or destroys these radicals.

Microbes that do not possess this enzyme are unable to grow in the presence of oxygen because oxygen is toxic to them. These are called anaerobes, a term derived from Greek words meaning without air.

Aerobic micro-organisms reduce the oxygen during respiration, so lowering the E_h value of the food. Anaerobic organisms have the same effect on the E_h, although the process involves substances other than oxygen.

Aerobes will, however, multiply only where there are high E_h values. So, when the redox potential sinks below 0, the growth conditions are more favourable for anaerobes.

In the middle E_h range, there is a transition stage where micro-aerophillic and facultative organisms can grow.

Food products usually have a low redox potential and it varies throughout the product. The surface of a product, for instance, may have a higher redox potential than deeper layers – the cosmos of a micro-organism is really very small!

Small pieces or particles of food are more exposed to oxygen than large ones because the ratio of their surface area to their body mass is higher. So, techniques like mincing, trimming, stirring, mixing and even squeezing food increases the food's exposure to oxygen. On the other hand, techniques like vacuum packing, the addition of reducing compounds (such as ascorbic acid) and heating processes have the effect of maintaining a low redox potential.

Stock control, storage and display

Have you ever rummaged in a kitchen cupboard at home only to discover that an essential ingredient for your meal is missing? Exasperating, isn't it? You can imagine the trouble a food business would get itself into if it failed to keep sufficient supplies of the foods and ingredients its customers wanted.

Why store food?

No food business has the time to pop out to buy ingredients and products every time they are needed, but convenience is only one aspect of the benefits of storing some foods. Even if your business buys all or many fresh ingredients on a daily basis, it still needs to store some staple products.

Large manufacturing and retail companies have sophisticated stock-producing and stock-ordering systems that allow them to fulfil annual seasonal demands and even to provide for activities such as barbecues that are so influenced by unpredictable weather.

Storing foods enables companies to provide customers with instant year-round supplies, even when particular produce is out of season. Rapid forms of transport and purpose-designed packaging allow foods to be imported from around the world every day.

The budgetary benefits from bulk buying and storing food are self-explanatory, as cost-effectiveness is fundamental to every company.

Smaller retail and catering companies are rarely able to predict *precisely* what their orders will be day to day or week to week, so storing food allows them to even out the peaks and troughs of demand and to satisfy their customers at the drop of a hat.

There is another advantage to storing food, although it is not perhaps the first thing you would think of in an affluent country: that is, to help to avoid famine, an issue that is still of the greatest importance in many parts of the world.

Making storage work to best advantage

We should perhaps remind ourselves that all these benefits assume that the food is stored in such a way that it retains its eating quality (its appearance, flavour, smell, texture and nutritional value) as well as remaining safe to eat. As we mentioned in Part 1, contaminated and spoilt food must be thrown away, which increases costs instead of controlling them.

Placing on the market

Shops need to store food on display, but the principles discussed in this chapter apply equally to food on display, in a warehouse or in a stock room.

Product specifications

Whether you are buying from a market gardener, from a wholesaler or from a manufacturer producing your own-brand products, you need to know exactly what should be arriving at your door. This helps you to keep control of the safety and quality of food, as well as the quantities and type of the products the business requires. All criteria for foods entering your company should be shaped by your risk assessments.

Large companies can usually insist on very detailed product specifications, including such things as microbiological standards and tolerances, levels of additives or residual pesticides and types of packaging. They often insist on audits, certification systems and laboratory analysis (for high-risk foods) before any products reach their doors.

Smaller businesses may have less scope to specify criteria for all their raw materials. However, reputable suppliers now have their own specifications for the goods they sell, so small companies can compare their own requirements against those specifications for such things as the ripeness or degree of washing of a raw food.

Record keeping

You need to keep accurate and up-to-date records of all foods and ingredients that come into and go out of your workplace, even if some of the information is logged by a central buying or stock-control department. The documents are essential to help you to:

- manage stock profitably and efficiently

- control the safety of food – by helping to assess any safety risks from particular foods, for example

- maintain your own company standards

- provide records, if required, that demonstrate due diligence to client companies and environmental health officers

- identify and trace the *source* of food supplies and *where products have been sold* (this traceability is particularly important for manufacturers, retailers and large catering companies that outsource their meals, because their products are distributed widely)

- identify and remove products from processing or sale if a problem is discovered with a particular batch or brand – glass contamination, for example

- take any necessary action, such as changing procedures, if illness is linked to any product sold by your company

- fulfil the legal requirement to have procedures based on the HACCP principles.

Staff who are involved in any aspect of record-keeping and their supervisors must be given appropriate training.

Dealing with food deliveries

The controls you put in place for accepting or rejecting deliveries of food to your premises will help to minimise the critical control points along the food flow for individual products and ingredients.

You may wish to designate individual members of staff who are authorised to accept or reject consignments of goods. Be certain to include the criteria for receiving food deliveries in their training programmes.

Transport, delivery and loading areas

It is best to consider delivery vehicles and loading areas as an extension of food premises so they must also be designed, maintained and operated in ways that safeguard food from contamination, microbial multiplication or spoilage.

Storage areas, especially in larger businesses, are often linked directly to delivery and loading areas. The same dock and entrance are often used for both delivery and loading. However, there are circumstances – such as abattoirs – where the fresh meat should not be loaded in the same place where live animals may be brought in. In some food premises a double-entry system is used where goods are unloaded through one door into an unpacking area and only then distributed through another door into the storage areas. Smaller businesses must do whatever is practicable to secure a safe workflow (see page 246).

Someone must be given the responsibility for checking the condition of food delivery vehicles when they arrive at the factory. Vehicles used for delivering food should ideally be specifically designed for the purpose and must be kept clean. If the vehicles are used for delivering different types and batches of food or for delivering goods other than food, then they must comply with legal requirements designed to protect food from contamination (see page 165). They should be refrigerated if they carry high-risk or highly perishable foods.

Receiving deliveries

Products must be checked as soon as they arrive and the food must be stored immediately afterwards. Large supermarkets often dictate strict delivery slots to their suppliers. Smaller businesses should do whatever they can to negotiate suitable delivery times with their suppliers. This is particularly important for small and medium catering companies, such as restaurants and pubs, which are often hard-pressed to find enough staff to check in deliveries during service periods such as lunch. If food is not checked immediately, problems can be difficult to resolve later. If high-risk and frozen food is not stored immediately, the cold chain may be broken and the food may become unsafe to eat.

Acceptance criteria

Every food business should have clear criteria for accepting or rejecting food deliveries. You need to check the details for different foods, but the key points are to ensure that the food is:

- fresh and within the date mark (see page 352)
- at the correct temperature
- contained in clean, undamaged packaging that is properly labelled – with a date mark and traceability code, for example
- free from pest infestation.

The reasons for rejecting a delivery of food are likely to include:

- high-risk or perishable foods delivered at a danger zone temperature
- frozen food delivered thawed or partly thawed
- packaging damaged, dirty or wet
- cans dented, bulging, rusty or leaking

- signs of mould or other forms of spoilage

- an expired date mark

- a date mark that gives insufficient time to process or sell the food

- inadequate labelling or documentation.

Rejection procedures

You need to establish with your suppliers agreed procedures for dealing with rejected products or consignments. This may involve placing food in quarantine (see page 356).

Shelf life and date labelling

The shelf life of a food depends on its nature and type of preservation. The manufacturing and processing sector of the food industry carries out many tests to determine shelf life: obviously, the longer the shelf life can be extended, the more profitable it is likely to be.

Pathogens and spoilage organisms

Some foods, such as canned, bottled or dehydrated foods, have an extremely long safe storage period because most bacteria have been destroyed or the conditions are too harsh for remaining bacteria to multiply. Roughly the same conditions that allow for the multiplication of pathogens are ideal for the multiplication of spoilage organisms – just think back to the chapter on microbiology in Part 3. The foods that are likely to pose safety problems are generally the same ones that will readily support the multiplication of spoilage organisms.

Date marks

Use-by dates are a legal requirement for packaged high-risk foods that require refrigeration. *Display-until* codes are voluntarily applied to packaging to help to maintain food safety and quality by indicating when staff should remove products from sale.

For this reason there are two legally recognised categories of date mark for food:

- use by

- best before.

Use by

This date mark, which usually gives a date only a few days after the date of purchase, states a day, month and year. It is a legal requirement for packaged high-risk foods to have a *use-by* date if they are not ambient shelf stable and therefore may become a health hazard. It is also an offence to sell them after the *use-by* date has expired. As you can see, the *use-by* date is largely concerned with food safety rather than quality.

Best before

This date mark applies to foods other than those covered by a *use-by* date and usually allows for a far longer storage period. The *best-before* date is, as the name suggests, largely an issue of quality, although safety may also be involved. The manufacturer is in effect making a statement that the food will be at its best – of the quality they would wish consumers to enjoy – up until the date given.

Undated

Some foods do not have to be date marked. They include raw fresh fruit and vegetables, provided that they have not been processed by cutting or peeling; wine and vinegar; and cooking salt and sugar.

The principles of storage

The best way to store food depends upon three factors, which are the:

- amount of food to be stored
- type of food to be stored
- length of time in storage.

There is obviously a vast difference between storing breakfast cereals in a guest house and storing half a million tonnes of grain in a granary. Although the scale is vastly different, many of the other necessary conditions are similar. In the case of a guest house a small dry goods store would suffice, whereas in the granary would need large grain silos.

Let us use some typical ingredients of a traditional British breakfast to deal with the type of food to be stored. What is the difference in the storage requirements for breakfast cereal, grapefruit, sausage, bacon, egg, bread, milk, tea and coffee? The most significant difference is that some require refrigerated temperature control and some do not. How does the scale of storage count? In bulk storage the relative humidity may also need to be controlled.

Account has to be taken of how long something needs to be stored – is it hours, days, weeks, months or years? This determines, for example, whether the storage facility should be chilled, deep frozen, humidity controlled or just clean and tidy.

All round essentials

The mention of 'just clean and tidy' in the previous paragraph has no doubt alerted you to some basic requirements for storage areas, no matter what their size, type or purpose. The following paragraphs outline these storage prerequisites.

Suitable for the purpose

This seems an obvious point to make, but you need to equip food premises with adequate storage space for the type of goods being stored and to ensure that any shelves, racking, pallets, packaging and containers conform to any relevant food legislation. There should be separate stores for non-food items such as cleaning equipment and chemicals, the latter ideally in a lockable facility.

Whatever the size or type of food business, food must be kept in suitable storage in appropriate conditions.

Provision should be made for the separate storage of different types of food, which may have varying requirements, such as those affecting temperature, gaseous atmosphere, stacking, accessibility and different stages of preparation – for example:

- canned and bottled food
- dairy products
- dry goods and cereals
- fish
- frozen food
- fruits

- liquids

- open food

- packaged food

- raw meat

- ready-to-eat food

- shellfish

- vegetables.

Designed so that different foods can be stored separately

Raw foods and high-risk foods that are cooked or ready-to-eat must be kept apart, ideally in separate storage areas. However, where space for storing raw or high-risk foods is so restricted that there is room for only one refrigerator, then raw foods must be stored *below* cooked and ready-to-eat foods so they cannot cause contamination from dripping juices or blood.

Protected from contamination

Contamination comes in many forms, as we have already discussed. Apart from the possibility of falls, spills and transfer of contaminants, there are also issues of quality to consider. For instance, as we saw earlier in Part 4, some foods readily absorb odours from other foods, so becoming tainted. Care should therefore be taken to store separately anything which is liable either to pick up a taint or to give one.

Windproof and waterproof

The store, whether it be an outdoor silo, a small larder, a large walk-in cold store or a self-standing refrigerator, should be constructed in a way that excludes the draughts but is well ventilated to prevent condensation. It may seem incongruous to talk of a refrigerator housed in a kitchen as needing to be windproof and waterproof, but the same general principle does apply as it needs to be made of non-porous materials and sited out of draughts.

Protected from light

Some foods react with light, especially sunlight, and change colour. In the case of potatoes, green patches and sprouts are produced that contain concentrations of the natural poison solanine. This is why potatoes should be stored away from sunlight.

Storing any food in direct sunlight is likely to affect temperature control, which may compromise food safety and quality. Make sure that the lighting is correct and that shading, such as blinds, is provided where necessary.

Easy to clean

All surfaces, especially those that come into contact with food, should be designed and be of such materials that they are easy to clean.

Keeping storage areas clean and free from clutter helps to:

- reduce the possibility of contamination of the food

- minimise the possibility of harbouring pests by reducing potential shelter, nesting places and supplies of food

- show up damaged packaging or signs of pest infestation clearly

- maintain proper stock control.

Pest proofed

The main reasons for pest proofing storage areas are to:

- eliminate possible contamination of the food or the premises from rodents, birds or insects

- prevent economic loss due to damage caused by the voracious appetites of pests.

Free from pests

Even if storage areas are properly pest proofed, they should still be monitored for the presence of pests – because pests are great opportunists – and any infestation should be dealt with immediately.

Storing and retrieving food

As well as inspecting food when it is delivered, staff need to check the integrity of food packaging and the quality of the food throughout its storage time and just before use, sale or dispatch. The frequency of inspection depends on the food: high-risk foods, for example, need to be checked daily.

Rotation

Ensure that supervisors emphasise the importance of placing the stock with the longest shelf life at the back of shelves, *behind* stock that is approaching its expiry date. With some kinds of storage facility, such as chest freezers, this may mean placing the food with the longest shelf life *underneath* food with a shorter shelf life.

The whole point of this way of storing and retrieving food, known as stock rotation, is to help to ensure that a product with a short shelf life is used before one that can be stored safely for longer. This is sometimes expressed as the FIFO system – meaning *first in, first out*.

While the phrase makes good sense to managers, it may need to be used with caution, if at all, with staff. They sometimes interpret it to mean that they should use stored food according to the time when it was *delivered*, regardless of the length of its shelf life.

Some food premises, such as supermarkets, have to deal with an extra unplanned form of stock rotation. This is caused by customers who rummage through displays to find the item with the longest lasting date mark and therefore the longest safe storage period. Managers of such premises must always be aware that, no matter how carefully they have had products rotated and arranged according to good practice, the stock may become thoroughly mixed up about two hours after opening for business.

Staff need to be trained how to store and retrieve food from storage areas: both food safety and occupational safety are at stake!

Quarantine

Suspect food
If in doubt, throw it
out.

Make sure that every member of staff who may be asked to receive a delivery of goods or to store or retrieve food from storage knows what to do if he or she suspects that food safety may have been, or will be, compromised.

This may involve placing food in quarantine. This is both a system and a place for keeping suspect food securely apart from other stock. Any product that appears to be spoilt or damaged must be examined thoroughly to ascertain their compliance with company criteria and their fitness for human consumption.

Depending upon your company procedures, the food may then be returned to the supplier or, if there is any doubt about its fitness, it may be destroyed so that it does not re-enter the food chain.

Making it easier for others

- Train designated staff to take responsibility for receiving and checking deliveries of goods to your premises.

- Make clear the criteria for accepting or rejecting deliveries.

- Create clear procedures in your food safety policy for dealing with spoilt food or food in damaged packaging.

- Insist that food is stored immediately after the delivery has been checked.

- Make sure that all staff know where and how to store different types of food and where to store non-food items.

- Emphasise the importance of storing high-risk and highly perishable foods before others such as dry and canned goods.

- Explain how rough handling can accelerate spoilage and cause contamination.

- Arrange a demonstration of how to stack shelves carefully without overloading but leaving enough space between goods for air to circulate freely.

- Emphasise and re-emphasise the importance of time and temperature control.

- Insist that all storage areas are kept clean and tidy.

- Encourage staff to report evidence of damage or signs of infestation.

- Make sure that stock is adequately rotated and that date marks are observed.

Feature

Extended shelf life

When archaeologists examined bottled food from a boat that sank more than 100 years ago they found that it was still safe to eat, even though it had lost its usual smell and appearance. The steamboat *Bertrand* was carrying preserved bottles of food, such as brandied peaches, oysters, plum tomatoes, honey and mixed vegetables, to the new goldfields of Montana, when it sank in the Missouri river in 1865.

The combination of a preservation method and suitable packaging certainly stood the test of time for food on the *Bertrand*. The process used, which we now know as *canning*, emerged from the Napoleonic wars. Malnutrition had been common in the French armed forces, so in 1790 Napoleon offered a huge prize for a new way of preserving food for his troops. French chef Nicholas Appert discovered that heating food sufficiently in sealed glass containers kept the food tasty and safe to eat.

It was to be another 50 years before the French chemist Louis Pasteur explained the the link between spoilage and microbial activity and the science behind the

preservative effect of heat-treatment. While Pasteur's name is familiar for the process that reduces pathogens in milk and other foods, Appert's name lives on as an alternative term for *commercial sterilization* (see page 338).

In 1810 the Englishman Peter Durand patented a method of preserving food in tin-plated wrought-iron containers. At first they were opened with a hammer and chisel. Today, with easier opening methods, almost 200 billion cans of food are produced worldwide each year. Appert's method has not been changed radically but the foods that are canned and the metals used have developed. Carbonated soft drink canning began in 1940 and aluminium was introduced in 1957.

Management matters

Cleaning and pest control services are sometimes outside the direct control of food managers. Even so, you must ensure that your company has in place and maintains proper procedures for cleaning and disinfection, the disposal of rubbish and waste and pest control.

Inadequate cleaning procedures can cause, or fail to control, a large number of hazards including:

- microbiological contamination – for example, when food debris is not removed from food contact surfaces promptly and thoroughly

- microbiological multiplication – for example, when food-contact or hand-contact surfaces are not cleaned and disinfected promptly

- cross-contamination – for example, when the same cleaning equipment, such as a cleaning cloth, is used in areas designated for the storage or preparation of raw foods as well as in areas set aside for preparing cooked or ready-to-eat foods

- physical contamination – for example, from debris from brushes and mops, or from grease or burnt food and other food debris that could contaminate the next batch of food that is prepared, or from packaging materials that are not disposed of properly and promptly

- chemical contamination – for example, from the purchase of cleaning chemicals that are not food-safe, the use of inappropriate dilutions of chemicals, the unsuitable storage of cleaning chemicals close to food or the storage of chemicals in food containers

- pest infestation – because particles of food and undisturbed areas attract pests.

Ignoring pest management could have a dire impact upon your company's legal record, budget and profits and could lead to serious illness or injury, so:

- establish clear procedures that are easy for staff to follow

- ensure that all food staff clean as they go

- emphasise the importance of keeping all parts of the premises clean at all times

- store food off the floor in pest-resistant packaging or containers and make sure that staff replace lids securely

- teach staff how to check and rotate stock

- encourage staff to report any sign of infestation.

Effective pest management may require cultural and educational changes in your business and better teamwork that involves everyone from the cleaning staff to the senior managers. Hazards from inadequate pest control include:

- bacterial contamination – carried or excreted by pests

- cross-contamination – particularly from flying insects that move from food to food or from sources of contamination, such as rubbish tips, to food premises

- chemical contamination – from the careless use or residual traces of pesticides

- physical contamination – from their bodies, droppings and nest materials.

Temperature control throughout the food chain is an important key to producing safe food and all food-contact staff should be given the opportunity to learn how microbial survival and multiplication affect the safety of food. All aspects of temperature control are important, of course, but you may wish to take the hint from the statistics about the main factors that lead to food poisoning (see page 75) and particularly reinforce the message about safe cooling, holding temperatures (both cold and hot) and reheating, if you permit reheating at all.

Managers have a crucial part to play, not only in emphasising 'safe' temperatures and setting a good example in their own everyday work, but also in ensuring that:

- workflow takes full account of temperature control and not just contamination hazards

- there are procedures for every aspect of temperature control that are clear to all and easy for every member of staff to follow.

As with so many other aspects of food safety, this may involve management teamwork. In a large organisation this could involve chefs and warehouse, distribution and sales managers, for example.

Dealing with a crisis

Imagine the scene: you turn up at work one morning to find your way barred by television crews and newspaper reporters. They ask you about a food poisoning outbreak. People are in hospital. Some are critically ill. A child is just holding on to life. Your business may be responsible. Would you like to comment?

Most people would regard this as a crisis. Even when a company thinks it has done everything possible that a responsible organisation can do, mistakes and the unforeseen can occur, leaving the business in the glare of hostile publicity. In the period before the cause of an outbreak of food-borne illness has been discovered the spotlight may well fall on the innocent and the guilty alike. So how do you prepare for the day when it could fall on you?

Preparation, preparation, preparation

Planning is your best insurance policy. Many food companies do not have any kind of crisis plan, so, when things go wrong, they really do go horribly wrong, often ending up by ruining the business. But how can you possibly plan for and manage a crisis? After all, a crisis is by definition a period of severe difficulty.

The ancient origins of the word (from Greek, Latin and Middle English) hold the clues, because a crisis can also be translated as a time of decision or as a *turning point*. Assuming that your company already does everything possible to protect consumer health and can justify a defence of due diligence under food safety legislation, a crisis management plan can make difficult and urgent decisions easier to make. Provided that no one dies and provided that the adverse publicity leaves you some customers, you may even eventually strengthen the business by improving your food safety systems.

Getting ready

The time to start your planning is now, not when the press is baying at your door. At that point you will need to put all your energy and clear thinking into dealing with the immediate situation. You need to have a three-stage plan of actions to be taken:

- in advance, as a matter of course
- during a crisis
- after a crisis.

This chapter outlines issues you should consider and actions you could take to plan for and manage an event that we all hope will never happen – after all, the whole point of this book is to help you to *prevent* such situations. Although we deal only with crises affecting food safety, the general management advice holds good for many other kinds of crisis, so you may wish to put it into the bigger picture of managing the business.

Planning ahead

Perhaps your company already has a crisis management plan. If so, is it up to date, comprehensive and well practised? Does everyone know about it and understand their part? Will it work if key people are on holiday or ill or just out of the office? Does it include a strategy for dealing with the media? Is there a press spokesperson? Do managers know what to say and how to say it? Do they know what *not* to say? Do they realise that their actions could make or break the company?

If you do not already have a plan, or the plan needs an overhaul, a good way to start is by thinking about what could go wrong – a complaint of food poisoning or a product recall, for example. Unless you have a realistic view of what might happen, you will not be able to plan for it. Ask yourself questions such as:

- what are the things that could go wrong – what is the very worst that could happen and what are the things most likely to happen?

- how would consumers (and the general public) be affected?

- what would the fallout be for the company – a minor inconvenience or bankruptcy; refunding the cost of a tin of beans, or paying out millions in damages; a minor dent in your reputation or the death of the business?

- what would you tell customers – how could you keep their confidence and their custom?

Once you have a general idea of the kind of crises that could happen in your business you can start planning for specific situations, such as dealing with a complaint of food poisoning or a product withdrawal.

Consider different scenarios

Initial information about a problem could come from many sources. Your planned response will probably need to be shaped by the source of the information and the perceived seriousness of the problem. Typical sources include:

- suppliers

- trade organisations

- customers

- consumer organisations

- local environmental health practitioners

- government departments or the Food Standards Agency

- the police

- blackmailers

- the media

- contacts in the food industry.

There are numerous possible responses. For example, your strategy for dealing with a blackmailer, however serious the threat, may be to give no publicity at all. In contrast, your response to the possibility of physical contamination may be to withdraw the product and recall it from the market, which could involve the maximum publicity in a bid to inform as many consumers as possible.

Establish a crisis team

As well as considering a range of response strategies you need to designate the members of the team who will go into action at the first sign of a problem, co-ordinating the company's responses and deciding what to say to the staff, press and public. The team members will vary depending on the type of crisis and the size and nature of the business but there should usually be a core group. In a larger company the team would probably include all the following people:

- senior manager or director able to take major decisions

- marketing or sales manager

- legal expert

- food safety expert

- quality assurance manager

- production manager

- press spokesperson

- external food safety or management consultant.

Owner-managers and managers of small businesses may need to draw upon the help of nominated outsiders in a crisis, as one or two people are unlikely to cope with doing everything when the pressure is on.

Appoint a spokesperson

Someone in the crisis team needs to be designated as the spokesperson who deals with any approach from journalists. Having one person in this role improves the chance of putting across a single, consistent message and minimises the possibility of confusion in the media and among consumers. It may not matter whether the spokesperson is the managing director, the food safety manager, the sales director or a member of the canteen staff. What *is* important is that the person should be capable, unflappable, believable, genuinely concerned and well briefed.

Draw up a communications policy

Communication lies at the heart of all business relationships, as it does of most human relationships. It can lose customers or gain them, it can give you a good press or a bad press and it can turn a crisis into a disaster or into an opportunity.

Consider two managers faced with a crisis. One tells the press, "We have never had a problem before so I don't see how this can be our fault." The other says, "We have been working very hard to find out exactly what has caused this problem. We will keep you informed as soon as we know anything. In the mean time, we have taken the following precautionary steps..." Customers are much more likely to forgive the second company than the first.

Try to involve your spokesperson and the other members of the crisis team in drawing up the communications policy. Don't forget to keep your staff, suppliers and customers in the picture as you scurry to deal with reporters. Staff may become anxious or even unco-operative in the absence of hard facts.

Remember too that many people show some of their best characteristics in a crisis, if they are given the chance to do so. After a bomb destroyed a large part of the Docklands area of

London in 1996, customers rallied round with help that enabled one company to get itself back on its feet. There are no hard and fast rules for your communications policy, but it is worth considering the following suggestions.

Put customers and the public first
Treat customers and the public with respect. Don't interrupt or be dismissive, but acknowledge their point of view, even if they are rude or misinformed. Show that you take their concerns seriously and appreciate their right to information.

Be honest and direct
Leave it to experts to find out the facts. Don't deny or accept responsibility until the evidence is in, but explain what you are doing to resolve the crisis. Little lies can become big lies when dealing with a crisis, so all communications must be truthful and above reproach. Any attempt to hide or misrepresent the facts will probably come out eventually – not only will you have more explaining to do, but your credibility will be in tatters.

Be prepared, practical and positive
Focus on the constructive measures you have taken to improve the situation. Decide in advance what you are going to say. Don't be tempted to make up ad hoc answers.

If a crisis occurs

Management during a crisis is different: normal roles and rules may be suspended temporarily in the interests of dealing with the emergency. In this situation you need to think quickly, clearly and with a view of the big picture.

Teamwork is even more important than before and managers must put the interests of public health first, followed by the long-term interests of the company – ahead of financial targets, deadlines, personal concerns or egos. There may need to be even greater flexibility than normal if production or service is to continue because even greater attention will need to be paid to food safety and product quality.

Going into action

As soon as you are aware of a crisis, bring your crisis management plan into action. Make sure that members of the crisis team meet immediately.

Among the questions they should ask themselves are:

- what has happened?
- who is already affected?
- who else could be affected?
- why has it happened – can this be ascertained immediately with any certainty?
- what can the company do to correct the situation immediately?
- is additional specialist advice required from outside the company?
- should production or service be halted?
- should a product withdrawal or recall be instigated?
- who will liaise with officials such as environmental health practitioners, Food Standards Agency representatives or the police

- what should be done to ensure that no one destroys, interferes with or disturbs potential evidence, such as suspect food?

- when is it appropriate to issue a press statement?

- what can be done to maintain good customer relationships?

Devising a plan

The team must place actions in order of priority in a staged plan. Some things will need to be done immediately, others later in the day, others the following day, and still others weeks or months later, or once the crisis is over. Team members must consider how to prevent the problem recurring as well as solving the immediate problem – and the immediate problem must, of course, take precedence. However, the solution to the problem usually leads to ways of preventing a recurrence.

Dealing with foreseeable problems

Take time to think through how well your company is prepared for dealing with a range of possible events, such as a customer complaint or allegation of food poisoning; an official investigation following an outbreak of food-borne illness; circumstances where a product withdrawal or recall might be required; and attempted bioterrorism.

Complaints and allegations – averting a crisis

Nobody wants customer complaints, but every company gets them. If handled badly, a complaint could turn into a public relations disaster, whether or not the allegation were justified. If handled well, it could actually improve customer or brand loyalty. Make sure that you create and make clear to staff the procedure to be followed. You might decide that all complaints should be referred immediately to a supervisor or manager, or you might create a form to be filled in by any staff member of staff and the customer. Whichever procedure you choose, make certain that everyone is aware of the importance of remaining polite and attentive, without admitting liability.

Keep records of complaints, whether they are eventually justified, disproved or malicious. Use them to review food safety (and customer relationship) procedures and to record any appropriate corrective action. The procedure should also indicate when the public health authorities should be notified, and who should do this.

Recording

Examples of information that should be recorded include:

- the name and contact details of the person making the complaint

- the date of the complaint

- the product – name, type, size – or service involved

- the nature of the complaint

- where and when the product or service was bought

- any date-marking

- the identification coding.

Investigation

The complaint should then be investigated and analysed by a supervisor, manager or experienced member of the company, with the help of staff as appropriate. The following questions are among those that should be answered.

- What needs to be done immediately to deal with the complaint?
- Is there an imminent threat to public health?
- Do the authorities need to be involved?
- Are there any other complaints linked to this product?
- Are there any other complaints linked to this batch/lot number?
- Are there any other complaints linked to this customer – is he/she a persistent or malicious complainer? (The comments of a persistent complainer should be taken seriously, but they should be viewed in context.)
- Is there anything in the process records or HACCP records for the day of production or service that give a clue to the root cause of the complaint?
- How serious is the complaint – is it likely to be a one-off or is it an indication of an underlying problem?
- What needs to be done to prevent recurrence of the complaint?

Action and review

Whatever action you take, it should be in proportion to the hazard, the scale of the risk and the likely timescale of the risk. You should ensure that you thank the person who complained for bringing the matter to your attention and let him or her know, briefly, what action has been taken as a consequence.

Ensure that complaints are analysed as part of your reviews of food safety procedures and practices: they are negative events that can be used in a positive manner. Complaints which are perceived by customers as being dealt with in a positive manner are likely to receive positive feed back. The opposite is very clearly also the case.

The role of investigating authorities

Let us backtrack for a moment. Why might a local authority environmental health practitioner (EHP) approach your business other than for a routine inspection or at your request for advice? The legal duties of EHPs include safeguarding food so that it is fit for human consumption. This involves generally monitoring the food chain and food operations and also specifically includes:

- investigating consumer complaints about food
- investigating allegations of food-borne illness
- investigating outbreaks of food-borne illness
- taking action to recall products from sale that are suspected of being, or known to be, harmful.

These activities not only protect consumers and public health, but they also help to exonerate innocent food businesses if they are accused of blame.

Outbreak of food-borne illness

Let's take an outbreak of food-borne illness as an example for dealing with a crisis. Your business might become involved in an investigation if there is an outbreak. While a case is just one incidence of illness, an outbreak is a cluster, in time or place, of cases of illness caused by a particular organism.

The Health Protection Agency (HPA) continuously researches and monitors infectious diseases, chemicals, poisons and radiation, and plans for and co-ordinates responses to health emergencies. It is responsible for co-ordinating the investigation of national outbreaks of food-borne illness and for ensuring consistency in dealing with local outbreaks. It also advises on the withdrawal or recall of food products.

There is a well-established system of Food Alerts involving local authorities, the Food Standards Agency and the medical authorities. If an outbreak is significant, an outbreak investigation team is then set up to co-ordinate all actions that need to be taken to deal with the problem.

Outbreak investigation team

The size and composition of an investigating team varies but the core members are:

- a consultant in public health medicine

- one or more environmental health practitioners/officers

- a consultant microbiologist

- administrative support staff.

Depending on the circumstances, the team may also include some or all of the following specialists:

- a consultant in infectious diseases

- press officers

- an infection control nurse

- a veterinarian

- a general practitioner (GP)

- a public analyst

- a toxicologist

- a virologist

- representatives of government departments and agencies.

The investigation

All investigations follow a similar pattern, involving interviewing patients and establishing what they have eaten in a period before the onset of symptoms. The team tries to find a common feature, either a type of food or an individual product that all the victims have eaten, or a restaurant or shop that has supplied them.

If any suspect food is still available in the home, restaurant or shop, it is taken away for analysis.

Other actions that the investigating team might undertake include:

- taking clinical and environmental samples

- inspecting suspected premises

- identifying the need for medical care facilities

- agreeing measures to control the outbreak and prevent further spread, for example by means of exclusion of personnel, withdrawal of foods thought to be hazardous or the closure of premises

- determining the issuing of advice to the public and professionals and the setting up of a helpline

- issuing press releases and dealing with the press

- liaising with government departments and agencies

- producing a report that includes any lessons learnt from the outbreak.

Why your business?

Outbreak investigations are undertaken to safeguard public health, not to make the lives of food managers difficult. So, while you must always do everything possible to *prevent* food-borne illness, you also need to be *prepared* for the authorities to knock on your door and to tell you that they 'think' there may be a problem with one of your products.

Whatever you do, do not be tempted to try to send them packing just because they said 'think'. You are legally obliged to co-operate, but from a business viewpoint, if there is even the remotest possibility that you may have a problem, then it is in your interest to reveal it anyway so that it can be dealt with.

Best interests

Keep in mind your responsibilities for safeguarding public health and business wealth by:

- bringing your crisis management plan into action

- carrying out your own internal investigation with external help if necessary

- co-operating fully with the authorities

- not destroying, disturbing or interfering with evidence.

Benefiting from the investigation?

How does an investigation end up exonerating or pointing the finger of blame at a particular product or business? In fact the results of investigations are often inconclusive.

The origin of the problem is sometimes discovered promptly because the test samples reveal that all the patients were affected by the same organism found in samples of the suspect food. Things rarely happen quite so neatly and, however diligent the investigators may be, they often have to rely on educated guesswork and epidemiological evidence (findings about the spread of the illness) to determine the likely cause. Sometimes it is impossible to make even an informed guess as to the cause. Usually, however, a tentative conclusion is formed. Even if there is only the slightest hint that your company could be responsible in some way, do bear in mind that the investigators would be foolhardy to draw a provisional conclusion without having satisfied themselves that they have sufficient evidence to justify it.

Whatever the outcome, use the lessons learnt or suggested to review, and possibly modify, your HACCP system and overall standards of food safety.

Product withdrawals and recalls

Product withdrawals and recalls are protection measures to prevent products being eaten that could harm consumer health. They involve removing products from sale or use before they harm consumers. A product withdrawal is a procedure initiated by a company to locate products that it has already supplied to other businesses. A product recall is a procedure to remove products from the market. It asks customers to return suspect products to the retailer for replacement or a refund. Withdrawals and recalls can affect a single batch or an entire production run.

The procedures can be initiated by food companies themselves or may be ordered by the Food Standards Agency (FSA) after issuing a Food Alert (see page 403). The principle of traceability helps manufacturers, retailers and the food authorities to establish where a suspect food or ingredient originated and where it is stored or on sale.

The procedures can stem from a consumer complaint – parts of a rat have been found in a cereal bar or glass fragments found in a jar of jam, for example. They can result from the manufacturer's own discovery that ingredients in a product are not as stated on the packaging, or that an allergen has been included but a consumer warning information is missing. They can also arise from lapses of food safety control identified by a company's own food safety systems, such as HACCP.

The impact of withdrawals and recalls

Withdrawals can avert both food safety problems and bad publicity if they are organised swiftly. Recalls are a necessary strategy of damage limitation. Recalls can be quite costly, as they may result in expensive actions to locate, block, place in quarantine, dispose of and replace the product. Even so, a well-organised recall action is still less costly than the loss of reputation and possible health problems that could arise if the product stayed on the market and affected an untold number of consumers. Ensure that your procedures take into account the likely length of time it would take for the information to come to the attention of suppliers, purchasers and the public, as appropriate.

Examples
Cadbury
In the summer of 2006 chocolate manufacturer Cadbury was obliged to withdraw and recall from the market more than one million chocolate bars after seven of its products were linked to traces of the pathogenic bacterium *Salmonella* Montevideo. The source of the contamination was said to have come from waste water from a pipe leaking over a production line at its Herefordshire factory. Forty-two people fell ill and three needed hospital care. In July 2007 the company was fined £1 million, with more than £152,000 costs, after pleading guilty to nine offences, including a failure to notify the authorities of positive test results for *Salmonella*. The company subsequently spent £20 million on changes aimed at ensuring that the problems never recurred.

Sudan dye adulteration
In 2005 the Food Standards Agency issued a Food Alert for Action, ordering the removal of more than 600 products from shop shelves after they were found to be contaminated by an industrial additive called 'Sudan I' or 'Solvent Orange' in ground chilli and curry

powder. The orange-red powder, which has been linked to a possible increased risk of cancer, is used mainly to colour auxiliary chemicals, such as waxes, oils, solvents and polishes, but before 2003 the additive was also used for colouring various foods. Following the removal of the products from the market the FSA created the Food Incidents Task Force to create guidelines for dealing with such large-scale problems.

Bioterrorism

Although it may not immediately spring to mind, the food industry is one of the business sectors that has been affected by acts of terrorism in various parts of the world. Before the eleventh of September 2001 most large responsible food manufacturers had some form of crisis management plan covering such things as accidental product contamination, malicious tampering, serious customer complaints, product withdrawal or recall procedures, press and public relations and damage limitation.

Although these issues remain crucially important, some of the emphasis has now shifted to controlling the risk of malicious attacks on the whole food chain, often described as *bioterrorism*. In America, for example, the food system has been identified as one of the eight most critical aspects of life that could be harmed by terrorist interference. As a consequence systems of 'food defense' have been created.

Managing the threat

Food is a global business and the threat has the greatest impact on the manufacturing, processing, storage and distribution sectors of the food industry around the world.

In a medium or large company you might not have any direct responsibility for formulating policies for dealing with the threat of food terrorism, but, as a manager, you need to be aware of the general issues, be familiar with company policy and be clear about what your staff need to know and to do. In a small business you may find that biosecurity measures fit fairly easily into everyday safety procedures. Whatever the size of your company, the main issues you need to consider are:

- management

- people

- premises

- vehicles.

You do need to remember that many of the issues involved could be construed as interfering with human rights, so care should be taken to recognise this when formulating policies and carrying out procedures.

Management

There needs to be some kind of crisis management team responsible for ensuring that there are adequate company policies and procedures in place. The management team should have a documented product security procedure that is communicated to staff, suppliers, customers and the appropriate authorities. However, it should be kept in mind that, although personnel should know enough about the procedure to make it workable, many of the details should be restricted to those who really need to know. The procedure should cover issues including risk assessment, unusual occurrences, incoming mail and packages, information technology, ingredient isolation and contract storage.

Risk assessment

The risk assessment should identify the measures that are most likely to have the greatest impact on reducing the risk of deliberate tampering with food.

Unusual occurrences

Management and staff should be trained to recognise and report any unusual occurrences. What are unusual occurrences? It is for the company to define this, but they could include such things as unexpected deliveries of goods or out-of-the-ordinary behaviour by colleagues, visitors, suppliers, customers or sub-contractors that could have a negative effect on the product.

Incoming post and packages

There should be a written procedure for handling suspicious mail and packages, whether delivered by mail or courier, and all personnel should be well-trained in the procedure.

Information technology

The usual precautions concerning the use of and access to computers and data, the installation of firewalls and so on should be followed. Computer-based systems can also be used for tracking vehicles and stock, for instance using a bar code and traceability codes.

Ingredient isolation – quarantine

There should be a written procedure for isolating and removing any contaminated or suspicious ingredient or material. This may need to differ from the usual quarantine procedures. Self-evidently, full production should not be resumed until everything has been satisfactorily resolved.

Contract storage

Many manufacturers use contract warehouses for the storage of both raw and finished product. These premises should also be considered in your procedures even if they have an effective system of their own.

People

Entrance to the premises should be controlled by a system for identifying people. In the case of employees this can of course form part of their normal checking-in procedures.

As part of ordinary safety and emergency precautions, all visitors should sign in and out with the date and time of arrival and departure; a note of the person being visited; the purpose of their visit; name of their company and vehicle registration number. The standard signing-in procedures to food premises should also normally include visitor declarations that they are not suffering from a list of health issues identified as being problematic. As a security measure, visitors who are not known by the person being visited should also be asked to show some form of identification and should be accompanied at all times.

Staff should of course be trained in food security issues. This training should include such topics as:

- company-specific rules

- recognising and dealing with the signs of and evidence for tampering

- reporting instructions

- the criminal nature of tampering with or deliberately contaminating food.

Premises

There should be clear policies about not only who should be allowed access to the premises but also where they should be allowed access. All unused entrances should be closed securely, bearing in mind fire and emergency requirements. Where practicable, the outside area of the premises, including transport parking areas and silos, should be securely fenced and have a controlled entrance/exit gate. All keys, identification badges and visitor passes should be listed in a register and the visitor whereabouts known and regularly checked.

Vehicles

Vehicles should be parked in designated areas. Visitor parking should be in a clearly marked area, preferably separated from staff and management parking, and in an area that is clearly visible to either the security staff or to other staff members who have been briefed to keep the car park under scrutiny. Delivery and dispatch vehicles and their drivers should be allowed access only to areas essential for their work.

When a crisis is resolved

Some crises are never truly resolved and some organisations never recover, typically those that failed to draw up, or implement, a crisis management plan. Assuming that you have a plan and have put it into action, you stand a good chance of pulling through. This is not the end of the story as there are still some vital things to be done.

Thank anyone who has been involved in helping to put things back on a normal footing, whether staff, suppliers, consultants or customers. After all, appreciation can go a long way. If appropriate, thank customers for their patience. Work with specialists, such as environmental health officers, to make certain that lessons have been learnt and measures are in place to prevent anything similar happening in the future. Take the time to evaluate and revise your crisis management plan. What was good about it? What did not work so well and could be improved? What came up that was not covered by the plan?

From crisis to opportunity?

It may seem like a disaster at the time, but, if you handle it well, a crisis can end up strengthening your business rather than destroying it. After all, you should now have enhanced food safety mechanisms in place, a workforce united by having pulled through difficult circumstances and customers who respect you for the professionalism, integrity and honesty with which you handled the situation.

Making it easier for others

- Create a simple procedure for dealing with customer complaints or allegations.

- Prepare a crisis management plan.

- Make certain that everyone knows what to do if the worst happens.

- Work as a team with a single external voice.

- Emphasise the importance of co-operation with investigating authorities.

Integrated management

Hats, rats, buildings, temperature, training, personal hygiene, personal habits, extrinsic factors, intrinsic factors, critical control points, critical limits, tolerances and teamwork – just a few of the topics we have discussed so far. We cannot pretend that food safety is anything but a vast subject, so how can you make your knowledge work well for your company, for consumer safety and for profit?

Suggestions about ways to manage the details of food safety have been provided throughout the book, but you may feel it would be advantageous to pull all these points together into a workable, comprehensive, easy-to-understand and easy-to-operate system.

The idea of implementing overall control systems is not new. Some industry and certification bodies have developed hygiene registration systems which take different types of food safety management systems (including farm-to-fork approaches and HACCP) and provide an all-embracing concept.

Many companies have developed individual guidelines for good practice (such as good manufacturing practice – GMP), often in preparation for, or as the first step towards, official certification of quality management. But what can *you* do to integrate all aspects of food safety?

Pulling everything together

A Swiss scientist, Friedrich Untermann, suggests that we think about food safety management as being rather like a house.

You do not start building a house with the roof, of course, but with the foundations. Only then do you work upwards. You might want to think of the foundations and basement as being the design, construction and equipping of the premises. On the floors above are fundamental requirements such as personal hygiene, cleaning and disinfection, pest and waste control, temperature and humidity controls and the separation of clean and dirty processes. At roof level you have the food safety control measures appropriate to your particular company.

Beyond the basement

All of your control measures need to be within the framework of your organisation's overall business aims and stated policies. Many companies publish a food safety policy, which states the company's intention to meet its legal obligations to provide safe products and its responsibilities towards its customers. It may also include an organisational flow chart indicating where management responsibility lies.

Detailed statements about policies and the ways in which staff should implement them are usually integrated in operational standards or staff manuals or software. They usually include topics such as personal hygiene, temperature control, storage and transport control, physical contamination, disposal of unfit stock, dealing with visitors, reporting illness, product recalls and allegations of food poisoning. Examples are given on the following two pages.

Personal hygiene

Product safety and product hygiene depend on the behaviour, attitude and action of staff and there is no chance of implementing an effective food safety system if the people who run it are not aware of the basic personal hygiene rules. All food handlers must be trained thoroughly and supervised diligently and other staff, such as finance managers, administrative staff, maintenance staff and sub-contractors must also be made aware of the impact that they could have upon the safety of food. Policies usually include the company's rules about the access and movement of personnel, eating and drinking on the premises, jewellery and personal adornment, protective clothing and personal cleanliness.

Visitor policies

As well as dealing with the actions of staff, a company also has to deal with visitors such as external maintenance engineers, cleaning staff, pest controllers, customers and suppliers. As they could all pose a threat to food safety, you should formulate rules for areas other than public access areas. These might cover such issues as how to authorise admission to the premises, insisting that visitors wear suitable protective clothing (supplied by the company) and observe all in-house hygiene rules, and whether visitors should be accompanied at all times. You should also consider displaying the company hygiene rules in reception areas and at entrances to production areas. You may wish to make part of the procedure for admission to the site a requirement for visitors to read the rules and to sign to confirm that they have read and understood them.

Glass, blade and brittle plastics registers

Sharp objects are on top of the list of physical contaminants. A written policy can state the company's attitude towards preventive measures and describe appropriate controls. In high-risk areas all sources of glass and brittle plastics should be either eliminated or protected. If you cannot achieve this immediately, establish a schedule for replacing breakable objects. Use the list of such items to help you to check the state of these objects regularly, record breakages and describe corrective actions. A blade register describes the cutting tools authorised by the company. Any other unauthorised tools, such as knives with break-off blades, should be banned from the premises.

Incident reports

A food safety incident (or food hygiene incident) is anything visible or easily detectable that might endanger the safety of the consumer – for example, glass fragments in a food room, traces of physical or chemical contamination, accumulating waste, or unauthorised items or utensils in food areas. It might also be under- or over-use of particular ingredients.

To introduce a reporting system you need to establish a list of types of event that could compromise product safety – your hazard analysis will already contain most of this information – and state the procedures for dealing with it.

Not only will an incident reporting procedure allow records to be kept of the incident itself, but it will also provide a permanent note of the resulting corrective action. This information can then be fed back into the review of hazards and assist you generally in gauging the company's potential weak points for food safety.

Setting priorities

Successful managers, whatever their line of business, are usually skilled at organising and setting priorities for their work time and good at establishing priorities for spending company funds. Faced with a list of known hazards and their risks in your workplace, would you know where to begin to prioritise repairs and improvements?

There is not room in this book to discuss all the possible aspects of how you could decide on priorities, but two examples may help you to consider some underlying principles. For the sake of the examples, let's assume that a senior manager, auditor or environmental health practitioner has asked for some specified improvements. Two of them are to:

- provide soap at the wash-hand basin and a notice reminding people to wash their hands

- provide diffusers for every fluorescent light or provide shatterproof tubes.

Soap and notices
Soap and notices are relatively cheap. Soap is essential for proper hand washing and a legal requirement. A failure by food handlers to wash their hands, or to wash them adequately, is thought to be a factor in many incidents of food poisoning. Even a simple risk assessment and cost-benefit analysis would show that this requirement is relatively cheap, simple to carry out, relatively effective and can be carried out quickly by someone with little or no technical knowledge or skills.

Shatterproof tubes and diffusers
Both these items can be expensive. It is rare for shattering tubes to contaminate products and such incidents are relatively easy to monitor. Problems are usually associated with either the changing of the tube or with a physical impact, say from a ladder or long pole, that breaks the tube or diffuser. Even a simple risk assessment or cost-benefit analysis would show that this requirement is expensive, relatively difficult to carry out, relatively ineffective and requires time and some expertise to install.

Diligence
What would operate in a food business's favour in any formal proceedings would be to show a prioritised list showing *when* any repair or improvement would be carried out and the reasoning behind the list. Even if the court didn't fully agree with the list, it is unlikely to overlook it if it was competently compiled.

Engaging specialists

An indication of a confident manager is that he or she knows when to ask for help. That help might be towards running a training programme, operating the pest control measures, setting up a quality assurance system, buying food equipment, helping to build a team or myriad other aspects of the business. The help might come in the form of someone within the company or an external specialist or consultant.

Some advantages

One advantage of engaging outsiders is their distance from the day-to-day issues and, with a good consultant, extensive knowledge of the industry, sector or practice or extremely specialised know-how. For example, before submitting themselves to an external audit, many companies obtain an independent judgement. This has the advantage that it will not result in consequences such as the withdrawal of a contract to supply a client or the refusal of a licence or certificate.

Sometimes the consultant is engaged at an early point – he or she is employed to support the company on their way towards objectives such as writing and communicating parts of the quality handbook or complex targets such as setting up a better HACCP system or making a product comply with a technical standard.

Often a consultant provides expertise to clients who require a particular type of knowledge or service for a specific period. In other situations, companies implementing a major project may need additional experienced staff to assist with increased work during that time – and this might include interim management. Whichever it is, a consultant is usually a temporary companion who is employed only for a particular project or problem and who usually leaves the working relationship when the purpose of his assignment has been met. The consultant may then offer further future services, such as regular reviews, on request.

Some disadvantages

The most famous comment about consultants is probably from management guru Robert Townsend who said that consultants are the people who borrow your watch to tell you the time, then walk off with your watch. In the food industry suspicion of consultancy has generated an unofficial 'translation' of HACCP as Hire A Consultant Create Paperwork.

There can be considerable problems if any system is so closely aligned with and dependent upon an individual consultant or outside provider that your company's own staff cannot make it work. This can manoeuvre a company into a position where it is forced to continue to depend on the consultant, or to risk a difficult-to-resolve system failure. In the past, this has sometimes been a problem with consultancy about HACCP systems. At the end of the day, any paperwork, written procedures or complete manuals must work for the appointing company.

Considerations

So, what should you consider before bringing in outside assistance? The following suggestions may help.

Think through whether you really need somebody to work out something that your company will need to operate itself once the consultancy has finished. Bear in mind that it would probably be better to work together in partnership. If you decide that you do need to hire somebody for a job you conceive as being too difficult or too specialised for members of the company staff and management, work out in advance how you will be able to take over when the consultancy has finished.

Work out exactly what the role of the consultant should be – coach, trainer, expert, mentor, facilitator, for example. Who is to work with the consultant and how will he or she fit in? How much responsibility are you prepared to delegate? Will the project involve staff training by the consultant? Will the consultant be responsible for product safety issues that have an impact on your clients or the end consumers? Are *you* prepared to be challenged?

Consider what steps you are going to take to check the consultant's credentials – you might glean some questions from those suggested for training providers on page 270. Remember that however good a consultant may be, he or she cannot free your company from its responsibilities – the consultant can only assist. Always make it clear what you want the scope of the work to be. At the end of the day the consultant is your service provider – no more and no less.

Managing food safety

Systems work only if they are used properly, monitored and reviewed – and that requires confident and competent staff who know what they should be doing and understand why they should be doing it. It also requires up-to-date, motivated supervisors and managers who lead by good example. Never forget that you need to continue your professional development as a manager and as a leader. The investment in training, motivation and systems is in time, energy, commitment and money, but prevention is always less costly than the cure.

A manager like you with the responsibility for food safety has a big and continuous task, but food safety is indeed achievable, provided that you manage it diligently.

Reference

Measurements and symbols

Abbreviations

Mass and volume

kg	kilogram (1,000 kg = 1 metric ton)
g	gram
µg	microgram (one millionth of a gram)
l	litre
ml	millilitre
cu	cubic (cubic metres are, for example, also expressed as m^3)

Linear measurement and area

km	kilometre
m	metre
cm	centimetre
mm	millimetre
µm	micrometre or micron (one millionth of a metre, also expressed as $10^{-6}m$)
nm	nanometre (one billionth of a metre, also expressed as $10^{-9}m$)
sq	square (square metres are, for example, also expressed as m^2)

Chemical symbols

CO_2	carbon dioxide
H	hydrogen
H_2O	water
N	nitrogen
NH_3	ammonia
NO_3-	nitrate
NO_2-	nitrite
O	oxygen
O_2	free (or molecular) oxygen
O_3	ozone

Others

a_w	available water; moisture
C	the Celsius temperature scale (often referred to as centigrade)
E_h	oxidation-reduction (or redox) potential
pH	scale of acid and alkali

Examples of numbers expressed to the power of ten

10^3	1 thousand	1,000
10^6	1 million	1,000,000
$6x10^6$	6 million	6,000,000
$25x10^6$	25 million	25,000,000
$50x10^6$	50 million	50,000,000
10^9	1 billion*	1,000,000,000
$25x10^9$	25 billion	25,000,000,000
$16x10^{10}$	160 billion	160,000,000,000

* This is the internationally recognised billion. The old British billion was 10^{12} or 1,000,000,000,000.

Pathogenic organisms

These tables provide an at-a-glance reference to the most common causes of food-borne diseases. Under the heading 'Type of illness' we have given the classification used in this book, followed, where appropriate, by a note of other classifications you may encounter in other publications written in English. The onset and duration periods are typical average ranges for the organism and are based on the findings of a Department of Health working group.

Bacteria

Bacillus cereus

Rod-shaped, aerobic, spore-forming, toxin-producing Gram-positive.

Type of illness	Bacterial food poisoning – *Bacillus cereus* poisoning. (Alternatively, classed as a bacterial intoxication, or as a toxin-mediated infection.)
Cause of illness	One of two kinds of toxin: 1) released in the food before it is consumed (emetic syndrome), and acts on the upper gastro-intestinal tract 2) released in the body (diarrhoeal syndrome) in the intestinal tract.
Illness	1) *Emetic syndrome* Onset time: 1-5 hours. Symptoms: mainly vomiting, abdominal pains, sometimes diarrhoea. Duration: 6-24 hours. 2) *Diarrhoeal syndrome* Onset time: 8-16 hours. Symptoms: watery diarrhoea, abdominal pains, sometimes vomiting. Duration: 24-48 hours.
Carrier status	None.
Source	Soil, dust and vegetation. Very common in the natural world.
Food commonly involved	Cereals, grains, rice and rice-based products, corn, cornstarch and products containing cornstarch, soya beans and soya products, meat, fish, milk, vegetables, pasta and tofu.
Control measures	Preventing cross-contamination. Controlling time and temperature during preparation and holding, such as cooking, cooling and hot-holding. Storing in temperature-controlled conditions (usually under refrigeration). Avoiding reheating food.

Brucella

Rod-shaped, aerobic, Gram-negative, zoonotic.

Type of illness	Bacterial food-borne infection – brucellosis, Malta fever (*B. melitensis*) or Bang's disease (*B. abortus*).
Cause of illness	Enteric fever, invasion of the bloodstream. The infection can occur as droplet infection (inhaling *Brucella*-infected dust), contact infection or food-borne infection.
Illness	Onset time: 5-30 days (*B. melitensis*). Symptoms: fever, headache, general weakness, depression, generalised muscle aches. Duration: can turn into a persistent chronic stage for years.
Carrier status	Yes.
Source	Intestines of sheep, goats and cattle; also found in deer, caribou and dogs. Occurs worldwide but especially in Mediterranean countries, Central and South America and Central Asia.
Food commonly involved	Milk, dairy products and meat products.
Control measures	Controlling time and temperature, especially during pasteurization or sterilization of milk and milk products. Observing high standards of hygiene in slaughterhouses. Excluding infected employees from handling food.

Campylobacter jejuni

Micro-aerophillic, Gram-negative, spiral-shaped rod, toxin-producing, zoonotic (can infect humans and animals).

Type of illness	Bacterial food-borne infection – campylobacter-enteritis.
Cause of illness	Acute infectious bacterial diarrhoea and gastro-enteritis caused by the invasive abilities of the organism. Only a few cells are required to cause infection (low infective dose). The common route is cross-contamination. Human-to-human transmission is of minor significance.
Illness	Onset time: 2-5 days, sometimes longer. Symptoms: watery and bloody diarrhoea, fever, headache, abdominal pain and nausea. Potential complications: meningitis, septicaemia, Reiter's syndrome, Guillain-Barré syndrome, Miller-Fisher syndrome. Duration: 2-7 days, but relapses are common and the patient can be infectious for 10 days or more.
Carrier status	Yes.
Source	Wild birds (such as seagulls, crows and feral pigeons), poultry, sheep, cattle, pigs, sewage and untreated water supplies.
Food commonly involved	Raw meat and offal, poultry, raw milk and untreated water sources.
Control measures	Strictly controlling time and temperature during the pasteurization or sterilization of milk and milk products. Preventing cross-contamination, particularly by effective cleaning and disinfecting and by separating utensils and equipment used for preparing raw and cooked foods. Observing high standards of personal hygiene. Using only potable sources of water.

Clostridium botulinum

Anaerobic, Gram-positive, rod-shaped, spore-forming, neurotoxin-producing. The spores are highly heat resistant.

Type of illness	Bacterial food poisoning – botulism. (Alternatively classed as a bacterial intoxication.)
Cause of illness	Consumption of an exotoxin – a highly toxic neurotoxin – produced on the food. Infant botulism is caused by the consumption by babies and young children of botulinum spores which then germinate in the intestine.
Illness	Onset time: 12-36 hours. Symptoms: double vision, difficulty in speaking and swallowing, headache, nausea, fatigue, constipation, vomiting, dizziness, muscle paralysis and damage to the nervous system. Mortality rate: 30 % -65 % . Duration: 1-10 days, although longer is common. Death is likely to occur within eight days of the onset of symptoms unless an anti-toxin is given.
Carrier status	None.
Source	Soil and water.
Food commonly involved	Meat, fish and vegetables; inadequately processed low-acid foods; home-canned products; vacuum-packed meats and other vacuum-packed foods; continuous stockpots; baked/jacket potatoes that have not been subject to effective temperature control. Infant botulism is often caused by spore-contaminated honey.
Control measures	Strict control of time and temperature (botulinum cook), especially in canning, bottling and vacuum packing.

Clostridium perfringens

Anaerobic, Gram-positive, rod-shaped, spore-forming, toxin-producing.

Type of illness	Bacterial food poisoning. (Alternatively, classed as an intoxication or as a toxin-mediated infection.)
Cause of illness	An enterotoxin. (Spores are formed in food as it cooks. When the food is cooled too slowly, the spores germinate and multiply. After the food is eaten, the organism sporulates in the intestine, releasing an endotoxin.)
Illness	Onset time: 8-18 hours. Symptoms: diarrhoea and abdominal pain; fever and vomiting are rare. Can be fatal for elderly and immuno-compromised people. Duration: 12-24 hours.
Carrier status	None.
Source	Human and animal intestinal tract, soil, dust, spices.
Food commonly involved	Cooked meat and poultry, gravy, sauces, spices, various foods that have been cooled too slowly.
Control measures	Strict control of time and temperature, especially in cooking, cooling and reheating. Avoiding reheating more than once, if at all. Preventing cross-contamination (eg. raw vegetables and cooked foods). Cleaning and disinfecting food preparation areas and utensils thoroughly and regularly.

Escherichia coli

Rod-shaped, aerobic and facultative anaerobic, Gram-negative, toxin-producer. This bacterium is naturally present in the human intestine and only some types are pathogenic.

Type of illness	Bacterial food poisoning. The illnesses are known by various popular names such as traveller's diarrhoea. (Alternatively, classed as an intoxication.)
Cause of illness	One of several enterotoxins invading intestinal cells and destroying the intestinal lining.
Illness	Onset time: 12-72 hours is usually quoted, but varies between hours and several days depending on the organism and the health of the person. Symptoms: can include acute abdominal pain, fever, watery or bloody diarrhoea, kidney damage and failure. The illness can be life threatening, especially to those in the 'at risk group'. Duration: 1-14 days.
Carrier status	Yes.
Source	Humans and animals, especially cattle; the natural environment including water; sewage.
Food commonly involved	Beef, especially minced beef (as in beefburgers), and meat products (including gravy); raw milk; milk products; fish; drinking water; some unpasteurized fruit juice products, such as cider.
Control measures	Cooking thoroughly and observing strict time and temperature control – for example, the internal temperature of beefburgers. Preventing cross-contamination. Observing strict personal hygiene. Using potable water. Ensuring the safe disposal of sewage.

Escherichia coli serotype O157: H7 (also referred to as VTEC)

Type of illness	Bacterial food-borne infection. (Alternatively, classed as an intoxication or a toxin-mediated infection.)
Cause of illness	Shiga-like toxins – verotoxin, verocytotoxin. The toxin causes damage to the intestinal epithelial cells. Blood vessels are damaged and bleeding occurs. The infective dose is very low and can be as few as 10 cells.
Illness	Onset time: varies between hours and several days depending on the number of bacteria ingested and the health of the person; 48 hours is typical. Symptoms: fever, vomiting, abdominal pain and diarrhoea. Potential complications: a second stage – haemolytic uremic syndrome (HUS) – can follow, which is characterised by kidney failure and loss of red blood cells. Can be life threatening.
Carrier status	Duration: variable; typically 1-8 days.
Source	None.
Food commonly involved	Intestinal tract of cattle and sheep; birds. Beef (particularly minced beef) and meat products, raw or underpasteurized milk and drinking water.
Control measures	Controlling time and temperature. Cooking food thoroughly. Avoiding cross-contamination. Observing strict personal hygiene, especially with regard to hands.

Listeria monocytogenes

Facultative anaerobic, rod-shaped, Gram-positive, psychrotropic, halophilic.

Type of illness	Bacterial food-borne infection – listeriosis.
Cause of illness	Bacteria invade body tissue and bloodstream, creating changes in the composition of the red blood cells. Non-pregnant, healthy individuals are usually resistant to infection, but may be life threatening to unborn babies, pregnant women, the elderly and individuals with weakened immune systems.
Illness	Onset time: 1-70 days, typically up to 21 days. Symptoms: fever, septicaemia, meningitis, nausea. Potential complications: abortion, premature birth, still-birth. Duration: depends on symptoms.
Carrier status	Yes.
Source	Soil, water, sewage, human and animal carriers.
Food commonly involved	Raw milk and raw-milk products such as soft cheeses, ready-to-eat foods such as prepared salads, coleslaw, cook-chill products, sausages, pâté and raw vegetables, salad vegetables and seafood.
Control measures	Observing thorough hygiene practices in abattoirs and dairies. Strictly controlling time and temperature during the pasteurization or sterilization of milk and milk products. Washing (and treating, where appropriate) vegetables and salad ingredients. Preventing cross-contamination. Observing high standards of personal hygiene. Using only potable water supplies. Warning labelling. Avoiding serving raw milk and raw-milk products to susceptible individuals, particularly pregnant women and nursing mothers, as the bacterium can affect unborn children or breast-fed infants. Observing the use by dates of refrigerated foods with the greatest care.

Mycobacterium tuberculosis and Mycobacterium bovis

Rod-shaped, Gram-positive, zoonotic, aerobic rods with exceptional resistance to drying processes and chemical disinfectants.

Type of illness	Bacterial food-borne infection – tuberculosis.
Cause of illness	Enteric fever; invasion of the bloodstream. The infection can occur as droplet infection, contact infection or food-borne infection. Direct infection of the lung by inhalation only needs very few cells.
Illness	Onset time: 4-12 weeks. Symptoms: pulmonary or extra-pulmonary tuberculosis. The initial infection usually goes unnoticed. Duration: can turn into a persistent chronic stage.
Carrier status	Yes.
Source	Human carriers, cattle, some wild animals such as badgers, opossum and deer.
Food commonly involved	Raw milk and dairy products.
Control measures	Strictly controlling the time and temperature during pasteurization and sterilization of milk and milk products. Not using raw milk or raw-milk products. Excluding infected employees from handling food. Preventing cross-contamination. Observing high standards of personal hygiene.

Salmonella species

Large group of rod-shaped, facultative anaerobic, Gram-negative bacteria.

Salmonella Enteritidis and *Salmonella* Typhimurium

Type of illness	Bacterial food poisoning – salmonellosis. (Alternatively, classed as an infection.)
Cause of illness	Invasion of the body by large numbers of bacteria (typically, 100,000 per gram of food) which have already multiplied on the food.
Illness	Onset time: 6-96 hours, typically 12-48. Symptoms: diarrhoea, vomiting, fever, abdominal pain. Can be life threatening, particularly for people in the 'at risk group'. Duration: typically 1-7 days, but can last up to three weeks.
Carrier status	Yes.
Source	Human and animal intestinal tracts and faeces. The infection route is via raw foods of animal origin, such as meat, poultry, eggs and egg products and milk, or via faeces and fertilisers – for instance, on vegetables. Insects, birds, vermin and domestic pets are also sources.
Food commonly involved	Meat and meat products, poultry, eggs and egg products such as mayonnaise, raw milk, dairy products, fish and seafood, some beansprouts such as alfalfa.
Control measures	Observing high standards of personal hygiene. Controlling time and temperature, especially in cooking, cooling and reheating. Preventing cross-contamination: strict separation of raw and cooked foods. Cleaning and disinfecting thoroughly. Ensuring effective pest management.

Salmonella Typhi and *Salmonella* Paratyphi

Type of illness	Bacterial food-borne infections – *S.* Typhi: enteric fever, typhoid/typhoid fever (not to be confused with typhus, which is an infectious disease caused by Rickettsiae); *S.* Paratyphi – enteric fever, paratyphoid.
Cause of illness	Enteric fever: invasion of the bloodstream at a very small infective dose.
Illness	Onset time: 3-56 days; typically 12-20 days. Symptoms: fever, spleen enlargement (*S.* Typhi), severe diarrhoea. *S.* Typhi is fatal in 2 % -10 % of cases. Duration: up to 40 days; typically 10-14 days. Paratyphoid is less severe than typhoid and its occurrence is more sporadic.
Carrier status	Yes.
Source	Human carriers (*S.* Typhi); human and animal intestines (*S.* Paratyphi).
Food commonly involved	Milk, dairy products, drinking water, meat and seafood.
Control measures	Using only potable water supplies. Ensuring the safe disposal of human faeces. Observing strict personal hygiene and kitchen hygiene. Controlling time and temperature thoroughly, especially during cooking and pasteurizing. Using shellfish only from approved sources. Excluding infected persons from handling food. Ensuring effective pest management.

Shigella dysenteriae

Rod-shaped, facultative anaerobic, Gram-negative, acid tolerant.

Type of illness	Bacterial food-borne infection – shigellosis (bacillary dysentery).
Cause of illness	A powerful toxin (Shiga toxin) which inhibits protein synthesis in the invaded cells. The minimum infective dose is very low.
Illness	Onset time: 1-3 days. Symptoms: watery, sometimes bloody diarrhoea, stools with blood and mucous, fever, abdominal pain, severe dehydration and sometimes vomiting. Duration: normally up to 2 weeks; depending on symptoms and treatment, the patient can excrete the organism for several months even after the symptoms have stopped.
Carrier status	Yes.
Source	Human carriers.
Food commonly involved	Milk, eggs and egg products, water, flour, vegetables, fruits, salad vegetables, shellfish, salads and dairy products.
Control measures	Using only potable water. Controlling the disposal of waste water and sewage. Observing high standards of personal hygiene and kitchen hygiene. Controlling time and temperature. Excluding infected persons from handling food. Ensuring effective pest management.

Staphylococcus aureus

Round (coccal), facultative anaerobic, Gram-positive, halophilic. Some are toxin-producers.

Type of illness	Bacterial food poisoning – staphylococcal gastro-enteritis. (Alternatively, classed as a bacterial intoxication.)
Cause of illness	Exotoxin poisoning when large numbers of the bacteria are toxin-producers. Illness is usually caused by consuming the toxin, not the living organism.
Illness	Onset time: 2-6 hours. Symptoms: acute vomiting, diarrhoea, nausea, abdominal pain and sometimes collapse. Body temperature may drop. Duration: 12-48 hours.
Carrier status	Yes.
Source	Human body – nose, throat, skin, hands and hair, and in boils, pimples, sties, septic lesions, burns and wounds – and animals.
Food commonly involved	Ham, poultry, egg products, dairy products, potato salads, raw goat's and cow's milk, cream and cheese, and almost any other product of animal origin or product touched by hand.
Control measures	Observing high standards of personal hygiene especially with regard to handwashing. Excluding people with skin infections, colds and so on from working with food. Controlling time and temperature, especially when cooking, cooling and reheating.

Vibrio parahaemolyticus

Comma-shaped, facultative anaerobic, Gram-positive, halophilic.

Type of illness	Food poisoning. (Alternatively, classed as an infection.)
Cause of illness	Invasion of the body by large numbers of bacteria (about 10,000 per gram of food) which have multiplied in food.
Illness	Onset time: 4-96 hours; typically 12-24 hours. Symptoms: vomiting, diarrhoea, abdominal pain, fever and dehydration. Can be life threatening to people in the 'at risk group'. Duration: up to 7 days.
Carrier status	Yes.
Source	Marine shellfish and fish, especially from warm waters. (Some species of *Vibrio* are naturally present in some marine creatures.) Also food from sewage-contaminated marine waters.
Food commonly involved	Fish and shellfish including clams, oysters, lobsters, crabs and prawns.
Control measures	Buying seafood only from approved sources, and checking legal requirements and quality standards for supplies. Controlling time and temperature. Avoiding serving raw or lightly cooked seafood, especially to those in the 'at risk group'.

Yersinia enterocolitica

Rod-shaped, facultative anaerobic, Gram-negative, psychrotrophic.

Type of illness	Bacterial food poisoning – yersiniosis. (Alternatively, classed as an infection.)
Cause of illness	Invasion of the intestinal tissue by the living organism.
Illness	Onset time: 1-14 days; typically 3-7 days. Symptoms: diarrhoea, fever, headache and abdominal pain. Potential complications: reactive arthritis, mesenteric lymphadenitis, terminal ileitis and pseudo appendicitis. Duration: up to 40 days.
Carrier status	Yes.
Source	The natural environment, including soil and water, and animals.
Food commonly involved	Milk and milk products, egg products, raw meat (especially raw pork), vegetables, poultry and vacuum-packed products.
Control measures	Controlling time and temperature, especially with chilled products. Observing high standards of personal hygiene. Using only potable water.

Viruses

Hepatitis A

Type of illness	Viral infection – hepatitis.
Cause of illness	Viral infection. Transmission usually occurs via the faecal-oral route. People can harbour the virus for six weeks before showing symptoms and are infectious for about one week before symptoms appear.
Illness	Onset time: 15-50 days. Symptoms: fever, nausea, vomiting, abdominal pain, liver disease, jaundice. Duration: 1 week-several months.
Carrier status	Yes.
Source	Human intestinal tract. Faeces, urine and blood may be infected.
Food commonly involved	Water, raw shellfish, raw vegetables and any food prepared by bare hands. Ready-to-eat foods, such as salads and bakery products, are often implicated.
Control measures	Ensuring the highest standards of personal hygiene, especially with regard to hand washing. Controlling time and temperature, especially when cooking. Avoiding cross-contamination.

Norovirus (previously known as Norwalk and Norwalk-like viruses)

Type of illness	Viral infection – Norwalk gastro-enteritis/Norovirus gastro-enteritis.
Cause of illness	Viral infection, often associated with traveller's diarrhoea and transmitted by the faecal-oral route.
Illness	Onset time: 1-2 days. Symptoms: fever, nausea, projectile vomiting, diarrhoea, abdominal pain. Headache and fever are possible. Duration: 1-3 days.
Carrier status	Possible.
Source	Human intestinal tract. Sewage-contaminated water.
Food commonly involved	Raw shellfish, raw vegetables, salads, fruit, water.
Control measures	Observing the time and temperature rules, especially for cooking. Avoiding cross-contamination. Observing high standards of personal hygiene, especially with regard to hand washing. Buying seafood only from approved sources. Taking special care when storing live mussels and cockles. Avoiding serving raw or lightly cooked seafood, especially to individuals in the 'at risk group'.

Rotavirus

Type of illness	Viral infection – rotavirus gastro-enteritis.
Cause of illness	Viral infection. Once the virus has invaded the host cell, it is transported to the lysosomes (organs within the cell containing vital enzymes).
Illness	Onset time: 1-3 days. Symptoms: fever, nausea, vomiting and watery diarrhoea, often leading to dehydration. Duration: 4-8 days.
Carrier status	Probable.
Source	Human intestines and sewage-contaminated water.
Food commonly involved	Raw seafood, untreated water, raw vegetables and salad ingredients.
Control measures	Observing high standards of personal hygiene, especially with regard to hand washing. Avoiding touching food by hand. Controlling time and temperature.

Parasites

Type of parasite	Organism	Definitive host	Intermediate host	Food involved	Prevention
Protozoa	*Cryptosporidium parvum*	Humans, many mammals, reptiles and birds	None	Water, vegetables and fruit that have been washed with contaminated water	Observing high standards of personal hygiene. Using only potable water. Disposing of sewage safely. Cooking food thoroughly. Freezing below -20°C.
	Giardia lamblia	Humans, rats, beavers and muskrats	None		
Tapeworms	*Taenia saginata*	Humans	Cattle	Beef	Controlling time and temperature when cooking and freezing. Avoiding cross-contamination and contact with animals. Inspecting meat. Controlling water pollution and other forms of environmental pollution.
	Taenia solium	Humans	Pigs and humans	Pork	
	Diphyllobothrium latum	Humans	Crustaceans and fish	Fish	
	Echinococcus granulosus	Dogs	Humans	Food contaminated by dog faeces	
Flukes	*Fasciola hepatica*	Humans and cattle	Water snails	Watercress	Avoiding eating wild watercress and other water plants from non-approved sources.
Roundworms	*Trichina spiralis*	Humans, pigs and rats	None	Pork and horsemeat	Avoiding eating raw or undercooked meat. Cooking meat thoroughly. Pickling or freezing meat. Inspecting meat.

Mycotoxins

	Aflatoxin	Patulin	Ochratoxin	Ergot alkaloids
Producing organism	*Aspergillus flavus, A. parasiticus*	*A. clavatus, A. giganteus, A. terreus*	*A. ochraceus, Penicillium viridicatum*	*Claviceps purpurea*
Foods commonly involved	Nuts, cereals, dried fruits.	Fruit, fruit juices, bread.	Cereals, corn, nuts, dried beans, cocoa, coffee, soya beans.	Rye, other cereals involved.
Effect on humans	Carcinogenic, hepatotoxic. Acute symptoms: hepatitis.	Carcinogenic. Causes chromosomal changes in animal and plant cells.	Carcinogenic, hepatotoxic, nephrotoxic.	Neurotoxic. Can cause gangrene.
Common preventive measures	At source: fungus-free seeds, rapid drying processes, storage under controlled dry conditions. Also storage and transport under controlled anaerobic conditions; frozen storage (-18°C). Preservation criteria: a_w <0.8/pH <3 or >6.5.			

Chemicals

Pest control chemicals

Pesticides by formulation

Formulation	Examples
Baits	Most rodenticides, ant baits
Dusts (finely ground mineral or pesticide combined with a dry carrier)	Boric acid, diatomaceous earth, pyrethrum, silica aerogel, sulphur
Fumigants (poisonous gas)	CO_2
Granules (pesticides and carrier combined with a binding agent)	Many insecticides
Sprays: • aerosols • emulsifiable concentrates • flowables • micro-encapsulated materials • slurry • water-soluble concentrates • wettable powders	Pyrethrins Many pesticides Sulphur, copper compounds Many pesticides Bordeaux mixture (hydrated lime and copper sulphate) Insecticidal soaps Bacillus thuringiensis

Pesticides by function

Category	Examples
Attractants	Compounds, including pheromones (sexual hormones), that attract pests to traps or poisons
Repellents	Compounds that repel the target pest
Desiccants	Compounds that kill by adhering to insect cuticle, drying out the insect (eg. diatomaceous earth, silica aerogel)
Insect growth regulators (juvenile hormones)	Compounds mimicking insect hormones that regulate insect development
Poisons: • contact poisons	Materials that penetrate the skin or outer membranes and disrupt the physiology of the organism (eg. insecticidal soaps, pyrethrins)
• stomach poisons	Materials that attack the pest after it has ingested the poison (eg. boric acid)
• fumigants	Respiratory poisons that kill by suffocation (eg. CO_2 against storage pests)
• pass-throughs	Poisons that pass through an animal's digestive system and kill insects that attempt to inhabit the dung
Sterilants	Compounds, such as methyl bromide (which is used for fumigation), which kill many life forms.

Detergents and chemical disinfectants

Functions and limitations of cleaning chemicals

Category of aqueous cleaner	Approx. concentrations for use (%)	Examples of chemicals used	Functions	Limitations
Clean water	100	(Water usually contains dissolved air and minerals in small amounts.)	Solvent and carrier for soils and chemical cleaners.	Hard water leaves deposit on surfaces. Residual moisture may allow microbial growth on washed surfaces. Promotes rusting of iron.
Strong alkalis	1-5	Sodium hydroxide Sodium orthosilicate Sodium sesquisilicate	Detergents for removing fat and protein. Precipitate water hardness. Produce alkaline pH.	Highly corrosive. Difficult to remove by rinsing. Irritating to skin and mucous membranes.
Mild alkalis	1-10	Sodium carbonate Sodium sesquicarbonate Trisodium phosphate Sodium tetraborate	Detergents. Buffers at pH 8.4 or above. Water softeners.	Mildly corrosive. High concentrations are irritating to skin.
Inorganic acids	0.5	Hydrochloric Sulphuric Nitric Phosphoric Sulphamic	Produce pH 2.5 or below. Remove precipitates from surfaces.	Very corrosive to metals but can be partially inhibited by amines. Irritating to skin and mucous membranes.
Organic acids	0.1-2	Acetic Hydroxyacetic Lactic	Remove inorganic precipitates and other acid-soluble substances from surfaces.	Moderately corrosive but can be removed by various organic nitrogen compounds.
	0.1-2	Gluconic Citric Tartaric Levulinic Saccharic	Remove inorganic precipitates and other acid-soluble substances from surfaces.	Moderately corrosive but can be removed by various organic nitrogen compounds.
Anionic wetting agents	0.15 or less	Soaps Sulphated alcohols Sulphated hydrocarbons Aryl-alkyl polyether sulphates Sulphonated amides Alykl-aryl sulphonates	Wet surfaces. Penetrate crevices and woven fabrics. Emulsify oils, fats, waxes, pigments. Compatible with acid and alkaline cleaners and may be synergistic. Effective general detergents.	Some foam excessively. May be incompatible with cationic wetting agents.
Non-ionic wetting agents	0.15 or less	Polyethonoxyethers Ethylene oxide-fatty acid condensates Amine-fatty acid condensates	Excellent detergents for oil. Used in mixtures of wetting agents to control foam.	May be sensitive to acids.

Category of aqueous cleaner	Approx. concentrations for use (%)	Examples of chemicals used	Functions	Limitations
Cationic wetting agents	0.15 or less	Quaternary ammonium compounds	Some wetting effect. Antibacterial action.	Not compatible with anionic wetting agents. Inactivated by many minerals and some soils.
Sequestering agents	Variable depending on water hardness	Tetrasodium pyrophosphate Sodium tripolyphosphate Sodium hexameta phosphate Sodium tetraphosphate Sodium acid pyrophosphate Ethlyenediamine tetra-acetic acid (sodium salt) Sodium gluconate with or without 3% sodium hydroxide	Form soluble complexes with metal ions such as calcium, magnesium and iron to prevent film formation on equipment and utensils. See also strong and mild alkalis opposite. Phosphates are inactivated by protracted exposure to heat.	Phosphates are unstable in acid solutions.
Abrasives	Variable	Volcanic ash Seismotite Pumice Feldspar Silica flour Steel wool Chore balls made of metal or plastic	Combined with scrubbing action they remove dirt from surfaces. Can be used with detergents for difficult cleaning jobs.	Scratch surfaces. Particles may become embedded in equipment and later appear in food. Skin damage possible if protective gloves not worn.
Chlorinated compounds	1	Dichlorocyanuric acid Trichlorocyanuric acid Dichlorohydantoin	Used with alkaline cleaners to increase peptizing of proteins and minimise milk deposits.	Not germicidal because of high pH. Concentrations vary depending on the alkaline cleaner and conditions of use.
Amphoterics	1-2	Mixtures of a cationic amine salt or a quaternary ammonium compound with an anionic carboxy compound, a sulphate ester or a sulphonic acid	Loosen and soften charred food residues on ovens or other metal and ceramic surfaces.	Not suitable for use on food contact surfaces.
Enzymes	0.3-1	Proteolytic enzymes produced in cultures of aerobic spore-forming bacteria	Digest proteins and other complex organic soils.	Inactivated by heat. Some people become hypersensitive to products containing enzymes. Some have contained *Salmonella*.

Sickness – exclusion from work

The table summarises the Department of Health guidelines for dealing with food handlers who have been diagnosed with a food-borne illness (middle column) and symptom-free food handlers who have been in contact with someone suffering from a food-borne illness (right-hand column).

Organism/illness	Criteria for allowing a food handler to return to work when free from symptoms and after:	Criteria for dealing with a symptom-free food handler who has been in contact with sufferer
Aeromonas species	48 hours after they have passed a normal stool, but strict hygiene measures must be followed	No criteria
Bacillus species	as above	No criteria
Campylobacter species	as above	No criteria
Clostridium botulinum	No criteria	Treatment of those at risk
Clostridium perfringens	as *Aeromonas* species	No criteria
Cryptosporidium species	as *Aeromonas* species	No criteria
Entamoeba histolytica	3 negative stools	Microbiological screening
E. coli (excluding VTEC)	as *Aeromonas* species	No criteria
E. coli (VTEC)	2 negative specimens	Microbiological screening
Giardia lamblia	No criteria	Microbiological screening
Hepatitis A	7 days after onset of jaundice or other symptoms	No criteria
Salmonella species (except S. Typhi and S. Paratyphi)	as *Aeromonas* species	No criteria
Salmonella Typhi and S. Paratyphi	6 consecutive negative stool specimens have been passed at 2 weekly intervals starting 2 weeks after the completion of antibiotic therapy	3 consecutive negative stools have been passed at weekly intervals starting 3 weeks after the last contact with the case
Shigella species	When normal stools are being passed	None
Staphylococcus aureus	After any septic lesions have healed	None
Taenia solium	After treatment	Until treated
Vibrio parahaemolyticus	as *Aeromonas* species	None
Norovirus and Rotavirus	as *Aeromonas* species	None
Yersinia species	as *Aeromonas* species	None

HACCP decision tree

This decision tree is a traditional version based on the Codex Alimentarius decision tree for determining critical control points in the Hazard Analysis and Critical Control Point system.

Is there a hazard at this process step?

No

Yes

This is not a critical control point. Consider the next hazard.

Do preventive measures exist?

Yes

No

Change the process or modify the product.

Is the process step specifically designed to eliminate the hazard or reduce the risk to an acceptable level?

Is it essential to control the hazard for food safety?

Yes

No   Yes

No

This is not a critical control point. Consider the next hazard.

Could contamination occur or increase to an unacceptable level?

No

This is not a critical control point. Consider the next hazard.

Yes

Will a subsequent process step eliminate or reduce occurrence to an acceptable level?

No

This is a critical control point. Controls must be developed for food safety.

Yes

This is not a critical control point. Consider the next hazard.

Glossary

Acaricide – a **pesticide** designed to kill mites.

Acceptable daily intake (ADI) – the amount of a chemical, determined on the basis of all the known facts, that can be consumed every day for an individual's lifetime without causing harm.

Acid – a chemical compound that releases hydrogen ions (H+) when dissolved in water. A solution with a pH of less than 7 is acidic.

Acute disease – an illness in which the symptoms develop rapidly following infection.

Acute poisoning – the short-term adverse effect of eating food containing a high level of a toxic substance.

Additives – substances, such as preservatives, colourings and flavourings, which are deliberately added to food to improve its taste, appearance or shelf life.

Adulterant – a substance or item that adversely alters the nature of a food.

Aerobic – description of organisms, such as bacteria, that require 20 per cent oxygen in the atmosphere to be able to multiply.

Aflatoxin – a mycotoxin, produced mainly by moulds of the genera *Aspergillus* and *Penicillium*.

Alert – see **food alert**.

Alga (pl: algae) – simple plants, many single-celled, including the seaweeds.

Alkali – a chemical compound that releases hydroxide ions (OH-) when dissolved in water. A solution with a pH of more than 7 is alkaline. Such chemicals are highly corrosive, but are frequently used as **disinfectants** in low concentrations.

Alkaloid – one of a group of chemical substances which are produced by some plants (such as members of the nightshade family) and fungi, and which have a specific effect on the animals that consume them. Alkaloids include nicotine, cocaine, morphine and atropine.

Allergen – a substance, usually a protein, in food that makes certain people ill, even though the food is harmless to others. The allergen prompts the immune system to create **antibodies**, as if the body were under attack.

Allergic reaction – symptoms of illness caused by an **allergy**.

Allergy (to food) – an identifiable, reproducible immunological response to food **allergens** that results in a variety of symptoms, some of which are life threatening.

Ambient shelf stable – a description of foods that can safely be stored at ordinary room temperatures for a specified period.

Ambient temperature – the environmental temperature, often used to describe 'normal' room temperature.

Anaerobic – description of organisms, such as bacteria, that require the absence of oxygen to be able to multiply. Obligate anaerobes are poisoned by oxygen.

Anaphylactic shock – an especially severe type of **allergic reaction** with possible life-threatening consequences.

Anatomy – the study of the form and structure of an organism.

Antibiotic – a substance, such as penicillin, that is produced by micro-organisms and destroys or inhibits the growth of bacteria.

Antibody – a natural protective chemical. A blood protein which counteracts the growth and harmful action of **antigens** (foreign bodies or substances) such as bacteria, pollen grains or allergens.

Antigen – a substance, such as a bacterial

toxin or food allergen, that triggers the formation of an **antibody**.

Antiserum (pl antisera) – blood serum containing **antibodies** which act against specific **antigens**.

Antitoxin – an **antibody** produced in response to a bacterial toxin.

Appertizing – another term for commercial **sterilization**, named after the Swiss-French chef Nicholas Appert. See also **commercially sterile**.

Aseptic – free from contamination by **micro-organisms**. Often used to describe a method of packaging.

Atmosphere – the gases surrounding Earth: the air we breathe.

At risk group – people at greatest risk from food-borne disease, including pregnant women and unborn children, breast-fed infants, the very young, the elderly and people who are ill or convalescing or who have weakened immunity to disease.

Atropine – a poisonous alkaloid produced by members of the nightshade family.

Audit (food safety) – a systematic examination of a company's activities and results to determine whether they comply with the company's documented procedures and standards and to determine whether the activities, procedures and standards are suitable to achieve the stated objectives. Often conducted by an independent consultant.

Authorised officer – someone legally authorised to act in matters relating to food safety in the UK.

Autotroph – an organism that can synthesise organic compounds from inorganic sources. **Photosynthesis**, where sunlight is used to convert carbon dioxide and water into organic compounds, is an example of autotrophism. See also **heterotroph**.

A_w – water activity: the moisture available to an organism. It is defined as $a_w = P/P_o$ where 'P' represents the vapour pressure of the food and 'P_o' represents the vapour pressure of water at the same ambient temperature. The a_w of pure water is 1, so food has an a_w value below 1.0.

Bacteria (s: bacterium) – ubiquitous single-celled micro-organisms of various shapes, most of which are harmless, or even beneficial, to humans but which also include a small number of **pathogens**.

Bacterial growth curve – the changes in the size of a bacterial colony (the population development), as recorded on a graph. The development of the population of an organism.

Bacterial monitoring – continuous observation or checking of bacterial contamination.

Bacterial spore – a dormant form of some bacteria that enables survival under adverse conditions. (See also **endospore** and **spore**.)

Bacterial toxin – a poisonous substance produced by pathogenic bacteria.

Bactericide – a substance that kills bacteria.

Bacteriology – the study of bacteria.

Bacteriophage – a virus that is parasitic within bacteria.

Base/basic – another term for **alkali**/alkaline.

Batch – a group or set of identifiable products obtained from a given process under practically identical circumstances and produced in a given place within one defined production period.

Best before – a date marked on food that indicates the period within which the food is at its best.

Biodegradable – the capability of a substance to be decomposed (broken down) relatively rapidly by the natural biological action of bacteria and other microbes into harmless constituents that disappear into the environment.

Binary fission – reproduction by splitting in two: the way in which most bacteria multiply. An asexual form of reproduction, typical of bacteria, in which a 'mother' cell splits into two identical 'daughter' cells.

Biocide – a poisonous substance that harms or kills living organisms.

Biodegradable – a substance that will naturally decay over time without producing noxious substances.

Botulinum cook – a method of high temperature food preservation designed to kill the spores of the pathogenic bacterium *Clostridium botulinum* and to reduce the spores of spoilage organisms to a level accepted as being safe for human health.

Budding – an asexual form of reproduction, typical of yeast, in which several 'daughter' cells sprout from one 'mother' cell.

Canning – a preservation method in which food is hermetically sealed in metal, glass or plastic containers and heat treated until it is commercially sterile.

Carcinogen – a substance with the ability to trigger cancer.

Carrier – a person who shows no symptoms of an infectious disease, but who carries it and may transmit it to others.

Carry-over effect – the accumulation and transmission of a chemical. The consequences of toxic substances being carried from one food in the food chain to another until they accumulate in the body fat tissue or organs of animals used for human food. The chemicals can be secreted in human breast milk.

Case – a single incidence of illness.

Catalyst – a chemical that initiates or accelerates a chemical reaction without

changing itself in the process.

Cell – the functioning unit of most organisms.

Cell division – an asexual method of reproduction whereby a cell divides into two, each half containing identical genetic information. (See also **binary fission**.)

Cell membrane – the layer between the cell wall and the inner cellular space in bacterial, fungal and plant cells which controls the interactions of the cell with its surrounding medium.

Cell mortality – the death rate of cells.

Cell wall – a strong and rigid structure surrounding bacterial, plant and fungal, but *not* animal cells. The cell wall is largely permeable.

Certificate of analysis (CoA) – a confirmation that the chemical or microbiological analysis of a product is within the limits stated in a specification. It does not cover physical or other properties of the goods supplied.

Chemical contaminants – so-called non-biological chemicals which are accumulated in food as a consequence of environmental pollution. They include heavy metals, radio nuclides and industrial hazards, such as dioxins, other polychlorinated compounds and polyaromatic hydrocarbons.

Chemical energy – a form of energy involved in cleaning. (Also the energy stored within an atom or molecule which can be released by a chemical reaction.)

Chemical hazard – any chemical which is potentially harmful to the consumer.

Chemically clean – the removal of all residue and deposits from cleaning and disinfecting chemicals, usually by rinsing with potable water.

Chemical preservation – any process, such as the addition of salt and sugar to food during processing, which is designed to extend the shelf life of food by eliminating or restricting the multiplication of spoilage organisms.

Chemical residues – substances which are deliberately or accidentally added to, or brought into contact with, a food during its growth. Residues tend to be veterinary products, feed additives, pesticides and herbicides.

Chemistry – a science dealing with the composition of substances and their combinations and changes under various conditions.

Chronic disease – an illness in which the symptoms last for a relatively long time and may take some time to develop following infection.

Chronic poisoning – the effect of eating food containing a low level of a toxic substance over a long period.

Ciguatera – the most common type of fish poisoning, caused by eating fish that have consumed species of toxic algae.

Cilia – hair-like structures on bacteria which usually move.

Clean – free from soiling, food residue, dirt, grease, marks or other objectionable matter.

Clean as you go – the recognised good practice of cleaning up throughout food preparation and immediately after completing the task.

Cleaning – the process of making something clean; usually a combination of the application of **mechanical**, **chemical** and **thermal energy**. Also the first stage of any chemical disinfection process.

Cleaning schedule – a management plan for effective cleaning and, where appropriate, disinfection, detailing what, how and when something is to be cleaned.

Clean in place (CIP) – a method of cleaning without first dismantling equipment. Common in breweries and dairies for cleaning pipes that carry food.

Cocci – spherical bacterial cells.

Code of practice – advisory or guidance notes without formal legal status, the observance of which may help a due diligence defence. Statutory codes of practice are issued to **EHOS** and **EHPs** about enforcing legislation.

Codex Alimentarius Commission – food standards and advice organisation that formulated the seven Principles of **HACCP**. It is a subsidiary of the World Health Organization and the Food and Agriculture Organization of the United Nations.

Cold chain – all the stages in the handling of food that should be refrigerated, from the moment it is harvested, slaughtered or caught, right through to the point of sale. The stages could include processing, storage and dispatch.

Commensal – a description of a form of **symbiosis**. A close, harmonious, biological relationship between one organism (the commensal), such as a benign bacterium, and another, such as a human, in which the commensal benefits without harming the other organism.

Commercial freezing – the rapid freezing and storage of foods at temperatures below −18°C; typically at −22°C or colder.

Commercially sterilization – a method of high temperature preservation, also known as **appertizing**, in which **sterilization** is assumed but cannot be measured accurately. The process is designed to kill pathogenic micro-organisms. 'Sterilized' milk, for example, is treated in this way.

Competent authority– usually the **enforcement authority**.

Contact time – the period when a disinfectant must remain on, or surround, a surface in order to achieve disinfection.

Contaminant – any unwanted material, object or substance in food.

Contamination – any unwanted matter in food. The presence in food, or the process of transferring to food, or the introduction to food, of any contaminant, unwanted material, object or substance. Contamination may be biological, physical, chemical or allergen and may occur by direct or indirect means.

Controlled atmosphere packaging (CAP) – the precise adjustment of the composition of the air surrounding packaged food to prolong its shelf life.

Core temperature – the temperature measured at the centre or in the thickest part of food, or at the bone.

Corrective action – in **HACCP**, an action to be taken when there is a loss of control at a **critical control point** or a deviation from a critical limit for a CCP.

Critical control point (CCP) – in **HACCP**, the point at which the exercise of control over one or more factors could eliminate a hazard or minimise the risk from it. The point where control matters most.

Critical limit – in **HACCP**, the border between what is safe and unsafe. A value at a **CCP** outside of which the product would be unsafe.

Cross-contamination – the transfer of a contaminant from one contaminated product, such as raw meat, to another previously uncontaminated product, such as a ready-to-eat food.

Cryptosporidiosis – a form of food-borne illness provoked by the parasite *Cryptosporidium parvum*.

Cytoplasm – a complex semi-liquid suspension of enzymes, metabolic and end products inside the living cell.

Danger zone – an expression describing the preferred temperature range of pathogenic food-borne bacteria. Temperatures from 5°C to 63°C at which most food-borne pathogens multiply easily. The temperature range to be avoided for high-risk foods.

Date mark – a date or code indicating the period within which food should be consumed. Legally recognised date marks include *use by* and *best before* dates.

DDT (dichlorodiphenyltrichloroethane) – an organochloric compound used as a pesticide in the 1940s and 1950s which accumulates in the food chain.

Death (or decline) phase – the final stage of a **bacterial growth curve**.

Definitive (or primary) host – the host on or in which a parasite carries out its sexual stage. The terminal host of a parasite.

Dehydration – the process of removing water/moisture from a product. The medical condition resulting from the loss of body fluid.

Denature – to make a structural change in protein or nucleic acid by heat, chemicals or high or low pH.

Depuration – cleansing or purification of shellfish.

Detergent – a formulation of chemicals designed to facilitate the removal of food and grease particles from dishes, equipment, utensils, surfaces and so on.

Diarrhoeal syndrome – symptoms involving excessive and frequent loosening of the bowel.

Diarrhoeic shellfish poisoning (DSP) – ('diarrhetic' in American English) poisoning from shellfish that have become temporarily poisonous following the seasonal ingestion of toxic plankton.

Digestion – the process of breaking food down in the body so that its nutrients can be used by the body and waste products can later be removed (see **gastro-intestinal system**).

Dinoflagellatae – small protozoa (algae).

Dioxin – an extremely toxic substance formed, for example, by burning plastics.

Direct contamination – the route of contamination direct from the source of contamination to food. This is the case when, for example, a contaminated food touches, drips or falls onto an uncontaminated one.

Disinfectant – a chemical formulation or the application of heat (as steam or hot water) to achieve disinfection.

Disinfection – the reduction of **pathogenic micro-organisms** to a level accepted as being safe for human health according to current scientific understanding. Disinfection does not usually destroy bacterial spores. British Standard BS 5283 states that disinfection may not kill all micro-organisms but reduces them to a level which is neither harmful to health nor to the quality of perishable goods.

DNA (deoxyribonucleic acid) – the genetic material inside every cell of an organism.

Dormant – literally 'asleep'; used to distinguish inactive forms or stages in the life cycle of an organism, such as bacterial **endospores**.

Dosing – the dilution of cleaning chemicals to the correct concentration for safe and effective use.

Due diligence – a defence under The Food Hygiene Regulations 2006 (for England, Wales, Scotland and Northern Ireland) that every practicable measure was taken to avoid committing an offence under the Act.

Dysentery – infection of the lower bowel causing pain, fever and diarrhoea.

Ectoparasite – a parasite thriving on a host's body surface.

E_h – see **oxidation-reduction potential**.

EHEC – enterohaemorrhagic E. coli (see

VTEC.)

EIEC – enteroinvasive E. coli, which multiplies in the surface cells of the intestine and particularly affects the very young and the very old. A toxin is *not* formed.

Electrolyte – a liquid capable of conducting electricity due to the presence of positive or negative ions.

ELISA test – an immunological test method.

Emetic syndrome – acute vomiting, sometimes accompanied by abdominal pain and occasionally by diarrhoea, typically caused by Bacillus cereus.

Emulsify – to mix two liquids where one exists as a colloid (small particles dispersed within the other).

Endoparasite – a parasite living within its host in the tissues, organs or circulatory systems.

Endospore – the full name for an asexual **spore** that develops inside the cell of some bacterial genera when the bacterium is under threat; a dormant form, or stage, of some types of bacteria that enables the organism to survive unfavourable conditions.

Endotoxin – a **toxin** present inside a bacterial cell which is released when the cell disintegrates.

Enforcement authority – the authority responsible for executing and enforcing food hygiene legislation. This is usually the local council.

Enterotoxin – a **toxin** affecting the intestine.

Environmental health officer (EHO) or environmental health practitioner (EHP) – a food safety specialist, among other things. An officer authorised to carry out legal proceedings connected with food safety issues.

Enzyme – a type of protein that can trigger chemical reactions in an organism without itself undergoing any change.

EPEC – enteropathogenic *E. coli*. The serotype responsible for many cases of childhood diarrhoea.

Epidemic – the existence and spread of an infectious disease to a large number of people within a certain area.

Ergot – a mycotoxin from the fungus *Claviceps purpurea* that affects grain, particularly rye.

Ergotism – also called St Anthony's fire. An illness caused by the ingestion of ergot, with symptoms including hallucinations and gangrene.

ETEC – enterotoxigenic *E. coli*. The serotype responsible for 'traveller's diarrhoea'.

Exotoxin – a toxin released from the cell of a living bacterium into its surroundings.

Exposure – in public health, a state of having no protection from contact with something harmful.

Extrinsic contamination – contamination from sources other than the raw food itself.

Extrinsic factors – external factors (such as temperature and atmosphere) that influence the growth and survival of micro-organisms.

Facultative – optional. A description indicating that a micro-organism can live in a variety of conditions: either in the presence, or in the absence, of an environmental factor. For example a facultative anaerobe is a bacterium that can survive with or without oxygen.

Faecal coliform – an organism, such as *E. coli*, the presence of which indicates faecal contamination.

Farm to fork – a popular expression describing all the many possible stages from the moment of harvesting (fruit, grain and vegetable crops), slaughter (animals) or catching (fish) of food until it is eaten by the consumer. The phrase is commonly used to highlight the long chain of food safety controls that are necessary to ensure public health. Other phrases, such as 'plough to plate', are used in the same way.

Fascioliasis – an illness provoked by the liver fluke *Fasciola hepatica*.

Final consumer – the ultimate consumer of a foodstuff who will not use the food as part of any food business operation or activity.

Flagellum (pl: flagellae) – slender thread-like structure enabling bacteria to 'swim' in liquids.

Flatworms – worms with a flat body lacking blood vessels. Many parasites are flatworms.

Flipper – the first stage in the process of spoilage in canned foods that eventually creates a blown can.

Flora (microbial)/microflora – the assemblage of microbial species normally found in a particular habitat, such as the intestine.

Food – any substance, product or ingredient intended, or reasonably expected, to be ingested by humans. It can be raw, processed or partly processed and includes drinks, water and chewing gum. Food does *not* legally include live animals (unless they are prepared for sale), feeding stuff for animals, plants before they are harvested, medicinal or cosmetic products, tobacco or tobacco products, controlled drugs or residues and contaminants.

Food Alert – a formal notification issued by the **Food Standards Agency** for dealing with food-related problems. A Food Alert for Information warns local authorities and consumers about problems associated with particular foods or brands, while a Food Alert for Action gives information about specific action to be taken. Alerts are often issued in conjunction with a product withdrawal or recall by a manufacturer, retailer or distributor.

Food-borne disease/illness – a general description of any illness from contaminated food. In this book the phrase covers *any* type of illness that is caused, or is probably caused, by the consumption of contaminated food, water or other drink.

Food-borne infection – an infection caused by **pathogens** that are carried by food but are not dependent upon it.

Food business – legal definition: 'any undertaking, whether for profit or not and whether public or private, carrying out any of the activities related to any stage of production, processing and distribution of food'.

Food business operator – the person responsible for ensuring that the requirements of food law are met within the food business under their control. The person in charge at any time. Legal definition: 'the natural or legal persons responsible for ensuring that the requirements of food law are met within the food business under their control'.

Food-contact surface – any surface that comes into contact with food.

Food flow – the stages (such as growing, harvesting or slaughtering, transport, storage, preparation, display and sale) that a particular food follows from farm to fork.

Food handler – any person in a food business who, by his or her action, inaction, management, decision or advice can directly influence the safety of any food that is handled by that business at any stage.

Food hazard – anything in food that could make someone ill or cause them injury. A source of danger in food. Anything microbiological, chemical or physical in food that could cause harm to the consumer. Legal definition: 'any biological, chemical or physical agent in food, or any condition of food, with the potential to cause an adverse health effect.'

Food hygiene – all the individual measures involved in keeping food safe to eat. Legal definition: 'the measures and conditions necessary to control food hazards and ensure the fitness of food for human consumption taking into account its intended use'.

Food intolerance – a form of sensitivity to certain foods that usually arises from the body's failure to produce enough of the particular enzymes needed to break down and digest some types of proteins in a particular food. Unlike an **allergy**, a food intolerance does not involve the immune system.

Food poisoning – any illness caused by, or thought to be caused by, pathogens or toxins in food. The term is sometimes also used as a simple general term for all kinds of illness related to food.

Food safety – the protection of human health from harm from food by controlling *and* minimising the risks from food hazards. Also used to indicate the absence of harm to people from food.

Food safety policy/food hygiene policy – a document that makes clear a company's intentions towards, and objectives for, food safety standards.

Food spoilage – see **spoilage**.

Food Standards Agency (FSA) – an independent government department, with some regulatory powers, that protects public health and consumer interests in food from farm to fork, nutrition and diet. The **Meat Hygiene Service** is an executive agency of the FSA. Among other work relating to food safety and standards, the FSA represents the government in the European Union, oversees standards of legal enforcement by local authorities and, when necessary, issues **Food Alerts**. The Agency supports local authorities by funding training and making grants and other resources available. It also provides a wide range of information for both the general public and food businesses, particularly through its website.

Freezer burn – the accidental dehydration of food caused by large ice crystals formed when the freezing process is too slow or food thaws slightly and is refrozen. A form of food spoilage.

Fungal spore – the reproductive stage of fungi.

Fungicide – a **pesticide** designed to kill fungi.

Fungus (pl: fungi) – a group of micro-organisms (including moulds and yeasts) and macro-organisms (mushrooms and toadstools) with rigid cell walls.

Gastro-enteritis – inflammation of the mucous membrane of the gut.

Gastro-intestinal system – the stomach and intestines. The route taken by food and drink through the human body.

Gene – the smallest unit of heredity; a segment of DNA; a distinct sequence of nucleotides forming part of a chromosome.

Generic HACCP – a modified system of **HACCP**, also known as process-specific HACCP, that can be applied in food businesses such as restaurants and bakeries, where it would be impracticable to apply the system to each product.

Genetic material – genetic 'information'; the sum of all hereditary material.

Genus (pl: genera) – a classification category, ranking above species, of organisms sharing many characteristics.

Germination – the growth of endospores into vegetative bacteria. (Also applied to the initial stages of plant seed growth.)

Giardiasis – an illness caused by the parasitic **protozoan** *Giardia lamblia*.

Good hygiene practice – the basic steps that must be carried out and the basic systems that must be in place in any food business in order to be able to produce food that is safe to eat. The phrase is often used synonymously with **prerequisites** and **good manufacturing practice**.

Good manufacturing practice (GMP) – a term recognised worldwide for the management, quality control and testing of foods and pharmaceutical products. It is often used synonymously with **good hygiene practice** and **prerequisites**.

Gram reaction – a test that distinguishes important basic characteristics of bacteria.

Growth curve – see **bacterial growth curve**.

Growth optimum – the peak of a **growth curve**.

HACCP – an abbreviation, usually pronounced 'hassup', for Hazard Analysis and Critical Control Point, a system for identifying and assessing hazards to food safety and controlling the risks from those hazards. The ICMSF definition of HACCP is 'a systematic approach to the identification and assessment of the microbiological hazards and risks associated with food and the definition of means for their control.'

Haemagglutinin – a substance which causes the clumping together of red blood cells.

Haemoglobin – an oxygen-carrying protein in mammal blood.

Haemolysis – breakdown of red blood cells. It can have several causes eg. the action of micro-organisms, poisons or as the result of an allergic reaction.

Haemorrhage – loss of blood.

Halophile – a salt-loving or salt-tolerant **micro-organism**.

Hand-contact surface – any surface touched by hand. The surface may subsequently be touched by food, or micro-organisms on the surface may be transferred to food.

Hazard – a source of danger: any thing, condition or circumstance that could cause harm to the consumer. (See also **food hazard**.)

Hazard analysis – the systematic identification of food hazards and the estimation of their severity and the degree of risk from them. The term is applied to the first Principle of **HACCP** and to a generic form of HACCP.

Hazard Analysis and Critical Control Point – see **HACCP**.

Health Protection Agency (HPA) – the government's health watchdog in Britain. The Agency provides an integrated approach to public health protection by supporting the National Health Service (NHS), the Department of Health, local authorities, the devolved administrations, emergency services and other arms-length bodies. Three main centres deal with communicable disease surveillance and specialist microbiology; radiation, chemical and environmental hazards; and emergency preparedness and response, focusing on applied microbiological research and emergency response.

Heavy metal – a metal with a high relative atomic mass such as copper, lead and zinc. Such metals are a cause of environmental pollution.

Herbicide – a **pesticide** designed to kill unwanted plants or weeds.

Hermaphrodite – an organism that possesses both male and female reproductive organs.

Heterotroph – an organism that derives its nutrients from organic substances. (See also **autotroph**.)

High-risk food – a food, typically high in protein and moisture, that is at high risk of **contamination** by spoilage bacteria or pathogens and requires strict time and temperature control to remain safe to eat. High risk foods are sometimes referred to as 'high care foods' or 'potentially hazardous foods'.

Home authority – the local authority where a food business is based, or where its decision-making office is based. The home authority for a business with multiple branches is usually the local authority where the head office is located.

Host – an organism providing nourishment and shelter, on or within its body, for a parasite.

HTST – high temperature short time. A form of **pasteurization**.

Hurdle concept/technology – the controlled manipulation of factors essential to microbial survival and multiplication to increase the shelf life of food.

Hygiene – see **food hygiene**.

Hygiene Emergency Prohibition Notice or Order – processes under The Food Hygiene Regulations 2006 (for England, Wales, Scotland and Northern Ireland) for closing a food business because of a suspected imminent risk to health. A Hygiene Emergency Prohibition Notice is issued by an authorised officer and a Hygiene Emergency Prohibition Order, confirming the Notice, is issued by a court.

Hygiene Improvement Notice – a notice served by an authorised officer under The Food Hygiene Regulations 2006 (for England, Wales, Scotland and Northern Ireland), requiring improvements to be made to food premises.

Hygiene Prohibition Order – a legal procedure by which a court may ban the use of premises, equipment, food processes or treatment because of a risk of illness or injury from food; or may ban a proprietor or manager from working in a food business.

Immune system – the combined action of the body's various means of fighting infection.

Immunocompromised – having an impaired immune system.

Immunological – pertaining to immunity.

Incubation period – the length of time

between infection by an organism and the first appearance of symptoms of a disease; also known as 'onset'.

Indicator organisms – organisms that suggest faecal contamination and inadequate cleaning and disinfection.

Indirect contamination – contamination introduced by a **vehicle of contamination**.

Infection – the presence and multiplication of a pathogen in the body, producing disease. The process of infecting or stage of being infected.

Infective dose – the number of micro-organisms that have to be present to cause a disease.

Infestation – the presence, usually in large numbers, of a food pest.

Ingest – to eat or drink. To take food or other substances into the body by swallowing or absorbing. (Food is then **digested**.)

Inherent – existing within something; inbuilt.

Inorganic – not composed of organic (carbon-based) matter; mineral.

Insecticide – a **pesticide** designed to kill insects.

Integrated pest management (IPM) – a style of pest management based on co-operation between a food business client and a specialist pest control operator (PCO), dealing mostly with preventive measures.

Intermediate (or secondary) host – the host in which the larval stages of endoparasites, such as tapeworms, develop.

Intoxication – the state or process of poisoning by a chemical substance or the products of bacteriological action.

Intrinsic contamination – contamination associated with the food itself.

Intrinsic factors – inbuilt or inherent

characteristics such as nutrients, pH and a_w that influence the survival, growth and multiplication of micro-organisms.

Irradiation – the use of gamma radiation to destroy pathogenic and spoilage organisms in food.

Kinetic energy – see **mechanical energy**.

Lag phase – the first stage of bacterial growth in which an organism adapts to its surroundings and does not reproduce.

Leaching – the washing out of the soluble constituents of a solid by passing a solvent, such as water, through it. Heavy metals sometimes contaminate the food chain when they leach from landfill sites as a result of rain or underground water.

Learning spiral – a sequence of experiencing, sharing, adjusting, applying and communicating knowledge.

Log (or logarithmic) phase – the stage of rapid bacterial multiplication.

Log scale – a scale of measurement in which an interval of one unit represents a tenfold multiplication of the quantity measured. Bacterial growth is often measured on a logarithmic scale.

Macro-molecule – a molecule containing a very large number of atoms.

Malicious tampering – the intentional contamination of a product.

Meat Hygiene Service (MHS) – an executive agency of the **Food Standards Agency** responsible for the protection of public health and animal health and welfare in England, Wales and Scotland, and the enforcement of legislation in approved fresh meat premises such as slaughterhouses, cutting plants, farmed and wild game facilities and meat products premises. Work includes verification, audit and meat inspection services.

Mechanical energy – a form of energy, also known as **kinetic energy**, involved in the process of cleaning. Energy possessed by a body by virtue of its motion.

Mesophile – an organism preferring temperatures between 10°C and 55°C.

Metabolism – the sum total of the chemical changes carried out in the cells of a living organism.

Metabolite – a substance required for **metabolism** or which is formed in metabolism.

Micro-aerophile – an organism that does not require much oxygen.

Microbe – see **micro-organism**.

Microbial competition – microbial activity in which one type of micro-organism gains superiority over another.

Microbiological criterion – a way to 'define acceptability of a product, a batch of foodstuffs or a process, based on the absence, presence or number of micro-organisms, and/or on the quantity of their toxins/metabolites, per unit(s) of mass, volume, area or batch'.

Microbiologically clean – a surface or equipment on which the number of micro-organisms has been reduced to a level accepted as being safe for human health.

Microbiology – the science of the study of microbes.

Micro-organism – any organism that is so small that it can be observed only through a microscope.

Miracidium – free-swimming larval stage of a parasitic fluke.

Mobile – movable. (Compare with **motile**.)

Modified atmosphere packaging (MAP) – the preservation of food by controlling the chemical composition of the air in hermetically sealed packaging.

Moisture – in general discussion about food and food safety, the word refers to the water activity (see a_w) of food. Also used to describe dampness, condensed water/water vapour.

Monitoring – in **HACCP**, the measurement or observation at a critical control point (CCP) of the criteria which allow corrective actions to be taken.

Morphology – the science of the structure and shape of organisms.

Mortality rate – death rate.

Motile – capable of independent, or self-propelled, movement. Usually used to describe cells, but *not* animals or equipment.

Moulds – strictly aerobic filamentous **fungi** that can spoil food and cause food poisoning by poisonous metabolites (**mycotoxins**).

Multiplication – microbial reproduction, for instance by **binary fission** (bacteria) or **budding** (yeast).

Mutagenic – causing genetic alteration.

Mycotoxicosis – an illness caused by the toxins produced by some fungi.

Mycotoxin – a toxic substance produced by some fungi. Mycotoxins can cause serious acute and/or chronic diseases.

Myristicine – compound present in the oil of nutmeg.

Natural toxins – poisonous substances which are inherent in the product.

'nature or substance or quality' – a legal description of food, requiring all food sold to be constituted as the consumer is led to expect.

Nephrotoxic – damaging or poisonous to the kidneys.

Neurotoxin – a poison that acts on the nervous system.

Neutral – a pH of 7.0.

Nitrate – a naturally occurring chemical

used in agriculture and as a food additive which may cause food poisoning.

Nitrite – a chemical used as a food additive which may cause food poisoning.

Nitrogen – colourless, odourless, gas element (represented by the letter N) which makes up 78 per cent by volume of the Earth's atmosphere. It is an essential component of proteins and nucleic acids.

Nitrogen cycle – major environmental element cycle. Nitrates in the soil are taken up by plants and passed to animals through the food chain. Denitrifying bacteria return some nitrogen to the atmosphere.

Nitrosamine – a chemical compound that can cause food poisoning.

Nucleus – a structure within some types of cell (not bacterial cells) that contains DNA.

Obligate – describes a microbe that is obliged to live in particular conditions to survive – for instance, an obligate aerobe must have oxygen, while an obligate anaerobe must live in oxygen-free conditions.

Ochratoxin – mycotoxin produced by the genus *Aspergillus*.

Onset/onset period – see **incubation**.

Oocyst – cyst containing a reproductive cell formed by a parasitic organism.

Organic chemistry – the chemistry of compounds of carbon, whether natural or synthetic.

Organism – individual life form capable of maintenance, growth and reproduction.

Organoleptic – involving the use of the senses; the characteristics of food are often assessed by its appearance, smell, taste, texture and even sound, for instance the tapping of bread.

Outbreak – two or more linked cases of the same infection or food-borne illness; a cluster, in time or place, of cases of illness caused by a particular organism; a situation where the observed number of cases unaccountably exceeds the expected number.

Oxalic acid – poisonous acid with a sour taste, present in rhubarb leaves.

Oxidation – the process of oxidising, that is, reaction with oxygen or a chemical reaction involving the loss of electrons. Oxidation can spoil food. The turning brown of a cut apple is the result of oxidation.

Oxidation-reduction potential (E_h) – the value used to describe the ease with which a medium loses or gains electrons. It sums up the effects of both oxidising and reducing factors in food and is influenced by bacterial growth. Also known as **redox**.

Packaging – the legal definition is 'the placing of one or more wrapped foodstuffs in a second container' and 'the latter container itself'.

Paralytic shellfish poisoning – food poisoning caused by shellfish which have become temporarily poisonous following the seasonal ingestion of toxic plankton.

Parasites – plants or animals that derive shelter and sustenance in or on other organisms, thriving on their body substance or metabolites.

Pasteurization – a method of heat treatment of liquids, such as milk and beer, that destroys tuberculosis **pathogens** and reduces other pathogens to accepted safe levels for human health.

Pathogen – an organism that can cause disease.

Patulin – a mycotoxin produced by moulds of the genera *Aspergillus* and *Penicillium*.

Perigo factor – an incompletely understood phenomenon that occurs when nitrite is added before food is heated and produces an effect ten times more inhibitory than when the nitrite is added *after* heating.

Peripheral nervous system – the nervous system outside the brain and the spinal cord.

Permeability – the degree to which a surface or membrane will admit the passage of substances. Permeability depends on the structure or texture of the membrane as well as on the nature of the diffusing matter.

Personal protective equipment (PPE) – any clothing, equipment or device designed to protect food from contamination or the wearer from injury. In food businesses such items include rubber gloves, overalls, hats, hairnets and aprons.

Person in charge – the person given the authority by the employer to take charge of food premises at any given time.

Pest – an unwanted animal, including insects and birds, which contaminates or destroys food, or whose presence in food premises is undesirable.

Pesticide – a collective term for several groups of chemical substances designed to kill animal pests and noxious plants and protect crops and stored products. They include insecticides (insect control), rodenticides (rodent control), acaricides (mite control), herbicides (for plant protection) and fungicides (for controlling unwanted fungi, such as mould).

Phagetyping – a method of identifying bacteria by using host-specific viruses which only attack certain bacteria strains.

Photosynthesis – a process by which plants use sunlight to synthesise nutrients from carbon dioxide and water.

pH scale – a logarithmic scale used to express acidity or alkalinity, in which 7.0 represents neutral. A reading below 7 is acid, above 7 is alkaline. It can be defined as $-\log_{10}c$, where c is equal to the hydrogen ion concentration in moles per litre.

Phylum (plural: phyla) – a high-level category of taxonomic classification of organisms. Organisms are classified into hierarchies such as: kingdom, phylum, class, order, family, genus, species.

Physical contaminants – foreign bodies in food which can provoke both harm and/or disgust depending on their nature.

Physically clean – the state achieved when all visible or tangible evidence of dirt or residue or foreign material has been removed by cleaning from a surface or piece of equipment.

Physiology – science dealing with the normal functions of organisms.

Place on the market – to offer for sale, to sell. Legal definition: 'the holding of food ... for the purpose of sale, including offering for sale or any other form of transfer, whether free of charge or not, and the sale, distribution, and other forms of transfer themselves'.

Plasma membrane – see **cell membrane**.

Plasmid – a structure in a cell composed of DNA which can reproduce independently. Plasmids often control instructions for cell activities.

Poison – any substance which either kills or causes damage when introduced into a living organism.

Polyaromatic hydrocarbons – derivatives of phenol; often highly carcinogenic.

Polymerase chain reaction (PCR) test – a genetic test method depending on the activity of the individual replication enzyme taking place in the sample due to the DNA amplification.

Potable – safe to drink. Generally used to describe water treated for use as drinking water.

Predisposition – the tendency to suffer from a particular condition.

Premises (food) – any building,

establishment, place, vehicle, stall, moveable structure, ship or aircraft that is used for the purposes of a food business.

Prerequisites – essentials of good practice that must be established and carried out to ensure food safety. These are aspects of food safety that should be in place in any food business and must be operating to a good standard before attempting to implement a **HACCP** system. They include pest control, staff training, cleaning and disinfection, personal hygiene and waste management. The term is sometimes referred to as **good hygiene practice**.

Preservation (food) – methods of treatment designed to delay the natural processes of decomposition and to extend the period within which the food is at its best for consumption.

Primary production – the production, rearing or growing of primary products, such as by harvesting, milking and farmed animal production prior to slaughter. It also includes hunting and fishing and the harvesting of wild products'.

Prion – the abbreviation for proteinaceous infectious particle; an abnormal form of mammal protein found, for example, in the brain. Prions have been implicated in brain-wasting diseases of animals and humans, such as scrapie in sheep, bovine spongiform encephalopathy (BSE) in cattle ('mad cow disease') and variant Creutzfeldt-Jakob Disease (vCJD) in humans. The suspected role of prions in these illnesses is, however, still controversial. Prions are *not* viruses, although their impact has sometimes been associated with viruses in the past, and they have sometimes been known as 'virions'.

Product recall – a public health measure to remove contaminated or suspect food from the market. Publicity notifies consumers that they should return specified products to the retailer for a replacement or refund.

Product specification – a food company's detailed description for its suppliers of the content, design, composition and intended use of the product to be supplied.

Product-specific HACCP – the full, original form of **HACCP**, which is designed to be applied to one product through all its process stages.

Product withdrawal – a public health protection measure in which contaminated or suspect products are traced to purchasers and removed from the food chain before they go on the market.

Protozoan (pl: protozoa) – single-celled animal with a more complex internal structure than a bacterium. Some protozoa, such as *Entamoeba histolytica*, are pathogenic.

PSP – see **paralytic shellfish poisoning**.

Psychrophile – an organism preferring temperatures between –5°C and 20°C.

Psychrotroph – an organism preferring temperatures between 0°C and 35°C.

Qats/QUATS – quaternary ammonium compounds: non-corrosive disinfectants.

Quality assurance – ensuring the repeatability of a defined quality in a product.

Quarantine – the separation, isolation and labelling of contaminated or suspect products and ingredients until an informed decision can be made about what to do with them, for example placing them on the market, re-working them, returning them to a supplier, holding them for analysis or destroying them.

Ready-to-eat – food produced for immediate consumption, without further treatment (except heating in some cases). A food that is either eaten raw, or is not prepared or treated, (such as by cooking) immediately before it is eaten, in a way that would kill any pathogens present.

Recall – see **product recall**.

Re-emergent pathogens – a term created by the World Health Organization to describe the reappearance of pathogenic bacteria which were thought to have been eliminated.

Residue – small amounts of a substance that remain after the main part has gone.

Ribosome – a tiny particle within a cell consisting of RNA and associated proteins.

Retail – the legal definition is 'the handling and/or processing of food and its storage at the point of sale or delivery to the final consumer, and includes distribution terminals, catering operations, factory canteens, institutional catering, restaurants and other similar food service operations, shops, supermarket distribution centres and wholesale outlets'.

Risk – a measure, or scale, of the likelihood (or probability) that a hazard will occur, and the severity of the effect (or consequences) of the hazard. The legal definition is 'a function of the probability of an adverse health effect and the severity of that effect consequential to a hazard'.

Risk analysis – a process involving risk assessment, risk communication and risk management.

Risk assessment – a scientifically based process consisting of four steps: hazard identification, hazard characterisation, exposure assessment and risk characterisation.

Risk communication – the legal definition is 'the interactive exchange of information and opinions throughout the risk analysis process as regards hazards and risks, risk-related factors and risk perceptions, among risk assessors, risk managers, consumers, feed and food businesses, the academic community and other interested parties, including the explanation of risk assessment findings and the basis of risk management decisions'.

Risk management – the process (distinct from risk assessment) of weighing policy alternatives in consultation with interested parties, considering risk assessment and other legitimate factors, and, if appropriate, selecting appropriate prevention and control options.

RNA – ribonucleic acid; a nucleic acid present in all living cells which acts as a messenger for the control of the synthesis of proteins.

Rodenticide – a pesticide designed to kill rodents.

Sanitizer – term used in the UK for a chemical formulation combining the properties of a detergent *and* a disinfectant. In America the term is often used for *any* kind of chemical disinfectant. Compare with **detergent** and **disinfectant**.

Sanitizing/sanitization – another term for chemical disinfection used particularly in America. The American Food Code (model for food safety legislation) describes sanitization as the application of cumulative heat or chemicals on cleaned food-contact surfaces to create a 99.999 per cent reduction in pathogens of public health importance.

Scombroid poisoning – an illness from a toxin that can be formed in oily fish, such as mackerel and tuna.

Selectively permeable – describes a membrane that allows only a selection of substances to pass through it.

Serotyping – an immunological method for identifying bacteria by means of specific antigen/antibody reactions.

Severity – in **HACCP**, the magnitude or seriousness of the possible consequences of a hazard.

Shelf life – the period within which food is both safe for human consumption and at its best. The legal definition is 'either the period corresponding to the period preceding the use by [date] or the minimum [legally defined] durability date'.

Smoking (food process) – a method of introducing a smoked flavour to food products. The process may, in some cases, have a preservative effect.

Solanine – a poisonous compound present in nightshade, green potatoes and related plants.

Solute – the substances dissolved in a solvent to form a solution.

Source of contamination – point of origin of a contaminant.

Spoilage – any undesirable change in food that makes it unacceptable for eating. The natural process of ageing, deterioration, decay or 'going off' of food, or the contamination or adulteration that makes food decay rapidly.

Spore (bacterial) – contraction of 'endospore'; the dormant, survival form of *Clostridium* and *Bacillus* bacteria which is resistant to heat, acid, salt and most other adverse conditions. When conditions become favourable, the spores germinate and release vegetative bacterial cells. Unlike fungal spores, bacterial endospores do not multiply.

Spore (fungal) – a reproductive cell of a fungus.

Sporocyst – a parasitic fluke in the initial stage of infection.

Sporozoite – a motile spore-like stage in the life cycle of some parasitic protozoa.

Sporulation – spore production.

Stationary phase – a stage of the bacterial growth curve at which the bacterial population has reached its maximum.

Sterile – a condition in which all living organisms have been destroyed.

Sterilization – the destruction of all living organisms.

Stock rotation – the practice of using a product with the shortest shelf life before using a similar one with a longer shelf life.

Stored product pest – an insect, sometimes known as a storage insect, associated with foods such as grain, flour, herbs, spices and nuts that are often stored for long periods.

Substrate – a substance on, or from, which an organism lives, grows, multiplies or obtains its nourishment. Also a substance on which an enzyme acts.

Supplier's certificate – a supplier's guarantee to its customer that the product being supplied conforms to the purchasing company's specification. May also be known as a certificate of conformance (CoC).

Surfactant – a substance which increases the wetting or penetrating action of a detergent.

Swabbing technique – a bacterial monitoring technique involving the measurement of the uptake of micro-organisms from a surface and incubation in a standard or selective medium.

Symbiosis – the close association between two species, particularly where there is benefit to both species. See also **commensal**.

Target level – in **HACCP**, a specified value for a control measure that eliminates or minimises the risk from a hazard at a critical control point (CCP).

Taxonomy – the naming, description and classification of organisms.

Temperature – a measure, or scale, of the degree of hotness or coldness of a substance.

Temperature control – all aspects of food safety in which temperature, combined with time control, is used as a measure to eliminate a food safety hazard or reduce the risk from it. The most basic rules of temperature control regarding high-risk foods are to keep hot food hot and to keep cold food cold. See also **danger zone**.

Thermal energy – one of three forms of energy involved in the process of cleaning. Thermal energy is usually provided by hot water or by steam.

Thermophile – a heat-loving microbe that thrives at between 40°C and 80°C.

Time control – see **temperature control**.

Tolerance – in HACCP, a specified variation from the target level which is deemed to be acceptable for food safety.

Toxic – a description of *any* poisonous substance.

Toxin – a poisonous substance produced by some bacteria and fungi; usually a complex enzyme (a type of protein) which is fatal to other proteins. Organisms producing toxins are toxigenic.

Traceability – the ability to identify and follow food ingredients, food products, animal feed and other substances through all the stages of production, processing and distribution. A food safety system involving everyone in the food chain from farm to fork.

Trophozoite – the growing stage in the life cycle of some protozoan parasites.

Tuberculosis – a chronic bacterial disease, which may be food-borne, air-borne or by contact, caused either by the bacteria *Mycobacterium tuberculosis* or *M. bovis*.

Typhoid/typhoid fever – the illness caused by the bacterium *Salmonella* Typhi. The disease is also known as enteric fever.

Typhus – an illness, sometimes known as 'spotted fever' and not to be confused with typhoid/typhoid fever, which is caused by rickettsiae, a group of parasitic organisms.

Ultra heat treatment (UHT) – a method of temperature treatment, usually applied to milk, designed to reduce spoilage organisms and extend the food's shelf life.

Unfit (food) – food that is unacceptable for human consumption because of contamination, decomposition, the presence of foreign objects, or unacceptable flavours or smells.

Unicellular – having only one cell.

United Kingdom Accreditation Service (UKAS) – the only British accreditation body recognised by the Government to assess organisations that provide certification, testing, inspection and calibration services against internationally agreed standards.

Use by – the date indicating the last day on which food is safe to eat.

Vacuum packing – a type of food packaging where the air has been removed to create a vacuum which prevents the multiplication of aerobic organisms.

Vector – an animal, including an insects or a bird, serving as a **vehicle of contamination**.

Vegetative cell – a living, reproducing cell.

Vehicle of contamination – any substance, object or living being which carries contamination from one point to another. The route taken is known as indirect contamination.

Verification – in **HACCP**, the checking or reviewing of the entire HACCP system to ensure that it is operating according to plan.

Virion – a virus-like particle, sometimes discussed in connection with **prions**.

Virology – the scientific study of viruses.

Virulence – the degree or severity of harm that a pathogenic organism can cause.

Virus – an extremely small infective organism, ranging from $^1/_{10}$ to $^1/_{100}$ the size of one bacterium, that can multiply only within living cells. A virus particle consists of only a single strand of nucleic acid surrounded by a protein coat which acts as a protective shell and enables the virus to link itself to the surface of a host cell.

VTEC – verocytotoxin-producing *E. coli*. The term verocytotoxin refers to the type of cells it affects in laboratory work. It is an extremely virulent serotype of the bacterium, which is also referred to as the serotype O157:H7 and as EHEC (enterohaemorrhagic *E. coli*).

Water activity – see a_w.

Winter vomiting disease – viral infection, caused by Norovirus, that commonly affects children of primary school age.

Workflow – the logical route organised through food premises for food, food handlers, equipment and rubbish at each stage from the delivery of raw food to the dispatch, sale or service of finished products.

Wrapping – legal definition: 'the placing of a foodstuff in a wrapper or container in direct contact with the foodstuff concerned' and 'the wrapper or container itself'.

Xerophile – an organism that likes dry conditions and can survive at low a_w values.

Yeast – a microscopic unicellular fungus which can contaminate food and cause spoilage.

Zoonosis (pl: zoonoses) – a disease of animals that can also infect humans.

Sources of further help
Organisations and websites

Where no country is stated, the address is in the United Kingdom. When navigating large and complex websites it is sometimes quicker to use an external search engine, such as Google, than the site's own search facility.

Allergy Action
An independent advice and training organisation promoting awareness of potentially fatal food allergies
T: 01727 855294
E: info@allergyaction.org
U: www.allergyaction.org

Allergy UK
A British allergy charity
3 White Oak Square
London Road
Swanley, Kent BR8 7AG
T: 01322 619898
E: info@allergyuk.org
U: www.allergyuk.org/

The Anaphylaxis Campaign
A British charity for people with life-threatening reactions to peanuts and other foods
PO Box 275
Farnborough GU14 6SX
T: 01252 542029
F: 01252 377140
E: info@anaphylaxis.org.uk
U: www.anaphylaxis.org.uk

American Institute of Baking
An auditing, inspection and training organisation
U: https://www.aibonline.org/

British Broadcasting Corporation (BBC)
BBC News Online
U: http://news.bbc.co.uk/

British Hospitality Association
A national trade association for the hospitality industry
Queens House
55-56 Lincoln's Inn Fields
London WC2A 3BH
T: 0207 404 7744
E: bha@bha.org.uk
U: www.bha.org.uk

British Institute of Cleaning Science
A professional, educational and awarding body
9 Premier Court, Boarden Close,
Moulton Park
Northampton NN3 6LF
T: 01604 678710
E: info@bics. org.uk
U: www.bics.org.uk

The British Retail Consortium (BRC)
A trade association and standards body
2nd Floor, 21 Dartmouth Street,
London SW1H 9BP
T: 020 7854 8900
F: 020 7854 8901
U: www.brc.org.uk/standards/index.htm

British Standards Institution (BSI)
A standards and certification body
389 Chiswick High Road
London W4 4AL
T: 020 8996 9000
E: info@bsi-global.com
U: www.bsi-uk.com or www.bsi-global.com

Campden & Chorleywood Food Research Association (CCFRA)
The world's largest membership-based food and drink research organisation
Chipping Campden
Gloucestershire GL55 6LD
T: 01386 842000
F: 01386 842100
E: info@campden.co.uk
U: www.campden.co.uk

Centers for Disease Control
American centre for disease surveillance
U: www.cdc.gov

Chartered Institute of Environmental Health (CIEH)
Professional, educational and awarding body for food safety and other environmental health matters. Its commercial wing, Chadwick House Group Ltd (CHGL), publishes a wide range of food safety books and materials
Chadwick Court
15 Hatfields
London SE1 8DJ
T: 020 7827 5800
F: 020 7827 5865
E: customersupport@chgl.com
U: www.cieh.org

Codex Alimentarius Commission
A food safety and standards organisation: a subsidiary of the World Health Organization (WHO) and the Food and Agriculture Organization (FAO)
www.codexalimentarius.net
ftp://ftp.fao.org/codex/Publications/understanding/Understanding_EN.pdf

Communicable Disease Surveillance Centre (Northern Ireland)
British disease surveillance organisation
McBrien Building
Belfast City Hospital
Lisburn Road
Belfast BT9 7AB
T: 028 90 263765
F: 028 90 263511
E: cdscni@hpa.org.uk
U: www.cdscni.org.uk

Department for Business, Enterprise and Regulatory Reform
The UK government department concerned with trade and industry
U: http://www.berr.gov.uk

Department for Environment, Food and Rural Affairs (Defra)
The UK government department concerned with food and related matters
T: 08459 33 55 77
U: www.defra.gov.uk

Department of Health (DoH)
The UK government health department
U: www.doh.gov.uk

European Food Scientist
A free publication dealing with food safety, and food and drink processing, packaging and labelling
U: www.scientistlive.com

European Hygienic Engineering and Design Group (EHEDG)
A research, standards, certification and training body promoting food safety during the processing and packaging of food products
U: www.ehedg.org

European Law
Site summarising European law
U: www.europa.eu.int/eur-lex

Eurosurveillance
European disease surveillance organisation
U: www.eurosurveillance.org

European Union
The social, legal and economic organisation
of European member states
U: http://europa.eu/index_en.htm
For food issues –
U: http://europa.eu/pol/food/index_en.htm

Food and Drink Federation
A membership organisation representing
manufacturers, trade associations and
industry-specific groups
6 Catherine Street
London WC2B 5JJ
T: 020 7836 2460
F: 020 7836 0580
U: www.fdf.org.uk
In Scotland:
E: generalenquiries@fdf.org.uk
U: www.sfdf.org.uk

The Food Safety Authority of Ireland
The Republic of Ireland's (Eire's) food
safety and standards organisation
U: www.fsai.ie

Food Standards Agency
The UK's food safety and standards
organisation: a good source of information
and guidance on legislation and good
practice
U: www.foodstandards.gov.uk

Hansard
The official record of the UK Parliament
U: www.parliament.the-stationery-
office.co.uk/pa/cm/cmhansrd.htm

Health Protection Agency
The UK government's public health
watchdog
Central Office
7th Floor, Holborn Gate
330 High Holborn
London WC1V 7PP
T: 020 7759 2700/2701
F: 020 7759 2733
E: webteam@hpa.org.uk
U: www.hpa.org.uk

Health Protection Scotland
The co-ordinating body for Scottish health
matters
Clifton House
Clifton Place
Glasgow, G3 7LN
T: 0141 300 1100
F: 0141 300 1170
E: hpsenquiries@hps.scot.nhs.uk
U: http://www.hps.scot.nhs.uk

Her Majesty's Stationery Office
A source of copies of UK legislation and
government departmental reports
U: www.hmso.gov.uk

Institute of Food Science and Technology
British professional organisation for
the food industry
U: www.ifst.org

Institute of Hospitality
(formerly the Hotel & Catering
International Management Association)
A trade, professional and awarding body for
international hospitality, leisure and
tourism industries
Institute of Hospitality
Trinity Court, 34 West Street
Sutton
Surrey SM1 1SH
T: 020 8661 4900
F: 020 8661 4901
E: commdept@instituteofhospitality.org
U: www.hcima.org.uk

The International Food Standard
A standards organisation
E: info@food-care.info

International Organization for
Standardization (ISO)
The world's largest standards body
1, rue de Varembé, Case postale 56
CH-1211 Geneva 20, Switzerland
U: www.iso.org/iso/en/ISOOnline.frontpage

Local Authorities Co-Ordination Body on
Food and Trading Standards (LACOTS)
Organisation co-ordination and giving
advice to enforcement bodies
U: www.lacots.com

Ministry of Justice
The UK government department dealing
with legal matters
For the UK statue law database –
U: http://www.statutelaw.gov.uk/

National Assembly for Wales
Regional government for Wales
U: www.assemblywales.org

National Registry of Food
Safety Professionals
A professional, educational and awarding
body in the USA; sister organisation of
the CIEH
1200 East Hillcrest Street
Suite 303, Orlando, Florida 32803
U: www.nrfsp.com

Northern Ireland Assembly
Regional government for Northern Ireland
U: www.niassembly.gov.uk

NSF International
A standards, product certification and
educational body dealing with food safety
and public health and safety
International head office:
T: +001 734 769 8010
E: info@nsf.org
U: www.nsf.org
Europe, Middle East and Africa office:
NSF International
Kleine Kloosterstraat 6
1932 Zaventem
Belgium
T: +32 2771 36 54
E: europe@nsf.org
U: www.nsf.org

Office of Public Sector Information
Part of the UK National Archive,
incorporating Her Majesty's Stationery
Office
U: http://www.opsi.gov.uk
For on-line copies of legislation –
U: http://www.opsi.gov.uk/legislation/
index.htm

Parliament (UK)
U: www.parliament.uk

Public Health Laboratory Service
British disease surveillance organisation
U: www.phls.co.uk

The Royal Environmental Health Institute
of Scotland
Professional, educational and
awarding body for food safety and
other environmental health matters
3 Manor Place
Edinburgh EH3 7DH
T: 0131 225 6999
F: 0131 225 3993
U: www.rehis.org

The Royal Institute of Public Health (RIPH)
Professional, educational and awarding body for food safety and other public health matters. Proposing to merge with the RSH in 2008
28 Portland Place
London W1B 1DE
T: 020 7580 2731
F: 020 7580 6157
E: info@riph.org.uk
U: www@riph.org.uk

The Royal Society for the Promotion of Health (RSH or RSPH)
Professional, educational and awarding body for food safety and other public health matters. Proposing to merge with the RIPH in 2008
38A St George's Drive
London SW1V 4BH
T: 020 7630 0121
E: rshealth@rshealth.org.uk
U: www.rsph.org

Scottish Centre for Infection and Environmental Health
Disease surveillance organisation for Scotland
U: www.show.scot.nhs.uk/scieh

Scottish Parliament
Regional government for Scotland
U: www.scottish.parliament.uk/home.htm

The Scottish Retail Consortium
Part of The British Retail Consortium
PO Box 13737
Gullane, EH31 2WX
T: 0870 609 3631
F: 0870 609 3631
U: http://www.brc.org.uk

The Society of Food Hygiene and Technology
British professional, educational and awarding body
PO Box 37
Lymington
Hampshire SO41 9WL
U: www.sofht.co.uk

SQF Institute (Safe Quality Food Institute)
An international standards, certification and training organisation dealing with food safety and quality management systems
Rue de Grand-Chêne 6/4
1003 Lausanne, Switzerland
U: www.sqfi.com

United Kingdom Accreditation Service (UKAS)
The official British accreditation body for assessing, against internationally agreed standards, organisations that provide certification, testing, inspection and calibration services
21-47 High Street,
Feltham,
Middlesex.
TW13 4UN
T: 020 89178400
F: 020 8917 8500
E: info@ukas.com
U: www.ukas.com

United States Department of Agriculture (USDA)
American government department
U: www.usda.gov

World Health Organization
The United Nations' public health body, based in Switzerland
U: www.who.int/home-page

Books and articles

Lisa M Ackerley, 'Food Hygiene and Food Poisoning: A Study of Public Perceptions', PhD thesis, University of Birmingham, 1991

M R Adams and M O Moss, *Food Microbiology*, The Royal Society of Chemistry, Cambridge, 2000

A Dictionary of Biology, Oxford University Press, Oxford, 2000

Advisory Committee on the Microbiological Safety of Food, *Interim Report on Campylobacter*, HMSO, London, 1993

Michael Agnes (ed), *Webster's New World College Dictionary*, IDG Books Worldwide Inc, Foster City, California, 2001

Patricia Barnes-Svarney, *The New York Public Library Science Desk Reference*, Macmillan, New York, 1995

Lutz Bertling, *Erlaubt-Verboten in Gastronomie und Gemeinschaftsverpflegung*, Deutscher Fachverlag, Frankfurt a. Main, 1996

R C Bowman and E D Emmett, *A Dictionary of Food Hygiene*, Chadwick House Group Ltd, 1998

Frank L Bryan, *Hazard Analysis Critical Control Point Evaluations*, World Health Organization, Geneva, 1992

Codex Alimentarius, *Hazard Analysis and Critical Control Point (HACCP) System and Guidelines for Its Application*, 1997

Concise Science Dictionary, Oxford University Press, Oxford, 1996

Department of Health, *FSA Review of BSE Controls*, CJD Policy Unit, May 2000

Department of Health, *Management of outbreaks of food borne illness*, Department of Health, UK, 1994

Tim Deveaux, *Supervising Health and Safety at Work*, CHGL, 2003

Robert H Dreisach, *Handbook of Poisoning*, Lange Medical Publications, Los Altos, California, 1980

Dagmar Engel, *Hygiene – Eigenkontrolle in Bäckerei/Konditorei/Café*, Gildebuchverlag, Alfeld/Leine, 1998

Dagmar Engel, *HACCP in Training – Food Safety Principles Made Easy*, Chandos Publishing (Oxford) Ltd, Oxford, 2000

Dagmar Engel, *Teaching HACCP – Theory and Practice from the Trainer's Point of View*, Food Control, Elsevier Applied Science Publishers Ltd, No 2-3, 1998

Environmental Health News, Chadwick House Group Ltd, various editions 1999-2001

Food Standards Agency, FSA surveys, research, annual reports and press releases, 2001-2007

Faith Goodfellow, Faith Murray and Sabeha Ouki, 'Water-related chemical incidents: a national survey', *Health and Hygiene*, Volume 21 Number 2, The Royal Institute of Public Health and Hygiene, April 2000

Health Protection Agency, reports and web pages

Walter Heeschen, *Handbuch Lebensmittelhygiene*, Behr's Verlag, Hamburg, 1996

Norman E Hickin, *Household Insect Pests*, Associated Business Programmes Ltd, London, 1974

Director Publications, *Director* (magazine of the Institute of Directors), London, 2000-2007

Kushik Jaga and Harsha Duvvi, 'Risk reduction for DDT toxicity and carcinogenesis through dietary modification', *The Journal of The Royal Society for the Promotion of Health*, Volume 121 Number 2, June 2001

Michael Jacob, *Safe Food Handling*, World Health Organization, Geneva, 1989

James M Jay, Martin J Loessner and David A Golden, *Modern Food Microbiology*, Springer Science and Business Media LLC, New York, 2005

Allan Jones, Rob Reed and Jonathan Weyers, *Practical Skills in Biology*, Longman, Harlow, 2000

Lothar Leistner, 'User Guide to Food Design', *Food Preservation by Combined Processes*, European Commission, Brussels, 1994

Donald MacDonald and Dagmar Engel, *A Guide To HACCP – Hazard Analysis For Small Businesses*, Highfield Publications, Sprotborough, 1996

Michael T Madigan, John M Martinko and Jack Parker, *Brock Biology of Microorganisms*, Prentice Hall International Inc, 2000

Tom Makin, *Microbial Contamination of Potable Water and Mechanisms of Control* in conference papers of The European Union and Food Control Conference for the Estonian Industry, ABLI International Ltd, 1996

Norman Marriott, *Principles of Food Sanitation*, Van Nostrand Reinhold Company, Inc, New York, 1989

Adrian Meyer, 'Commensal Rodent Control' in *Proceedings of the 3rd International Conference on Urban Pests*, Executive Committee of the International Conference on Urban Pests, Prague, 1999

Klara Miller, *Toxicological Aspects of Food*, Elsevier Applied Science Publishers Ltd, London, 1987

R T Mitchell, *Practical Microbiological Risk Analysis*, Chandos Publishing (Oxford) Ltd, Oxford, 2000

Sara Mortimore and Carol Wallace, *HACCP – A Practical Approach*, Chapman & Hall, London, 1994

J W Munro, *Pests of Stored Products*, Hutchinson & Co Ltd, London, 1966

Claire Nash, *Food Safe to Eat*, VisàVis Publications, St Albans, 2002

Claire Nash, *Food Safety: First principles*, Chadwick House Group Ltd, 1998

Claire Nash, *Food Safety: First principles for manufacturing*, Chadwick House Group Ltd, 2006

Claire Nash, *Food Safety: First principles for retail*, Chadwick House Group Ltd, 2006

Claire Nash, *The Hygiene Challenge*, VisàVis Publications, St Albans, 1997

Claire Nash, *The Food Safety Training Pack*, Chadwick House Group Ltd, London, 2000

National Advisory Committee on Microbiological Criteria for Foods, *Hazard Analysis and Critical Control Point Principles and Application Guidelines*, US Food and Drug Administration, 1997

Richard North, *Some Observations on Food Hygiene Inspections*, Chadwick House Group Ltd, 1999

Notifications of Infectious Diseases, Public Health Laboratory Service, 2001

NSF International Conference and Exhibition, *Food Safety in Travel and Tourism*, conference papers, Barcelona, 2000

William Olkowski, Sheila Daar and Helga Olkowski, *Common Sense Pest Control*, The Taunton Press Inc, Newtown, 1991

John Postgate, *Microbes and Man*, Cambridge University Press, Cambridge, 2000

Hans Riemann, *Food-borne Infections and Intoxications,* Academic Press, New York 1969

Hans-Jürgen Sinell, *Einführung in die Lebensmittelhygiene,* Verlag Paul Parey, Berlin/Hamburg, 1985

David A Shapton and Norah F Shapton, *Principles and Practices for the Safe Processing of Foods*, Butterworth-Heinemann Ltd, Oxford, 1991

Heinrich Steinbrink, *Gesundheitsschädlinge*, Gustav Fischer Verlag, Stuttgart, 1989

Sue Stevenson and Claire Nash, *Food Safety Management*, Chadwick House Group Ltd, 2000

Sue Stevenson, Claire Nash and Alan Brereton, *Food Safety for Supervisors*, Chadwick House Group Ltd, 2006

TFIS, *Hazard Analysis and Critical Control Point* (HACCP Verification Manual), Technical Food Information Spectrum Inc, 1997

The Hutchinson Science Desk Reference, Helicon Publishing Ltd, Oxford, 1999

The Inquiry into BSE and Variant CJD in the United Kingdom, HMSO, October 2000

The Macquarie Concise Dictionary, The Macquarie Library Pty Ltd, New South Wales, 1998

The New Oxford Dictionary of English, Oxford University Press, Oxford, 1998

The Oxford Dictionary for Writers and Editors, Oxford University Press, Oxford, 2000

The Penguin Dictionary of Science, Penguin 1986

The Royal Society of Health, *Hygiene and*

Product Safety Management Systems for Food and Beverage Processing Companies (Accreditation Scheme), The Royal Society for the Promotion of Health, London, 1997

The Scottish Office, *The Investigation and Control of Outbreaks of Foodborne Disease in Scotland*, Department of Health, 1996

Clarence Wilbur Taber, (Clayton L Thomas (ed)), *Taber's Cyclopedic Medical Dictionary*, F A Davis Company, Philadelphia, 1993

Jill Trickett, *The Prevention of Food Poisoning*, Stanley Thornes Ltd, Cheltenham, 1996

J A Troller, *Sanitation in Food Processing*, Academic Press, New York, 1983

Report of the Committee on the Microbiological Safety of Food Parts I and II, HMSO 1990, 1991

Friedrich Untermann and Ulrich Dura, 'Das HACCP-Konzept: Theorie und Praxis', *Fleischwirtschaft*, 76 (7), 1996

Christopher Wills, *Plagues – Their Origins, History and Future*, Flamingo, London, 1996.

Page notes

We are pleased to acknowledge the following sources of information, comment or inspiration. We have endeavoured to include all sources, but will be glad to include additional information if appropriate. Page numbers are given in bold.

Part 1

15 The comment about the return of the customer was made by Robert Tyler, President of the British Meat Trades Federation, at a conference at the University of Reading, 20 January 1998.

Part 2

16 See the Food Standards Agency website at http://www.food.gov.uk and follow the links to the annual surveys.

20 Self-diagnosis of food poisoning based on research and press releases issued by the Food Standards Agency, 05 February, 2001.

21 Graphs based on data published by the Health Protection Agency, Statutory Notification of Infectious Diseases (for England and Wales); Health Protection Scotland, Scottish Centre for Infection and Environmental Health; and Health Protection Agency, Communicable Disease Surveillance Centre, Northern Ireland.

23 Food Standards Agency Annual Report 2005/2006 http://www.food.gov.uk/multimedia/webpage/annual report0506
For other estimates of the cost of food-borne illnesses, see also the *Explanatory Memorandum to the Food Hygiene (England) Regulations 2006 (2006 No.14)* and page 140 of *Food Microbiology*, M R Adams and M O Moss, Royal Society of Chemistry, 1999.

24 Aspects of this feature were inspired by 'The Importance of HACCP for the public and the economy', Yasmin Motarjemi, lecture at the International Food Safety HACCP Conference, Noordwijk an Zee, February 1997.

28 Due diligence: Food Safety Act 1990, Section 21.

33 *Environmental Management at Work*, GEMS Environmental Management Services (Editors: Claire Nash and Caroline Smith); Chadwick House Group Ltd, 1999.

Part 3

64 The table showing the effect on bacteria at different temperatures over time is based upon research published in *Practical Hygiene in the*

Foodservice Profession, SwissAir Catering Services.

70 For a more detailed discussion about the revised nomenclature of *Salmonella* species, see also James M Jay, Martin J Loessner and David A Golden, *Modern Food Microbiology*, Springer Science and Business Media LLC, New York, 2005.

79 The description of *Clostridium perfringens* (*C. welchii*): 'Clostridium welchii food poisoning', Hobbs B et al, *Journal of Hygiene*, 51 75-101, 1953.

83 For a more detailed discussion about cholera and to see a copy of the illustration mentioned, see Christopher Wills, *Plagues – Their Origins, History and Future*, Flamingo, London, 1996.

96 Health Protection Agency website www.hpa.org.uk/infections/topics_az/norovirus/faq.htm

146 More information about allergies and anaphylaxis can be found at www.anaphylaxis.org.uk and www.food.gov.uk/safereating/allergyintol/

151-169 Copies of legislation may be obtained through various websites, such as those of the Food Standards Agency (FSA), Her Majesty's Stationery Office (HMSO) and the European Union (see pages 415 to 419). Guidance on the legislation is also obtainable from the FSA website – example of URLs are:
www.food.gov.uk/foodindustry/regulation/hygleg
www.food.gov.uk/foodindustry/guidancenotes/foodguid/generalfoodlaw
www.food.gov.uk/foodindustry/regulation/hygleg/hyglegresources/goodpractice

Part 4

178 For a definition of severity, see also Frank L Bryan, *Hazard Analysis Critical Control Point Evaluations*, World Health Organization, Geneva, 1992.

182 R T Mitchell said in *Practical Microbiological Risk Analysis,* Chandos Publishing (Oxford) Ltd, Oxford, 2000, 'HACCP is the use of the simplest possible controls where it matters most'. The table at the bottom of this page is based upon

Hazard Analysis and Critical Control Point (HACCP) System and Guidelines for Its Application, Codex Alimentarius Commission, 1997 and on Hazard Analysis and Critical Control Point Principles and Application Guidelines, US Food and Drug Administration, as adopted by the National Advisory Committee on Microbiological Criteria for Foods, 1997. For information about systems based on HACCP principles, go to national food safety website and follow the links, such as ww.food.gov.uk/foodindustry/regulation/hygleg/hyglegresources/sfbb/ for Safer Food, Better Business.

188 Part of our definition draws on that of Frank L Bryan in Hazard Analysis Critical Control Point Evaluations, World Health Organization, Geneva, 1992, 'A CCP is an operation (practice, procedure, location or process) at which control can be exercised over one or more factors to eliminate, prevent or minimize a hazard.'

189 This decision ladder is adapted from original training materials developed by Dagmar Engel and Donald MacDonald in 1998. For a more conventional HACCP decision tree based on the Codex Alimentarius model, see page 395.

197-200 See pages 415 to 419 for details of the standards organisations mentioned.

230-233 The Food Standards Agency and Anaphylaxis Campaign have produced a wealth of information for food businesses of different sizes and in different sectors. Go to www.food.gov.uk/safereating/allergyintol/ then follow links to information about labelling, manufacturing, catering and so on, or try www.anaphylaxis.org.uk. We are grateful to the Anaphylaxis Campaign for permission to reproduce the top poster on page 230.

255-256 See pages 415 to 419 for details of the organisations mentioned. This feature draws partly on the work of Roland Cocker, Director of Cocker Consulting (http://www.cocker.nl). An article about food machinery by Andy Timperley, of Timperley Consulting (andy.timperley@tesco.net), can be found in Issue 47, 2006 of SoFHT Focus, the magazine of The Society of Food Hygiene and Technology.

268 A message from the bored: originator unknown. Reprinted by permission of John Frater, The Royal Environmental Health Institute of Scotland.

273 L M Ackerley, 'Food Hygiene and Food Poisoning: A Study of Public Perceptions', PhD thesis, University of Birmingham, 1991.

285 See pages 415 to 419 for details of the organisations mentioned.

287-288 This feature is based upon information on the Food Standards Agency's website www.eatwell.gov.uk/foodlabels/understandlabels/
See also www.food.gov.uk/foodlabelling/ull/

297 and **304** The diagrammatic parts of our illustrations are based on the 'Sinner diagrams' (Reinigungskreis nach Sinner), the models created by the former chemist at the Fa. Henkel company in Düsseldorf. Although these diagrams are widely used in continental Europe, we regret that, despite searches and enquiries, we have been unable to establish Sinner's first name or the date of publication of this influential model. The website of the University of Bielefeld includes information in German featuring the diagrams: http://dc2.uni-bielefeld.de/dc2/wsu-haush/kap_01.htm/

357 This feature draws on information on the website of the United States Fish and Wildlife Service's DeSoto National Wildlife Refuge www.fws.gov/midwest/desoto/bertrand.htm

372 Friedrich Untermann's model is generally known as 'the Untermann house'. See Friedrich Untermann and Ulrich Dura, 'Das HACCP-Konzept: Theorie und Praxis', in Fleischwirtschaft, 76 (7), 1996.

391 The tables are adapted from William Olkowski, Sheila Daar and Helga Olkowski, Common Sense Pest Control, The Taunton Press Inc, Newtown, 1991.

392-393 Adapted from 'Functions and Limitations of Cleaning Chemicals', with permission of the International Commission on Microbiological Specifications for Foods.

394 Chart based on Department of Health guidelines published in Communicable Disease and Public Health Volume 7 No. 4 December 2004. The original chart and other information is given on page 383 of Preventing person-to-person spread following gastrointestinal infections: guidelines for public health physicians and environmental health officers, prepared by a Working Group of the former PHLS Advisory Committee on Gastrointestinal Infections. It can be downloaded from www.hpa.org.uk/cdph/issues/CDPHvol7/No4/guidelines2_4_04.pdf

395 The decision tree shown here is based on that of Codex Alimentarius.

Index and Acknowledgements

Index

Acknowledgements

Many people and organisations have contributed directly or indirectly to the preparation of this book. Our published sources of information and inspiration are included in 'Books and articles' on page 420 and 'Page notes' on page 423.

For direct help towards this edition we would particularly like to thank Allergy Action; Roy Hayter, chef-proprietor, Lloyds Hotel, Llanidloes; Hazel Gowland, Food Adviser, The Anaphylaxis Campaign; Brian Hooker, of Hyburn Quality Services; John Hutchison, of Hutchison Associates; and Carole Milligan, Chartered Environmental Health Practitioner. As always, it was a delight to work with Mark Hackett, our illustrator.

Our thanks are also due to Alan Brereton, consultant food scientist; Nicola Bull, proofreader and indexer; Roland Cocker, of Cocker Consulting; Tina Garrity, Information and Communications Manager, Chartered Institute of Environmental Health; and Robyn West, proofreader and indexer.

For contributing material to the first edition we are particularly grateful to Ifan Payne and Justine Johnstone.

For help towards the first edition our thanks go to: Axiom Partners; Les Barker, Director, Environmental Solutions Partnership Ltd, London; David Barnes, C P Consultants, Devon; John Barrow, Managing Director, HACCP International Ltd, England; Derrick Blunden, Marketing Manager, International Food Hygiene, Positive Action Publications, England; Julia Bruce, assistant editor, VisàVis Publications; Martin Cole, International Commission on Microbiological Specifications for Foods, Australia; Alex Douglas, Higher Executive Officer, Scottish Executive, Edinburgh; Focus Public Relations, London; Tina Garrity, former Research Officer, Chartered Institute of Environmental Health; Tony Girdwood, Stobhill Hospital, Glasgow; Ann Goodwin, former Assistant Secretary, Chartered Institute of Environmental Health; Roy Hayter, chef/co-proprietor, Lloyds Hotel, Llanidloes; Herts Advertiser, St Albans; Ben Inns, Bedfordshire; Johnson Wax Professional, UK; Ned Kingcott, Chief Environmental Health Officer, Food Standards Agency, London; Maria Laybourn, Safeway Stores plc; Mary Locking, Epidemiologist, Scottish Centre for Infection and Environmental Health, Glasgow; Audrey Lynch, Senior Press Officer, Communicable Disease Surveillance Centre, Northern Ireland; McDonald's Restaurants Ltd, UK; Morris McAllister, Director, Food Standards Agency, Northern Ireland; Dick Madely, formerly Professor, Department of Virology, Newcastle University; Tom Makin, Consultant Bacteriologist, Royal Liverpool University Hospital; Carole Milligan, former Director, Environmental Solutions Partnership Ltd, London; Jenny Millward, Food Safety Team Manager, Birmingham Metropolitan District Council; Bob Mitchell, Head, Environmental Surveillance Unit, Public Health Laboratory Services, Colindale; Martin Müller, Germany; Richard North, consultant, Brussels and UK; Bill Reilly, Deputy Director, Scottish Centre for Infection and Environmental Health, Glasgow; Safeway Stores plc; the staff of The Science Photo Library, London; Julie Snelling, Senior Technical Enforcement Officer, Slough Borough Council; Mike Sweeney, Chief Executive, British Institute of Cleaning Services; Dee Waite, former Technical and Development Manager, Chadwick House Group Ltd; Alette Weaver, Head of Diet and Nutrition Surveys Branch, Food Standards Agency, London.

Picture credits